ABOUT THE AUTHORS

Ren Mei'e, born in 1913, received his B.S. from Central University in China and his Ph.D. from Glasgow University in Great Britain. He taught at Zhejiang University, Fudan University and Central University and directed the Institute of Geography of Nanjing under the Chinese Academy of Sciences. Currently he is a professor in Nanjing University and also an academician of the Chinese Academy of Sciences. As one of the best-known geographers in the country, he holds responsible positions in many academic organizations, including vice-chairman of the Council of the Chinese Geographic Society and of the Chinese Oceanographic Society. More than 200 of his writings have been published, including ones written in English and French that appeared in the magazines *Economic Geography* (United States), *Erdkunde* (West Germany) and *Annales de Geographie* (France). *Introduction to Karstology* is his most recent work, published by Commercial Press in 1983.

Yang Renzhang (1919-1971), a native of Dangtu County, Anhui Province, graduated from the geography department of Central University in 1941. She once served as head of the physical geography teaching and research section of the geography department of Nanjing University and was a member of the land hydrology committee of the Chinese Geographic Society and a committee member of the Chinese Association for Dissemination of Scientific Knowledge. Well versed in China's climate, hydrology and regional physical geography, particularly that of some dry areas such as Qaidam Basin and Inner Mongolia, she published a large number of academic works that have proved important contributions to the theory of the division of physical geographic regions. She was promoted to associate professor in 1963 and died in 1971.

Bao Haosheng was born in 1932 in Changshu City, Jiangsu Province. After graduating from the geography department of Nanjing University in 1956, he taught physical geography there. Under the guidance of Professor Ren Mei'e he surveyed the physical geography and regional geomorphology of Yunnan and Guizhou provinces. Many of his writings were published, and he was promoted to lecturer in 1964. In 1979 he was selected by the Ministry of Education, after a competitive examination, to study karstology under the famous geomorphologist Dr. J. N. Jennings of the Australian National University. He returned home at the end of 1981. In 1983 he was promoted to associate professor. Currently he is head of the natural resources teaching and research section of the geography department of Nanjing University, specializing in research on natural resources, regional physical geography and karstology.

CHINA KNOWLEDGE SERIES

AN OUTLINE OF CHINA'S PHYSICAL GEOGRAPHY

Compiled by *REN MEI'E*
YANG RENZHANG and *BAO HAOSHENG*

Translated by
ZHANG TINGQUAN and *HU GENKANG*

FOREIGN LANGUAGES PRESS
BEIJING

First Edition   1985

Hard cover: ISBN 0-8351-1191-1
Paperback: ISBN 0-8351-1192-X

Copyright 1985 by Foreign Languages Press

Published by Foreign Languages Press
24 Baiwanzhuang Road, Beijing, China

Printed by Foreign Languages Printing House
19 West Chegongzhuang Road, Beijing, China

Distributed by China International Book Trading Corporation
(Guoji Shudian), P.O. Box 399, Beijing, China

Printed in the People's Republic of China

PREFACE

The People's Republic of China is one of the largest countries in the world. It is also a country with the largest population. China's economic development and ever-increasing contacts between the Chinese and other peoples have made it a matter of importance to publish a scientific account of China's physical geography, one that will enhance foreign readers' understanding of China and promote academic exchange in the field of geography. Publication of this book was inspired by the founder of China's geographic studies, the late Professor Zhu Kezhen, former vice-president of the Chinese Academy of Sciences, who had mentioned this urgent need many times.

China's physical conditions are diverse. The years since the founding of New China in 1949 have seen a rapid development in geographical research and survey, and geographical and geological materials and data on Tibet, Qinghai, Xinjiang and Yunnan, where they were scarce or even nonexistent before Liberation, have been accumulated. In the course of our teaching and research over the past years we have left our footprints everywhere except Tibet and have made long-term surveys, particularly in Yunnan, Guizhou, Qaidam and Inner Mongolia. The present book was compiled from reports of our practical surveys and analysis of a great wealth of documents and materials. The views presented in the book, which are entirely our own, may not agree completely with those in other works, but we think our views are closer to objective reality. Comments and suggestions from readers are welcome.

This English edition was translated from the Chinese

edition published in August 1979. The original version was left basically intact, with only some necessary alterations of a few data as well as some additions and deletions. As a result of the swift development of China's economy and detailed geographical surveys since 1979 some material in the book needs to be revised or added.

Ren Mei'e
April 27, 1984
Nanjing University

CONTENTS

Part One GENERAL DESCRIPTION

Chapter I
INTRODUCTION

1. Area, Position and Territory

China is situated in the eastern and central part of Asia, on the west coast of the Pacific Ocean. The third largest country in the world, next to the Soviet Union and Canada, it has a territory of 9.6 million square kilometres — one-fifteenth of the land area of the world, or one-fourth that of Asia.

China's territory extends more than 5,500 kilometres from north to south. Starting from the central line of the Heilong River near Mohe in the north, it stretches to the Zengmu Reef on the southern fringe of the Nansha Islands in the South China Sea. Due to differences in latitude, the solar incident angle and subsequent lengths of day and night differ. The solar incident angle in Guangzhou in the south, for instance, has about 30 degrees difference from that in Mohe in the north. The shortest day on Hainan Island in the south is 11 hours and 2 minutes, and the longest is 13 hours and 14 minutes; while in places near Mohe these days are about 7 hours and 17 hours respectively.

From west to east, China's territory extends over 5,200 kilometres, starting from the Pamirs in the Xinjiang Uygur Autonomous Region and reaching the confluence of the Heilong and Wusuli rivers in Heilongjiang Province. The time difference from west to east is more than four hours, so that while it is about noontime along the Songhua River in northeast China, it is still early morning in the Pamirs.

1

China has a land frontier of over 20,000 kilometres. It borders Korea in the northeast; the Soviet Union and Mongolia in the north; Viet Nam in the south; and Afghanistan, Pakistan, India, Nepal, Bhutan, Burma and Laos in the west and southwest.

China's coastline extends from the mouth of the Yalu River in the north to the mouth of the Beilun River on the China-Viet Nam border in the south. This is a distance of more than 18,000 kilometres. Across the sea, China faces Japan, the Philippines, Malaysia, Brunei, etc.

Besides the Bohai Sea, an inland sea of China, the China mainland adjoins three sea areas which are, from north to south, the Yellow Sea, the East China Sea and the South China Sea. With the exception of the South China Sea, which has the features and depth of an ocean basin, the other seas are mostly shallow continental shelves, providing favourable conditions for the development of marine agriculture. The extensive continental shelves also contain rich oil deposits that are of great significance to China's national economy. East of Taiwan Island, there is a steep continental slope that stretches into the Pacific Ocean, to a depth of more than 4,000 metres.

China has more than 5,000 coastal islands, 85 per cent of which are scattered in the coastal waters south of the Hangzhou Bay and in the South China Sea. With an area of 36,000 square kilometres, Taiwan is China's biggest island. This is followed by Hainan Island, with an area of 32,200 square kilometres. The Diaoyu and other offshore islands in the northeast of Taiwan Province are China's easternmost islands while the Nansha Islands are its southernmost group.

A vast territory, considerable differences in latitude and longitude (more than 49 and 60 degrees, respectively) and its being in the eastern part of the Eurasian Continent, next to the Pacific Ocean — all these features contribute to China's unique physical geography.

2. General Characteristics of China's
Physical Geography

The general characteristics of China's physical geography
are as follows:

1) Owing to the differences in latitude from north to
south, China's extensive territory straddles the frigid-temperate, temperate, warm-temperate, subtropical, tropical and
equatorial zones. The warm-temperate and subtropical zones
combine to account for the biggest percentage (over 30 per cent)
of its total area while the tropical zone makes up about 8 per
cent. From the coast in the east to the hinterland in the west,
there is a gradual transition from humid and semi-humid regions to semi-arid and arid regions, with the humid regions
composing about 30 per cent of the country's total land area.
An adequate supply of heat and water, and the excellent relationship between these two in most parts of the country,
provide favourable conditions for agricultural development.
The types of vegetation and soils are distributed in relation
to natural zones from north to south.

2) Situated in the eastern part of Eurasia, on the west
coast of the Pacific Ocean, China has a climate which is
strongly affected by monsoons, with marked changes of high
and low pressures in winter and summer. The monsoons
greatly affect the atmospheric movement in East Asia. And,
unlike areas in the same latitudes in other countries, many
of which have turned into deserts and arid steppes, China's
subtropical regions are well-known agricultural areas, suitable for the growth of rice. This is because summer monsoon brings enough rainfall in the high-temperature season
to form hot and humid weather. The alternating monsoons
and their southward and northward movement have played
an important role in the formation and evolution of China's
natural landscape. The differences between the east and
west areas of China, as well as the gradual changes in nat-

ural zones from north to south in the eastern regions, are to a large extent influenced by the monsoon.

3) China has an extremely complicated topography, with mountains and plateaus occupying a large part of its land surface. The Tibetan Plateau, containing a number of big mountain ranges and often called the "Roof of the World", towers in the west. It includes Mt. Qomolangma, located on the China-Nepal border. This rises 8,848 metres above sea level, and is the world's highest peak. Northwestern China is an arid region where high mountains alternate with huge basins that include the Turpan Depression, which is well below sea level, and the Taklimakan Desert, one of the biggest in the world. Eastern China has broad alluvial plains and many medium and low mountains and hills. The mountains in different horizontal natural zones have varying structures of vertical landscape zones, which add to the complexity and variety of China's natural conditions. The Tibetan Plateau, which stands 4,500 metres above sea level and accounts for almost a quarter of the country's land area, disrupts to a great extent the horizontal natural zone structure found in the rest of China. In studying China's physical geography and the agricultural patterns of its various regions, it is imperative to take into full account the topographical conditions.

4) The economic activities of the Chinese people through the ages have brought about profound changes to the landscape. In the plains and hilly areas of eastern China, the natural forests were long ago destroyed or have been replaced, in some places, by tree farms and fruit trees. Only in mountainous areas can one find small patches of secondary forests. Vast plains have become cultivated land, and terraced fields have been opened in hilly areas for agriculture. On the vast desert basins of northwestern China, irrigation networks and oases have been built using river water fed by melting snow from the high mountains. Natural grasslands have been used to develop animal husbandry on the Inner Mongolia and Qinghai-Tibet plateaus, as well as in many

mountainous areas. In their thousands of years of productive activities, the Chinese labouring people have ceaselessly re-moulded nature and accumulated a wealth of experience in its utilization and transformation. Since Liberation in 1949, large-scale afforestation, water and soil conservation, irrigation projects and other activities have changed the feature of the country. Nature is now increasingly at the service of the people.

Chapter II
LANDFORM

1. Basic Contours of China's Landform

Mountains and plateaus occupy a large part of the land of China. Areas exceeding 500 metres above sea level account for 84 per cent of its land surface while those below 500 metres make up only 16 per cent (Table 1).

Table 1. China's Territory in Terms of Elevation

Elevation (in metres)	<500	500-1,000	1,000-2,000	2,000-5,000	>5,000
Percentages in total area	16	19	28	18	19

China's landform has five basic types: mountains, plateaus, hills, basins and plains. The highest mountains, those exceeding 5,000 metres, are snow-covered all year round and contain glaciers. Most of the high mountains, i.e., those from 5,000 to 3,500 metres above sea level, have no permanent snow covers or glaciers, but are strongly affected by frost-cracking and retain the marks of former glacial landforms. Medium mountains, of 3,500 to 1,000 metres in elevation, generally have steep slopes and deep valleys. The low mountains are below 1,000 metres. In the warm humid climate of eastern China, chemical weathering has an obvious effect on such mountains and, with strong erosion by running water, the

6

valleys have broadened, slopes have become gentle and the terrain has been so altered the contour of tectonic strike on the mountains has become less obvious. The hills, as a rule, are less than 200 metres in height with gentle undulations. It should be pointed out that there is a wide variation in the effect of natural forces on the vertical zones of mountains in different regions of China. For instance, the arid denudation belt in the northwestern high mountains can reach as high as 3,000 metres and above. Frost weathering appears at an altitude of 2,000 metres in the Greater Hinggan Mountains of northeastern China. The process of chemical weathering in the mountainous areas of southwestern China is particularly pronounced, reaching as high as 2,500-3,000 metres above sea level.

There is a vast difference in the altitude of various parts of China's land surface. Mt. Qomolangma, on the China-Nepal border, stands 8,848 metres above sea level while the surface of the Aydingkol Lake, the lowest part of the Turpan Depression in Xinjiang, is 154 metres below. The Tibetan Plateau generally rises 4,000-5,000 metres above sea level, while most of the plains in the eastern part of the country are 50-100 metres high. Many peaks of the Hengduan Mountains stand 5,000-6,000 metres above sea level, although the average elevation is about 4,000 metres, with a relative height difference of just over 2,000 metres compared with the adjacent valleys. This forms the terrain characterized by high mountains and deep valleys.

The general contour of China's landform is that the western part is higher than the eastern, as the terrain slopes gradually from west to east, forming a big three-step staircase. All the major rivers, such as the Changjiang (Yangtse River) and the Huanghe (Yellow River), flow eastward to enter the Pacific Ocean along this inclined plane. The topographical staircase begins with the Qinghai-Tibet Plateau, formed of the highest mountains and biggest plateaus. With an average altitude of 4,000-5,000 metres, this area is known

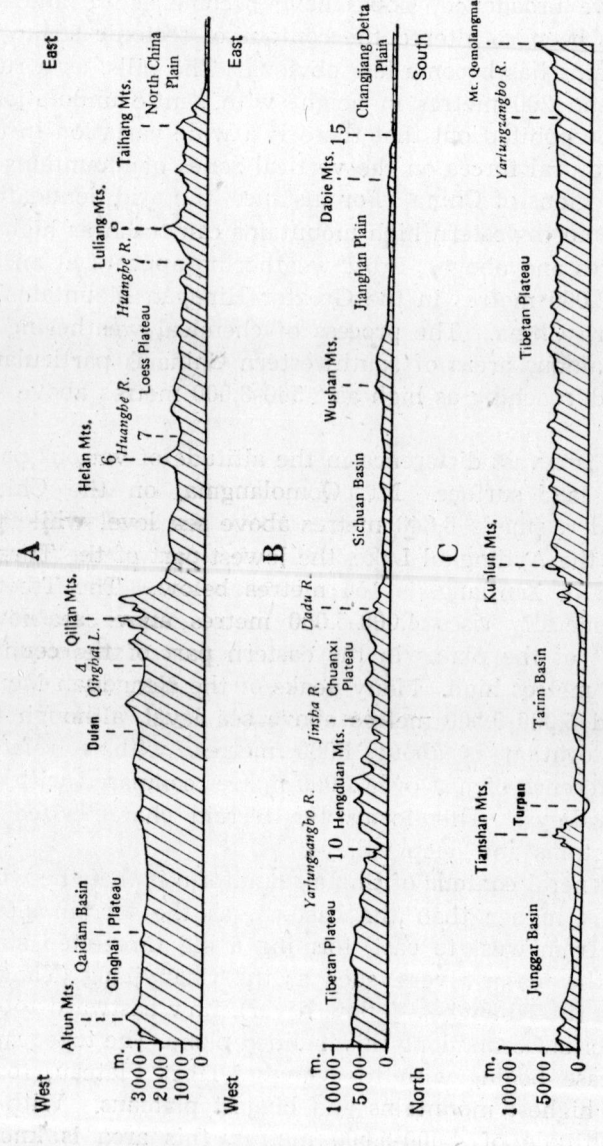

Fig. 1 Cross Section of China's Topography

A: Qinghai Plateau — North China Plain; B: Tibetan Plateau — Changjiang Delta Plain;
C: Tibetan Plateau — Junggar Basin

The world's highest peak, Mount Qomolangma, stands 8,848 metres above sea level.

The Great Wall rises and falls along the ridges
of the Yanshan Mountain chain in the east.

The natural forest of the Lesser Hinggan range in the Northeast.

Basaltic lava from volcanic eruptions beneath Wudalianchi Lake in the Northeast.

The highly eroded terrain of the Loess Plateau.

Grassland in Inner Mongolia.

The Taihu Plain is an important agricultural region. Here are fields along the shore of Taihu Lake.

The Three Gorges on the Changjiang.

Dujiangyan irrigation works, built during the second century B.C. in Sichuan Province.

Guangxi is famous throughout the world for its strange karst formations. This is a bird's-eye view of the myriad karst pinnacles at Yangshuo.

The Stone Forest at Lu'nan, Yunnan Province, is a typical karst formation remaining from the landscape of the Tertiary Period.

Rubber forest on Hainan Island.

Coral reef of the Xuande island group of the Xisha Islands.

Riyuetan (Sun and Moon Pool), located on the grand rift belt between the Yushan and Ali mountains, is a famous scenic spot in Taiwan.

Taklimakan, the largest desert in China.

Tomur is the highest peak of the Tianshan Mountains.

as the "Roof of the World". The second step, which extends from the outer rim of the Qinghai-Tibet Plateau to the Greater Hinggan, Taihang, Wushan and Xuefeng mountains, consists mainly of massive plateaus and large basins. East of the Qinghai-Tibet Plateau are the Inner Mongolian Plateau, the Loess Plateau, the Sichuan Basin and the Yunnan-Guizhou Plateau, while north of it are vast basins surrounded by huge mountain ranges, including the Tarim Basin between the Kunlun and Tianshan mountains and the Junggar Basin between the Tianshan and Altay mountains. The broad plains and hills in eastern China form the lowest step of the staircase, including, from north to south, the Northeast Plain, the North China Plain, the Huaihe Plain and the Middle-Lower Changjiang Plain. Stretching from northeast to southwest, these plains are almost linked to one another and form China's most important agricultural regions.

All three steps of the staircase are steep in the east and gentle in the west. For instance, from the North China Plain via Zhangjiakou to the Inner Mongolian Plateau, from Lianghu (Hunan-Hubei) Plain via western Hunan to the Guizhou Plateau, and from the Guangxi Basin to the Guizhou Plateau, there is a marked rise in each case of one step, which is 1,000-1,500 metres higher than the eastern plains. Further west, from the Yunnan-Guizhou Plateau to the Tibetan Plateau, which stands about 5,000 metres above sea level, another step is ascended (Fig. 1).

2.   Contributing Factors to the Landform

China's landform took shape as a result of the interactions of internal and external agents and the substances forming the earth's surface.

(1)   Effect of Geologic Structures on China's Macro-geomorphic Contour

The formation of China's macro-geomorphic contour, or

the outline of major mountains, plateaus, basins and plains, was mainly influenced by tectonic movements.

The well-known geologist Li Siguang (J. S. Li) divided China's tectonics into five systems: (a) the macrolatitudinal tectonic system; (b) the longitudinal tectonic system; (c) the north-east to north-north-east Cathysian tectonic system; (d) the north-west to north-west-west "Xiyu"-type tectonic system; and (e) the torsion tectonic system (such as the marginal arc). The pattern and strikes of China's mountains are closely tied up with these tectonic systems (Fig. 2).

According to their strike characteristics, China's mountain ranges can be classified as follows:

1) West-east ranges — mainly the Tianshan-Yinshan-Yanshan, the Kunlun-Qinling-Dabie, and the Nanling. Of these, the Tianshan-Yinshan and the Kunlun-Qinling most clearly reflect the latitudinal tectonic system. Influenced by the Cathysian tectonic system, the strike of the Nanling Mountains has undergone great change, though, generally speaking, the mountains still run west-east. All these mountains are important geographical boundaries in China. The Yinshan Mountains, for instance, constitute the margin of the Inner Mongolian Plateau; the Tianshan Mountains divide north and south Xinjiang; the Kunlun Mountains form the border between south Xinjiang and the Tibetan Plateau; the Qinling Mountains serve as the watershed between the Changjiang and the Huanghe, as well as the Huaihe and the Huanghe; while the Nanling Mountains are the barrier between the Zhujiang and Changjiang drainages. Customarily, the country is divided into north China, central China and south China by taking the Qinling and Nanling ranges as the boundaries.

2) North-south ranges — mainly the Helan, Liupan and Hengduan mountains. Geologically, the Hengduan Mountains in western Sichuan and northern Yunnan are formed of many bunches of north-south faults with very close folds. Geomorphologically they are a series of parallel high moun-

tains and deep valleys with a great disparity in their relative heights. To the south of central Yunnan Province, the Hengduan Mountains gradually spread out southward into Viet Nam and Laos.

3) North-east ranges — dominated by the Cathysian tectonic system, they are mainly distributed in the eastern part of the country, namely, to the east of the north-south tectonic belt. Here, a series of depression and upheaval belts were formed along the direction of the Cathysian tectonic system. Geomorphologically this finds expression in alternating basins, plains and mountains. There are, from west to east, a) Hulunbuir Basin-Ordos Basin-Sichuan Basin; b) Greater Hinggan Mountains-Taihang Mountains-Luliang Mountains-mountains in western Hubei, eastern Guizhou and western Hunan; c) Songliao Plain-Bohai Bay and North China Plain-Jianghan Plain-Beibu Gulf; d) the mountains in eastern Jilin-Liaoning, in Shandong and in the coastal areas of Zhejiang, Fujian and Guangdong, of which the local depressions are represented by the North Jiangsu Plain and the southern part of the Yellow Sea; and e) the sea basins of the East China and South China seas.

4) North-west ranges — dominated by the "Xiyu"-type tectonic system, they are mainly distributed in western China. These ranges include the Altay and Qilian mountains. They cut across mountains formed of north-east-east rifts and folds (the Altun Mountains) to shape the rhombic contour of huge inland basins, such as the Junggar, Tarim and Qaidam.

5) Arc-shaped mountain — mainly the Himalayan Mountains and mountains in Taiwan. The two ends of the Himalayan Mountain Chain project southward to form an arc. near Zayu, the east end of this range suddenly turns southward to become the Hengduan Mountains. The west end turns southward in the upper reaches of the Indus to form the south-south-west Sulaiman Range. The mountains in Taiwan are part of a marginal arc (west Pacific islands arc) along the coast of the East Asian continent. It starts from the Japan Islands and the

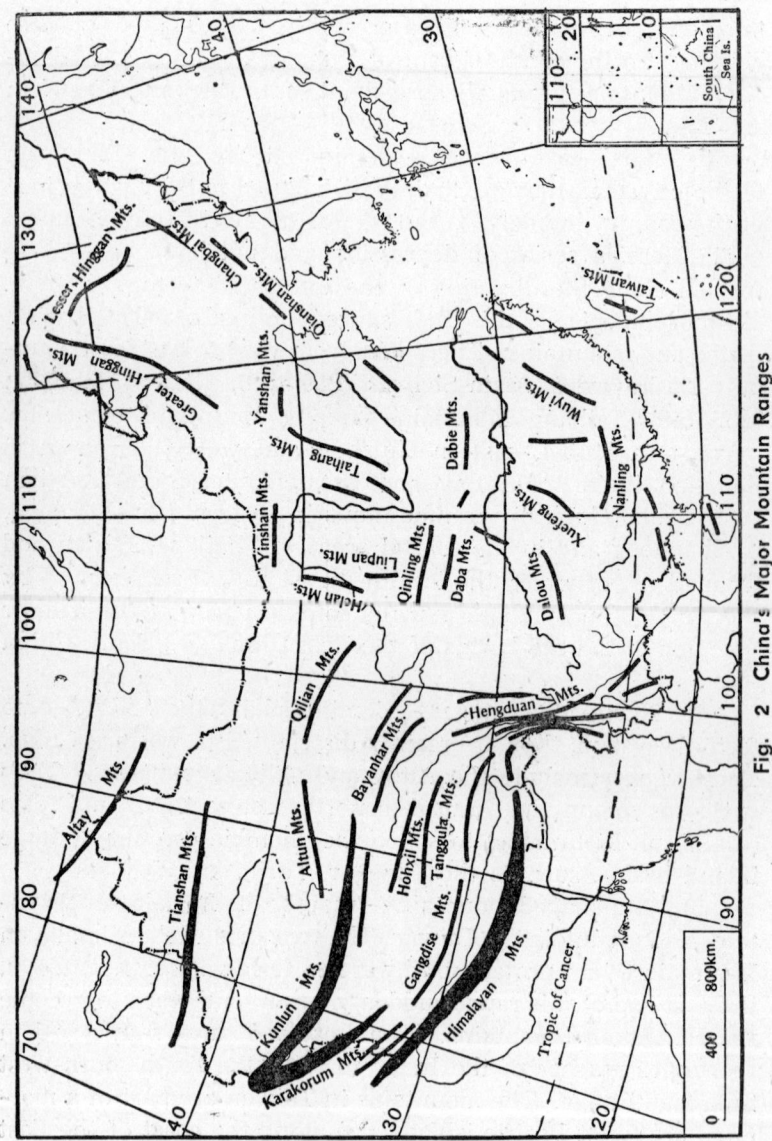

Fig. 2 China's Major Mountain Ranges

Ryukyu Islands and extends through Taiwan Island to the Philippine Islands, roughly forming an arc projecting eastward. Hence the name "island arc".

Generally speaking, these huge arc-shaped mountains and other macro-geomorphic features can be explained by the theory of plate tectonics. The Himalayan Mountains were formed as a result of two continental plates, the Indian plate and the Asian plate, knocking against each other. The former thrust under the latter at a small angle. The overlapping of the two plates fashioned a thick crust (70 kilometres thick, one of the world's thickest areas) and a high, precipitous relief. The enormous north-south pressure engendered by the collision of the Indian and Asian plates made the mountains in western China run roughly west-east. Under such pressure, the hard landmasses of the Junggar, Tarim and Qaidam basins broke into rhombic blocks, with their long axes running in a similar direction. Likewise, the northward thrust of the Indian plate collided with the Asian plate moving in an opposite direction, the stress release to the east and west brought about the abrupt southward turn in the east and west ends of the Himalayas. The mountains on Taiwan Island and the marginal arc along the coast of the East Asian continent were produced by the Pacific plate (the Oceanic plate) thrusting slantingly under the Asian plate at a relatively big angle. Since the crust of the Pacific plate is not very thick, no high and huge plateaus, or extra thick crust, have been formed in the eastern part of China. The series of north-east depressions and upheavals in eastern China were probably created by the Pacific plate squeezing and twisting the Asian plate.

Most of China's mountains which took form after repeated orogenic movement are of a polycyclic character. Generally speaking, however, the crustal movement prior to the Mesozoic Era had little direct relationship with present landforms, though it affected the latter's growth in terms of the character, strike and degree of folding. For instance, the karst rocks in southwestern China are related to Palaeozoic limestones.

The strike of the modern Qinling, Qilian, Tianshan and Altay mountains can be traced back to the fold zones of the Caledonian and Hercynian movement.

The Mesozoic Yanshan movement gave basic shape to China's geotectonic patterns, and this was also of decisive significance in determining China's macro-geomorphic framework. After this movement, with the exception of the Himalayas and some other areas, sea water receded from China's mainland and the scattered land masses linked up. Fundamentally, the Yanshan movement also determined the main orographic strikes in China as mentioned above: latitudinal, longitudinal, north-west and north-east. Many red-rock basins in central and south China were also formed by the Yanshan movement.

The Cenozoic Himalayan movement was of special importance in forming China's present macro-geomorphic structure. Aside from creating the huge Himalayan Mountains and the mountains in Taiwan, it engendered widespread rifting that gave rise to drastic vertical uplift and subsidence. This was the most important factor in bringing about the present topographical distinctions of China. What is known as the neotectonic movement mainly refers to the vertical uplift and subsidence in the Himalayan movement, particularly during its second episode between the Pliocene and the Pleistocene. Generally speaking, the elevated regions formed by the neotectonic movement are today's mountains and plateaus, while the subsiding regions are today's basins and plains.

The violent upheavals during the neotectonic movement occurred mainly in the western part of China, making this area generally higher than the eastern part. The Tibetan Plateau and the Himalayan, Kunlun and Tianshan mountains experienced the most extensive uplift. The axis of the Himalayas, for example, has risen nearly 3,000 metres since the end of the Tertiary Period. During this period, the piedmont depressions in the Tianshan and Kunlun mountains were covered with fine-grain sediments. Only during the Pliocene and the Pleistocene did there appear a boulder bed with a thickness of 6,000-7,000 metres. This shows that the high altitude of the Tianshan and Kunlun mountains has resulted from the violent uplift since the Pliocene. Simultaneously with such elevation, these mountains had violent local faulting, producing a number of graben intermontane basins with vast differences in relative heights, such as the Turpan Depression in the Tianshan Mountains. It is also because of this uplift since the Pliocene that the Yunnan-Guizhou Plateau has reached its present height of about 2,500 metres above sea level. Pliocene fossil regolith of the lateritic type left in some places on the plateau shows that these places were lowland at that time. Under the impact of the neotectonic movement, block uplifting continued in the Taihang, Daqing and Qinling mountains and high, steep fault cliffs often appeared on one side of them so that they stand towering on the nearby plains today.

The North China Plain, the Bohai Sea and the south section of the Yellow Sea in the eastern part of the country are all vast subsided areas resulting from this neotectonic movement. The thickness of Quaternary sediments of the North China Plain reached 500-600 metres and that of upper Tertiary and Quaternary sediments of the Bohai Sea and the south section of the Yellow Sea reached a total of 1,500 metres.

It is thus clear that China's geomorphic pattern was shaped in the Yanshan movement, while the present topographical distinctions are mainly the result of the Himalayan movement. Taking the north-south Helan-Liupan-Longmen-Ailau mountains as the line of demarcation, there are striking differences between the macro-geomorphic patterns east and west of it. Most of the mountains to the east of this line have a northeast to north-north-east strike. The absolute and relative uprise and subsidence in the neotectonic movement were, relatively speaking, not so marked (with the exception of the northern China region). Accordingly, both the absolute and relative heights of the terrain are not great, and the landform consists mainly of plains, low plateaus, hills and medium and low mountains. Most of the mountains to the west of the said de-marcation line have a north-west to north-west-west strike, with pronounced absolute and relative uplift and subsidence in the neotectonic movement. Hence both the absolute and relative heights of the terrain are enormous, and the landform consists mainly of large basins, extensive high plateaus and the highest mountains.

The contact zone of the two plates and the deep rift zones are where the crustal movement is most active, earthquakes and volcanoes are most numerous and terrestrial heat is most intense. For instance, China's earthquakes occur most numer-ously and frequently in the eastern part of Taiwan Province (including the seabed to the east of it) where the Pacific and Asian plates meet. The vicinities of the macrorift zones, where uplift and subsidence during the neotectonic movement were manifest, experience frequent macroseisms. Thus the Liupan Mountains, west Sichuan, Yunnan, the eastern foot of the Tai-hang Mountains and the southern foot of the Yanshan Moun-tains are all areas known for macroseisms. The earthquakes which occurred in Tonghai of Yunnan Province in 1970, in Xingtai (at the eastern foot of the Taihang Mountains) in 1966, and in Tangshan (at the southern foot of the Yanshan Moun-tains) in 1976 were major events. A strong earthquake often results in a conspicuous transfiguration of the earth's surface. For example, the Xingtai earthquake caused a 40-50mm. ter-restrial fluctuation over wide areas. The Tonghai earthquake brought in its wake a new rift which, extending for 60 kilo-metres in the Qujiang rift zone, cut across mountains and valleys with a horizontal heave of 0.14-2 metres.

The live volcanoes which have been active in Chinese his-tory are distributed in a similar pattern to the earthquakes. The highest volcano is Mt. Baitou at the top of the Changbai Mountains on the China-Korea border. It erupted in 1597, 1668 and 1702, leaving behind a crater lake, Tianchi, which has remained intact ever since. In 1720, a volcanic eruption took place on the upper reaches of the Namor River, a tributary of the Nenjiang. The lava flow blocked the Baihe River to form five lakes. The Datun volcano group in Taiwan is composed of 16 volcanoes, still active today. Sulphuric gas is often seen erupting from them. There are four live volcanoes under the sea to the east of Taiwan, one of which erupted in 1927. Generally speaking, China has only a small number of live volcanoes standing several hundred to one thousand or more metres above sea level and having a relative height of only 100 metres or so. They are thus insignificant to China's landform as a whole.

Often, in earthquake and volcano areas, there are hot springs and terrestrial heat. China has altogether 1,900 such springs, mainly in Yunnan, Guangdong, Fujian and Taiwan provinces. Quite a few are found on the Tibetan Plateau, some having a temperature exceeding 90°C., higher than the local boiling point; its highest hot spring is at a height of 5,500 metres in the Gangdise Mountains in Ngamring County. Geysers, seldom known in China, have now been found in the Xigaze area. Their water gushes four times a day, forming water columns more than 20 metres high.

(2) Effect of Climate on China's Landform

Aside from geologic structures, landform is affected by exogenetic forces. The character and intensity of such forces are, to a great extent, determined by climatic conditions, of which precipitation and temperature changes have an overall effect on the process and intensity of weathering, denudation, transport and accumulation.

Generally speaking, in eastern China running water has played a key role in shaping the local landform; but, with precipitation decreasing towards the northwest, arid denudation there gradually becomes predominant. In the big arid basins of northwestern China, annual precipitation is generally less than 200 mm., vegetation is sparse, temperature changes drastic, mechanical weathering strong, and wind erosion and accumulation obvious. These basins have large areas of sand dunes, gobi, and aridly denuded mountains with bare rocks and crisscrossing dry gullies; and piedmont diluvial plains are linked up, though not continuously. All told, China's desertland has an area of 1.3 million square kilometres, or 13.6 per cent of the country's land surface.

To the north of the Qinling-Huaihe line in eastern China, evaporation exceeds precipitation, surface runoff is inadequate and the drainage network sparse. But scouring by rainstorms and flood waters, dissection by rivers, and accumulation of mud and sand are notable; wind erosion and accumulation also have their effect. To the south of the Qinling-Huaihe line, precipitation increases, there is a well-developed network of waterways, erosion and dissection by running water has resulted in a broken, undulating land surface, while alluviation by running water has incessantly added to the accumulation on the plains. In the hot, humid areas of southern China, however, thick red regolith develops extensively due to the prevalence of chemical weathering. In some areas on Hainan Island, such regolith is 30 metres thick. Scoured strongly by rainstorms, the red regolith in places where vegetation is sparse often develops into a "landform of storm flow" which is responsible for the broken terrain in the hilly areas of southern China.

Dominated by high mountains and big plateaus, western China has a cold climate. There are present glaciers with snowline as high as 4,000-5,000 metres. The tongues of such glaciers may drop to 3,000 metres above sea level in some valleys. These high mountains worked over by present glaciers and Quaternary glaciers have developed a glacial landscape. In places not covered by snow, frost weathering is strong and extensive, and frostcracked rocks form talus and rock storm on valley slopes. Below the snowline the temperature is higher and there is low, sparse alpine vegetation on the accumulation of residual topsoil and slope wash.

These places are covered by snow for a fairly long period every year. With the thawing of snow in spring and summer, mud flow and mud-rock flow are often formed. These violently rush towards the foot of the mountains. Take Danghenan Mountain in the western section of the Qilian Mountains for example. The present snowline there reaches 4,300-4,500 metres and the low limit of frost weathering is 4,000 metres, while mud flow extends down to 3,200-3,500 metres.

Present glaciers are distributed widely in China, from the Altay Mountains in the north to the Himalayas and the Yulong Mountains in Lijiang, Yunnan Province, in the south, and from the Pamirs and Mt. Muztagata of the Kunlun range in the west to Mt. Gongga in western Sichuan in the east, stretching 2,500 kilometres either way. Initial estimates put the total area of China's present glaciers at 57,000 square kilometres. Most of them are valley and cirque glaciers. Melting alpine ice and snow are of great significance to agriculture and animal husbandry in the arid areas of northwestern China, and they supply water for irrigation in the oases and for urban use.

Mainly distributed in the northern part of northeast China and on the Qinghai-Tibet Plateau, perennial frozen earth covers 2.15 million square kilometres, or 22.3 per cent of the country's total area. It affects the smooth permeation of surface water, turning the earth's surface into marshes because of excessive dampness. It also hampers the down-cutting of running water while increasing its lateral erosion to make the valleys flat, shallow and broad. Such areas also have frozen-earth knobs and local solution downcast, all of which are unfavourable to transport and production.

Furthermore, in the history of recent geological development, China's climate has undergone changes of varying degrees, and land features born under palaeoclimatic conditions have remained in some areas. These are out of keeping with present agents. For example, traces of Quaternary glaciation are often seen on the mountains of western China, 2,700-3,500 metres above sea level. In the arid and semi-arid areas, a number of landforms, such as broad valleys, lakeside and river terraces, and a well-developed network of waterways, have been discovered, none of which are in keeping with erosion by modern running water. This shows that these areas had previously experienced humid and rainy climate. The frigid Qinghai-Tibet Plateau has a remnant tropical karst landform marked by mogotes, some of which are situated 5,100 metres above sea level. The existence of these left-over landforms contributes to the complexity of China's topography.

(3) Effect of Surficial Substances on China's Landform

China's landform is also greatly influenced by the composition, hardness and texture of surficial substances. The extensive particular landform shaped by substances composing the earth surface is typified by the loess landform in northern China and the karst landform in southwestern China.

By and large, China's loess is mainly distributed north of the Kunlun, Qinling and Dabie mountains. It lies roughly in an east-west belt on the outer rim of the desert areas of the temperate zone. Most well-known is the Loess Plateau embracing central and eastern Gansu, northern Shaanxi, and Shanxi. Averaging 1,000 metres or more in elevation, it occupies an area of 300,000 square kilometres. As a unique loess area, 100-200 metres thick, it is the largest of its kind in the world. Its loess is loose, liable to be scoured by rainwater and dissected by running water. The area has numerous gullies and its surface is badly carved, so much so that soil erosion is serious. As a matter of fact, 90 per cent of the silt in the Huanghe comes from the Loess Plateau. Its existence is, therefore, of paramount importance to the formation of the North China Plain.

With carbonatites covering 1.3 million square kilometres, or 14 per cent of its total area, China has the most extensive

karst area in the world. Guangxi, Guizhou and eastern Yunnan include the greatest part of this area. Since China straddles tropical, subtropical and temperate zones, it has a varied
karst landform, such as the tropical karst pinnacles in Guangdong and Guangxi, the subtropical karst hills and depressions in central China, and the temperate karst springs and
dry valleys in northern China. In particular, the tower karst
in the Guilin area of Guangxi is famous throughout the world.
Carbonate rocks not only result in the unique karst landform
but they constitute special soils and affect vegetation, thus
playing an important role in the formation of different regional landscapes in China.

3. Effect of Landform on the Formation of the Chinese Landscape and Its Significance in Economic Development

As the material basis of physical geography, China's complex landform — great difference in altitude between various parts of the country, sprawling plateaus and mountains,
vast plains, etc. — has a profound effect on the formation
and evolution of its natural landscape.

1) Geomorphic contour and its combination is one of
the main factors contributing to the characteristics of the
formation and evolution of natural regions. The massive
Qinghai-Tibet Plateau, which towers in western China, forms
a natural region in itself, characterized by frigid climate. It
affects the physical geography in vast sections of China by
obstructing or facilitating the movement of air currents and
by serving as the source region of a number of Chinese rivers.
In northwestern China, big basins are sandwiched between
high mountains, and that is why these basins are more arid
than some others elsewhere. Meanwhile, melting ice and snow
flow into the basins from the mountains, to form the struc-
tural model of a landscape stretching from the diluvial plains

at the mountain foot to the central parts of the big desert basins. In eastern China, the terrain is low and flat with numerous low mountains and hills that affect landscape differentiation only to a small extent. A number of ranges such as the Nanling, Qinling, Taihang and Greater Hinggan have different climatic conditions on both sides and thus become marked demarcation lines of regional differentiation.

Mountains have a profound effect on living things and climate and contribute to the formation of a vertical zonation of natural landscape. They have different structures of vertical zonality due to their different geographical positions, absolute and relative heights, sizes and shapes, and aspects and gradients of slopes. Stretching over wide areas, China's mountains are of many types and are located in different horizontal zones. This results in a great variety of complex vertical zonation which substantially enriches the content of China's physical geography and which, sometimes overlapping with the horizontal zones, complicates the regional differentiation of its natural landscape.

2) In the polycyclic process of the geological development of China's mountains, large quantities of igneous rock intruded into the mountains through the crustal movements of different ages. This constitutes a rich and varied resources for metallic ores. Piled up in some large depressions and basins (including continental shelves) were thick layers of sediments containing rich deposits of oil and natural gas.

3) China has vast mountain and hilly areas which are favourable for the development of a diversified economy and the rational integration of agriculture, forestry and animal husbandry. An important aspect of China's socialist construction, therefore, consists in fully and rationally using the natural conditions of these areas, while overcoming the unfavourable conditions for the expansion of production there.

Although plains account for only 12 per cent of the country's total area, they occupy as many as 1.1 million square kilometres in all. They extend over 3,000 kilometres from

the Song-Nen (Songhua and Nenjiang rivers) Plain in the
north to the Lianghu Plain in the south. In addition, there
are smaller delta plains, such as the Zhujiang Delta, as well
as intermontane basins. With flat land, fertile and thick soil
and a dense network of rivers and lakes, China's plains have
become main producers of grain and diversified economic
crops, thanks to the long years of meticulous cultivation by
Chinese peasants.

Moreover, the Chinese topography, in which the west is
higher than the east and in which there are great vertical differences in heights in southwestern China, has resulted in
ample hydraulic resources that permit the multi-level utilization of water power.

4) The unfavourable effects of geomorphic conditions
on economic construction are mainly the following: the rugged mountainous areas hinder construction of highways,
railways and other communication facilities; the massive permeation of surface water in karst areas causes underground
caverns to collapse; sandstorms in the desert areas are harmful
to production; and scouring of the areas of loess, red earth
and yellow earth by rainstorms causes soil erosion. But the
industrious and courageous Chinese people have full con-
fidence in overcoming natural difficulties. They have built
railways in areas of Sichuan Province which have been known
as natural barriers, in the karst areas where limestone caverns
abound, and in the Gobi and other desert areas despite frequent sandstorms. They have constructed terraced fields and
orchards in many mountainous areas, initially checking soil
erosion there. The planting of windbreaks and sand-fixation
forests in northwestern China has greatly weakened the invasion by dry wind and thus promoted the growth of agriculture and animal husbandry.

Chapter III

CLIMATE

1. Basic Characteristics of China's Climate and Its Formative Factors

With a vast territory, China is known for its varied climate, which is essentially monsoonal. Notable seasonal changes in the direction of the prevailing winds account for the marked differences in climate: dry and cold winter, and wet and hot summer with concentrated rainfall.

The main factors in the formation of China's climate are:

1) Solar radiation. China extends over nearly 50 degrees of latitude from north to south. Latitudinal differences in the amount of solar radiation are the basic factor behind the progressive decrease of heat from south to north. In winter, the total amount of solar radiation sharply decreases from south to north, and the temperature on the surface and near the surface layer of air falls likewise. During summer, daytime lengthens with an increase of latitude, compensating to a certain extent for the effect of the smaller angle of solar altitude. Thus the total amount of radiation received by the north nearly equals that received by the south, greatly reducing the north-south temperature difference.

In terms of the value of radiation equilibrium, except for areas north of Lat. 40°N., which show a negative value in winter months, most parts of China show a positive value throughout the year, with the income of radiative energy exceeding expenditure and the annual value of radiation equilibrium amounting to 50-70 kilocalories per square centimetre (Fig. 3). This shows that most parts of China have quite abun-

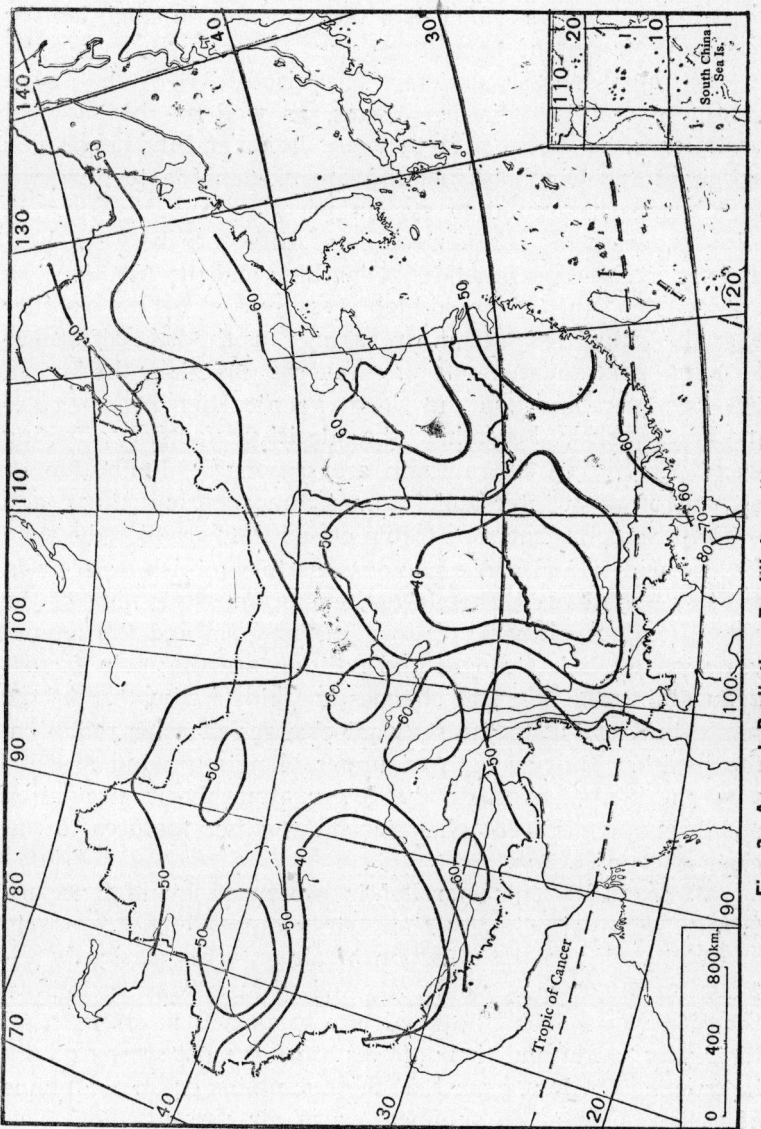

Fig. 3 Annual Radiation Equilibrium (in Kcal/cm²) in China

dant heat resources, which is a very favourable condition for the development of agriculture.

2) Monsoon circulation. The disposition of the Asian continent and its adjacent oceans, as well as the seasonal variation of the upper planetary circulation and the orographic action of the Qinghai-Tibetan Plateau, combine to give rise to a monsoon circulation system peculiar to East Asia. In winter, due to the considerable heat difference between land and sea in East Asia, the Mongolian high and the Aleutian low are well developed and cold high pressure controls the weather over the Chinese mainland. In summer, as the heat difference between land and sea acts in a reverse direction, the Indian hot low over land and the North Pacific High over sea are most powerful, becoming the decisive factors affecting weather. Spring and autumn are seasons of diminution or growth of the winter and summer atmospheric centres, and of the transition from one to the other; they are also the time for the winter and summer monsoons to diminish or grow in power respectively. The strengthening and weakening of the above four atmospheric centres in East Asia and the annual variation of their strength and position are the main factors determining the seasonal changes in China's climate. At the same time, owing to the seasonal changes of solar radiation, the position and strength of upper planetary wind systems vary markedly, affecting the lower atmospheric circulation and bringing different climatic and weather features to various parts of China.

3) Relief. China's relief is contoured by high mountains. The trend of many mountain ranges which are nearly at right angles to the direction of air currents, seriously affects the latter's movement. Blocked by numerous mountains, the cold waves from the north are weakened in strength on their way south, and their effects are felt most strongly only in crossing the lower parts of the mountains or on the plains of eastern China. In summer, warm air currents flow over the mountains bringing much rain to the windward slopes,

while the lee sides are hot and dry. The high mountains surrounding the inland basins in the northwest block moisture from the oceans and increase aridity there. The Tibetan Plateau, high in elevation and massive in size, exerts a great influence on East Asian atmospheric circulation. It intercepts and disturbs to a great extent the westerly air currents of the middle latitudes, and obstructs the moisture coming from the Indian Ocean. This gives rise to singular plateau airflows and is a factor affecting climatic and weather variations over wide areas of the country.

4) Ocean currents. The ocean currents that pass China's coasts are the warm Kuroshio (Black Currents) of the West Pacific and the China littoral current. The Kuroshios do not have much influence on China's coasts as far as the increase of temperature and moisture is concerned, because they are far from shore and because the winter monsoon blows off shore. The littoral currents, which move' southward from the Bohai Sea all the way to the Taiwan Straits, gain strength in winter because of the northwest monsoon. They are thus cold currents which help stabilize the air in the surface layer and reduce precipitation.

The aforesaid four factors affect China's climate interplay and condition one another. Their combined action gives China's climate the characteristics of a monsoon climate, as well as its extremely complex regional differences.

2. Atmospheric Circulation and the Advance and Retreat of Monsoons.

China has a typical monsoon climate. The vast territory produces marked regional differences as regards the position of circulation, the distance to the ocean and specific terrain, and these in turn lead to a considerable variation in the intensity and duration of monsoons as well as their influence on the climate. The following is a brief description of the formation and special features of China's monsoons, their circulation, their advance and retreat, the influence of the Tibetan Plateau on their circulation, and the action of the main weather fronts.

(1) Formation and Special Features of Monsoons

A monsoon is a synthetic phenomenon subject to the combined influence of the disposition of land and sea, atmospheric circulation and specific terrain. The heat differences arising from the disposition of land and sea in East Asia obviously upsets the distribution of the lower planetary wind belts in the troposphere, forming a strong monsoon pressure field. Therefore, such a heat factor is the fundamental cause for the formation of monsoons in China. The seasonal displacement of the upper planetary wind belts, resulting from seasonal changes in solar altitude, and the orographic action of the Qinghai-Tibetan Plateau are important factors contributing to the evolution of China's monsoons and to their complex changes.

The main features of monsoon circulation in China are its marked seasonal changes.

1) Marked seasonal changes of the general atmospheric circulation system. It changes from a pressure ridge of Long. 80°-90°E. and a coastal pressure trough in winter to a pressure trough of Long. 70°-80°E. and a coastal shallow pressure ridge in summer. This seasonal change, involving a nearly contrary phase, is almost unknown elsewhere in the northern hemisphere.

2) Marked seasonal changes of basic air currents predominating in China. In winter, northwest, north and northeast monsoons prevail in the lower troposphere while the middle and upper troposphere is controlled by westerlies. In summer, southwest, south and southeast monsoons dominate the lower troposphere, while the middle and upper troposphere is controlled by subtropical westerlies. Such noticeable seasonal changes of basic air currents are not only

rare in non-monsoon regions but also unique in the whole of the northern hemisphere.

3) Diametrically different predominant air masses in winter and summer. In the winter half-year, polar or modified polar continental air masses are predominant over China's mainland, mostly resulting in cold fronts and cold waves. In the summer half-year, many parts of China are influenced by tropical and subtropical marine air masses and tropical continental air masses, which often lead to typhoons, thunderstorms, tornadoes and other violent weather systems, as well as showers and torrential rains in the wake of cold fronts.

4. Diametrically different weather in winter and summer and distinct seasons. Winter is dry and cold with clear sky and little rain. Summer is damp and hot with rainy weather. In spring, the temperature rises rapidly over the land and the air is unstable, so the weather is windy. In autumn, the temperature drops sharply over the land and the air tends to be stable, so the weather is mostly clear. In short, China's climate is characterized by notable alternations of season, which present sharp contrasts in most areas.

(2) Circulation Situation

The regular seasonal changes of monsoons over China chiefly result from seasonal changes in the centres of high and low pressure in East Asia, while the monsoons' intensity, stability and scope are related to the character of these centres.

In winter, the Mongolian high becomes strong enough to control the whole mainland while the Aleutian low penetrates deeper and extends further to stay over the northern part of the North Pacific. The former is a centre of continental anticyclones and the source of the dry and cold polar continental air masses. The action of the cold air of the Mongolian high directly affects the specific features of China's winter climate and weather changes, such as severe cold and scanty rain and snow over a long time, repeated outbursts of cold waves and strong winds, frost and snowstorms in the wake of the cold fronts. The Mongolian high has little influence over the Yunnan-Guizhou Plateau, which is controlled by southwest warm currents formed by tropical continental air masses. The weather there is mostly sunny, warm and dry, becoming China's centre of warmth in winter.   At an altitude of 1,500 metres the westerly air currents in the western part of the Qinghai-Tibetan Plateau consist of two branches, south and north. The north branch moves across northwestern, northern, northeastern and eastern China towards the North Pacific. The south branch passes through the southern edge of the plateau to become southwest currents of rather high temperature and much moisture, causing prolonged cloudiness in winter over Sichuan and Guizhou provinces. Besides, an air current divergence zone appears over Shaanxi, Sichuan, Hubei and Hunan provinces where the northeast currents moving southward and the southwest warm and wet currents moving eastward merge to form a shear line (corresponding to it on the surface chart is the "Southern China Quasi-stationary Front"). Each time a shear line is formed, the southwest warm and wet currents glide upward along the shallow-layer cold air, often bringing about cloudy and rainy weather in southwestern and central China. At times when cold air comes down from the north, there is considerable precipitation in central and eastern China.

Spring is a transitional period as far as changes in barometric pressure are concerned. This is the season when the Mongolian high and the Aleutian low weaken and gradually leave China. At the same time, the North Pacific subtropical high gains strength gradually and its centre expands and moves westward; the continental low pressure also begins to take shape. Thus the four centres of action are all involved in the spring weather phenomena, forming a saddle field centred at Hetao (the Great Bend of the Huanghe). There is complex interchange of south and north air currents, frequent cyclonic actions and radical weather changes, and the wind direc-

tion is not so stable as in winter. With the northward movement of the westerlies in the middle latitudes and the notable
weakening of the south westerly jet stream, a cyclonic vortex
develops over Yunnan and Guizhou, resulting in more
frequent airflow and more moisture. In eastern China's coastal regions, however, there are more southerlies and considerably increased humidity at lower altitudes. Hence the
sustained rainy weather south of the Changjiang River. At
this time, weather in the northeastern and the northern part
of northern China is controlled by the northwest air currents because of the north westerly jet stream.

In summer, when the Asian continent becomes an extensive zone of low pressure and there is a zone of powerful
high pressure over the western North Pacific, the pattern of
barometric distribution is just the reverse of that in winter.
At this time, the weather in most parts of China is controlled
by subtropical and tropical systems. The dominant airflows
are rather deep and thick; the air currents between the earth's
surface and 3-5 kilometres above ground are basically similar,
and the greater part of the country has southwest winds.

The barometric situation undergoes gradual change between spring and summer. In early April, a centre of low
pressure appears over the mouth of the Heilong River in the
eastern part of the saddle field. With the rapid rise in temperature over the continent, this centre moves towards north
China; in summer it develops into a centre of low pressure over
China's mainland and joins the powerful low pressure in northern India. By then, the continental high pressure has disappeared, while the North Pacific high is at its best. The tropical
marine air masses coming from the North Pacific high form
the southeast monsoons, whose prolonged action covers a wide
area. When these prevail, moist air may penetrate northern
China all the way in from the Pacific and Indian oceans. In
late May or early June, the north westerly jet stream disappears, while the south subtropical westerly jet stream suddenly pushes northward; the Pacific high pressure ridge also

moves north and the upper east wind of low latitudes thrusts to the south rim of the Qinghai-Tibetan Plateau. Therefore, the southwest monsoon from the Indian Ocean influences southwestern China and the rainy season begins there. In eastern China, the rain belt steadily advances north along with the northward movement of the subtropical high pressure ridge. When this ridge arrives at the middle and lower reaches of the Changjiang, it may cause a prolonged mid-summer drought there, but it helps to create precipitation in western Sichuan and northwestern China. Meanwhile, Pacific typhoons begin to invade China's mainland. In the last 20 days of July, the south westerly airflow again thrusts northward as far as Lat. 40°N. where it usually joins the upper southerly airflow over the lower reaches of the Huanghe, contributing to the precipitation of the rainy season in northern China and the south part of northeastern China.

Autumn sees the summer circulation type passing over to the winter circulation type. In early September, when the Mongolian high again emerges over Central Asia, a polar high which takes shape at a fast pace may push southward to lower latitudes. Because the upper subtropical high remains at higher altitudes, overlapping on the lower high pressure, weather in most regions is stable, with clear skies. However, southwestern China is still influenced by the southwest airflow and has mostly rainy weather. In October, the westerlies move southward and the westerly currents in the middle troposphere are again divided into the south and north currents. As the south westerly jet stream gains in strength, the southwest monsoon retreats from the mainland. The east-wind circulation over Sichuan and Guizhou changes over to the west-wind circulation, resulting in what is called "autumn rains in western China". The clear autumn weather over China's mainland disappears, marking the change from the summer circulation type to the winter circulation type in East Asia. At this time, the Aleutian low begins to gain in strength and to expand, the Indian low retreats, and the air pressure in the centre of the Pacific high lowers significantly as it draws back to the southeast. After early November, the Mongolian high completely envelopes the Chinese mainland, giving rise again to the winter barometric situation. Dry and cold winter monsoons abruptly sweeps down south to control the climate for the whole of China.

(3) Advance and Retreat of Winter and Summer Monsoons

In the winter half-year, the whole mainland and offshore islands come under the influence of winter monsoons. Their southern limit may reach the South China Sea (Line 1 in Fig. 4) and their western limit may reach the east and north fringes of the Qinghai-Tibetan Plateau (Line 3 in Fig. 4), forming an orographic front. The southeastern section, which is a front surface between the winter continental cold air currents and the southwest warm air currents, is usually called the "Kunming Quasi-stationary Front".

In early March, the southern part of China begins to be influenced by summer monsoons (southeast monsoons) which then gradually advance northward. In late April when the summer monsoons prevail over southern China, central China begins to feel their influence. In mid-June, the summer monsoons prevail over central China and begin to influence northern China. In mid-July, the summer monsoons that prevail over northern China may affect south Inner Mongolia. In the first 20 days of August, the summer monsoons reach their northernmost position (Line 2 in Fig. 4), i.e., the northern limit of the summer monsoons. Areas to the west of this line, which are weakly influenced by the summer monsoons, remain dry throughout the year.

When the summer monsoons withdraw from north to south in, generally speaking, late August or early September, the winter monsoons move southward. They reach central China very soon and come down to southern China approxi-

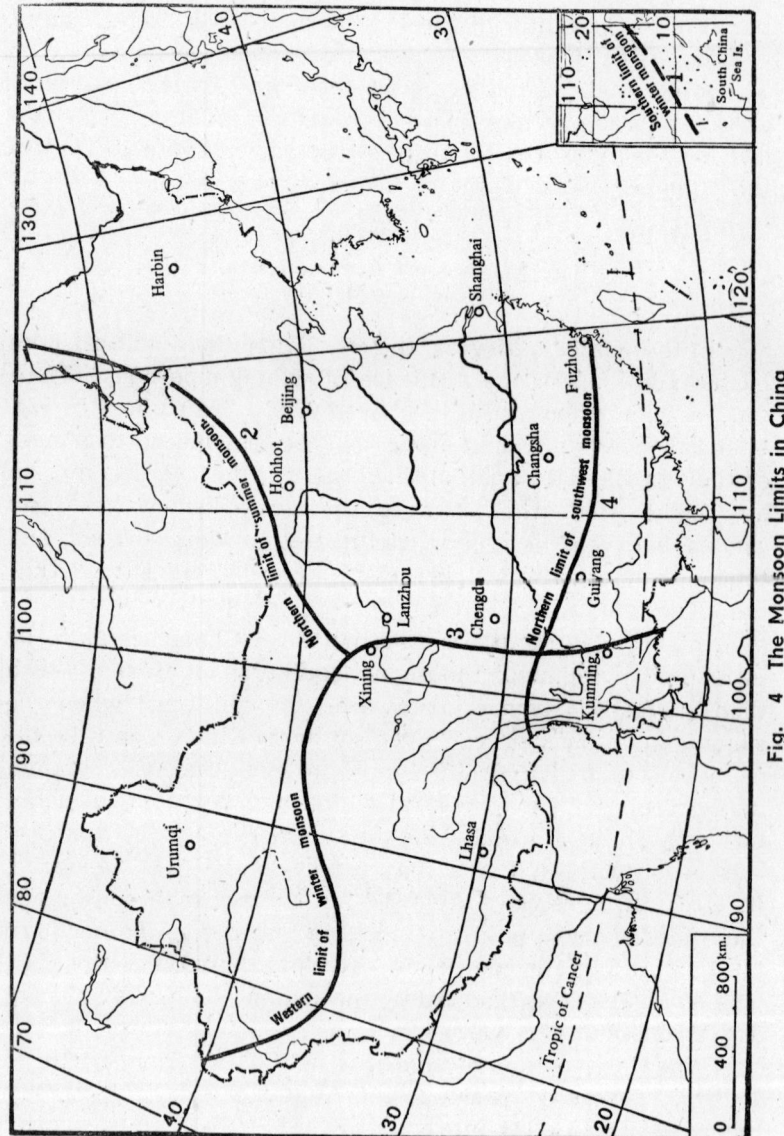

Fig. 4   The Monsoon Limits in China

mately at the end of September or beginning of October. From north to south, the winter monsoons sweep the whole of China in less than one month, marking the end of the summer monsoons' prevalence over the Chinese mainland. So it takes four months for the summer monsoons to invade southern China and prevail over the whole of the country. This shows that they come slowly but retreat quickly.

In summer, the southwestern part of China is also influenced by southwest monsoons, which explode northward in mid-June and, at their height, may move along the eastern rim of the Qinghai-Tibetan Plateau to reach somewhere north of Lat. 30°N. These monsoons may also affect the Zhujiang River basin, though they only reach the vicinity of Nanling Mountains (Line 4 in Fig. 4).

The winter and summer monsoons advance and retreat by distinct stages and entail marked changes in various weather phenomena and meteorological elements, most notable of which are spatial variations in rainfall. A large rain belt appears over the coasts of southern China in mid-May, and this later moves north in a regular pattern, reaching the north side of the Nanling Mountains in early June. It makes its first thrust in mid-June to reach the Changjiang. A second thrust in mid-July brings it across the Huaihe to the middle section of the Huanghe. The northernmost position is reached in mid-August. After August, the rain belt quickly moves southward.

(4) Impact of the Qinghai-Tibetan Plateau on Monsoon Circulation

With a massive area and an average height of over 4,000 metres, the Qinghai-Tibetan Plateau exerts tremendous influence on the middle-latitude atmospheric circulation in East Asia and over China's climate as a whole. Basing themselves on a systematic analysis of the general circulation and laboratory simulation, Chinese meteorologists have shown that the Qinghai-Tibetan Plateau creates a great dynamic disturbance and exerts notable thermodynamic influences over westerly circulation in East Asia, which helps to maintain and enhance the monsoons there.

The dynamic action of the Qinghai-Tibetan Plateau expresses itself mainly in the detouring and branching phenomena of westerly airflow in the vicinity and as a barrier to the south and north air currents. The plateau blocks westerly airflow on its western rim to create two branches of stable and strong west winds, or the south and north jet streams. The north jet stream, or southwest air current in the northwestern part of the plateau, bypasses northern Xinjiang to change into a northwest current which curves as an anticyclone. The south jet stream, or the northwest air current in the southwestern part of the plateau, bypasses the plateau to turn into a southwest current which curves as a cyclone. This gives rise to a circulation pattern with a ridge in the north and a trough in the south. Such a branching phenomenon usually begins in October and continues through to June. This phenomenon not only exists in the lower troposphere, but also may affect altitudes up to nine kilometres and higher. Furthermore, it brings about a "dead-water region" with little wind velocity on the windward and leeward sides of the plateau.

Acting as a barrier, the plateau prevents the advance of the westerly weather system, and directly blocks the southward invasion of cold air from the north and the penetration of the southwest monsoons into the interior. Moreover, it forces the southwest monsoons with moist air from India to remain in the southern part of the plateau, unable to penetrate deep into the inland areas of northwestern China, so that many topographic quasi-stationary fronts form in southern Xinjiang and Gansu to the north of the plateau. The resulting weather situation is characterized by a dry, cold winter and dry, hot summer. Besides, the plateau prevents India and Burma to the south from being influenced by cold wave in winter. The summer tropical storms, or typhoons, from the

Bay of Bangal are also blocked at the southern foot of the Himalayas.

As for the thermodynamic action of the Qinghai-Tibetan Plateau, first the plateau — a huge uplifted landmass — acts as an obvious cold/heat source for the surrounding free atmosphere in winter and summer. In winter, the plateau is colder than the surrounding free atmosphere and air moves out from it. Thus the impact of the plateau on winter monsoons is to increase the surface high pressure, thereby strengthening winter monsoon circulation. In summer, the plateau is warmer than the surrounding free atmosphere and the ascending movement of air currents over it is stronger than the ascending movement in the east. Thus air in the lower altitudes is transferred to the plateau, thereby enhancing the strength of the summer monsoons. Owing to the action of this cold/heat source, a cold high pressure forms in the western part of the plateau between October and April, a hot depression appears there from June to August, and May and September become the periods of transition from one to the other.

The forming of the cold high pressure and hot depression over the plateau results in a singular and complex structure of pressure and flow fields in the plateau area. A depression belt arises over India and Burma, south of the cold high pressure, while there is a high pressure belt north of the hot depression. The appearance of these high and low pressures had an important impact on the formation of drought in northwestern China and on the formation of rain at the southern foot of the Himalayas in winter.

Second, the heating action of the Qinghai-Tibetan Plateau in summer has tremendous impact on the general circulation in East Asia, which results in an obvious convergence in the middle and lower layers and an obvious divergence in the upper layers to form a unique subtropical high pressure, i.e., Qinghai-Tibet high pressure. The northward withdrawal of the westerlies over the plateau, the establishment of the easterlies to the south, the emergence of the upper high pressure and the hot depression over the area, the formation of the monsoon meridional circulation and other phenomena are all inter-related. However, the key factor in all of this is the heating action of the plateau. The formation and movement of the southwest monsoons and the strengthening and westward extension of the North Pacific subtropical high in summer are also due to such heating action.

Besides, the displacement of the Qinghai-Tibet high pressure has an important effect on the occurrence of drought and waterlogging over wide areas in eastern China. When the centre of the high pressure is west of 100° E., eastern China has more rain and is liable to suffer waterlogging; when its centre is east of 100°E., the same region has little rain, which sometimes means drought.

(5) Cold Wave, "Plum Rains" and Typhoon

Under the influence of the above-mentioned atmospheric circulation systems and with the advance and retreat of the monsoons as well as the southward and northward movement of the barometric belts, the air masses prevailing in China play varying roles in different seasons. The polar continental air masses and tropical marine air masses are present throughout the year; the former are particularly developed in winter while the latter are most prevalent in summer. Both types are the most important air masses existing in China. The confrontation of the polar continental air masses, tropical marine air masses and their modified air masses forms various fronts and produces corresponding weather phenomena, of which cold wave and "plum rains" are the most significant and peculiar to China's climate.

1) Cold Wave

In the winter half-year, strong cold air often invades China. But the area of its influence and the extent of the resulting temperature decrease varies greatly. Usually what is referred to as a cold wave is the strong cold air that causes a sustained and sharp drop in temperature over a wide area and has great influence on crop cultivation and other productive activities. As far as China is concerned, its meteorological departments stipulate that a cold wave refers to an attack of the invading cold air that causes temperature along the middle and lower Changjiang River and areas north of it to drop by at least 10°C. within 48 hours, brings the lowest temperature along the same section of the river down to 4°C. or below and produces a northerly wind of force 5-7 over the mainland and 7 or upward over the sea. A violent cold wave refers to the situation where the cold air makes the temperature drop by 14°C. or more within 48 hours, accompanied by a northerly wind of force 5-7.

Most cold waves that invade China originate in the deep, thick cold air of the Arctic Ocean. When they flow past nothern Siberia and the Mongolian People's Republic, they strengthen the continental high pressure. Then they burst into China and advance southward roughly along the following three routes (Fig. 5): The first route (west route) begins in Siberia, passes through Xinjiang, Gansu and the Loess Plateau, and extends all the way into the North China Plain. Then it moves southward in two branches. One branch moves through the Jianghuai (Changjiang and Huaihe rivers) Plain to enter the East China Sea as a fast-moving cold wave. This one is the coldest, driest and thickest. The other branch bypasses the Qinling Mountains and turns southwest to enter the Lianghu Basin in the middle reaches of the Changjiang. Then it moves quite slowly due to obstruction by the Nanling Mountains. After crossing the low passes of the Nanling Mountains, it penetrates Guangdong and Guangxi to reach the South China Sea. This route of cold air is the main one for cold waves invading China, and it has the maximum momentum and influence. It makes the temperature drop sharply, resulting in rainy and snowy weather over wide areas.

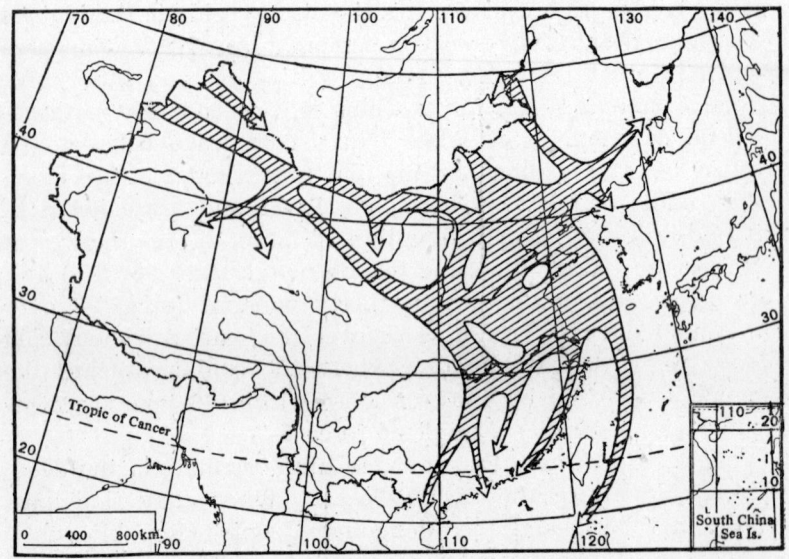

Fig. 5 Cold Wave Routes Within China

The second route (northwest route) starts from Western Siberia and the Mongolian People's Republic, and goes southward across the area of Hetao into the middle and lower reaches of the Changjiang and areas south of it, sometimes even reaching southern China. The cold waves along this route frequently cause strong winds and a lowering of temperature north of the Changjiang, while rainy and snowy weather may develop south of it. The third route (north route) starts east of Lake Baikal, moves past the northern part of northern China and the southern part of northeastern China, then turns southwest to spread southward via the lower Huanghe. It usually affects only areas north of the Changjiang. It is rather weak in strength and does not entail any sharp drop in temperature, though it can produce a northeaster over the Bohai and Yellow seas and the lower reaches of the Huanghe. And it can often lead to heavy snow and severe cold in spring along the lower Changjiang.

With the invasion of a cold wave, the wind mostly becomes northwesterly. Its velocity may reach upwards of 20 metres per second. In the north it is always accompanied by sandstorms. As it moves southward, it uplifts the moist modified polar continental air masses, thus forming cloudy, rainy or snowy weather. In the wake of the cold front, the weather becomes clear and very cold because it is enveloped by the dry polar cold air.

The cold wave generally travels at a speed of 20-30 kilometres an hour. South of the Changjiang, its velocity slows down greatly owing to deeper modification of the air mass and retardation by the terrain. On the average, it takes one day for a cold wave to move from Inner Mongolia to northern China, another day from northern to central China, and still another day from central to southern China. But when a violent cold wave comes down from the north, it can sweep the whole country within one or two days. According to statistical data, such cold waves affect the greater part of China between October and April at most only three or four times a year.

Between January 24 and 31, 1960, a violent cold wave hit China with an intensity rarely seen in the past two decades or more. Having invaded Xinjiang, it swept through the Gansu Corridor to reach the Changjiang valley, then entered the South China Sea through Hunan and Guangxi. Xinjiang and the areas south of the Changjiang experienced the maximum decrease in temperature, which plummeted as many as 26°C. in some places. Yining in Xinjiang registered the lowest temperature (-40.3°C.) ever recorded in its history. The cold wave invasion caused snowfall in the northwest and precipitation of 10-30 mm. south of the Changjiang. Precipitation in most parts of Guangdong and Guangxi reached 80 mm. (over 100 mm. in Guangdong's Foshan and Zhanjiang prefectures), and torrential rains, unusual in winter, were reported.

As a cold wave moves southward, it is repeatedly obstructed and weakened by mountains. The Nanling range is the last barrier in its southward march, and the areas south of the mountain range are markedly different as regards the extent to which they are influenced by the cold wave from those on the north side. In winter, the frequency of cold waves and strong cold air invading southern China is only half that in the Huanghuai (Huanghe and Huaihe) areas and one-third of that in the northeast. Moreover, the extent of temperature decrease in southern China during cold current invasion is generally smaller than in the northern regions. Take the January mean temperature for example. Temperature drops on an average 1.5°C. for 220 kilometres between the North China Plain and southern Hunan, but the average temperature difference is as high as 5°-6°C. for the same distance in the vicinity of the Nanling Mountains. This indicates what the obstruction of the Nanling Mountains means.

The invasion of cold waves have an obvious adverse effect on industrial and agricultural production. Frost over wide areas of China and the date of the initial frost are all closely related to it.

2) Plum Rain

"Plum rains", named for the time of year when plum trees ripen, constitute another important weather phenomenon, which results from the confrontation of air masses within China. Plum rains mean a weather process of continuous dampness and hotness and much precipitation that occurs between mid-June and early July in the middle and lower reaches of the Changjiang and the Huaihe River basin. They are produced by a plum rain front between a tropical air mass and a polar air mass, as well as by cyclones that continuously emerge over it. The rain belt that begins to push northward from the Nanling Mountains before June and the one that pushes towards the Huaihe and Huanghe River basins after July are the products of this plum rain front. With a great deal of vapour, the warm and wet tropical marine air mass provides the necessary condition for the formation of the plum rains, but the quantity of a plum rain is mainly determined by the frequency and intensity of the cold air moving down from the north, whereas the strength of the force in between the cold and warm airs is decisive to the positioning of the rain belt and the speed of its movement. With the advance of the southeast monsoon, the plum rain front reaches the Changjiang River basin in June and generally pushes swiftly into northern China in less than a month. If there is a high pressure over the Sea of Okhotsk and the Sea of Japan which retards the plum rain front in its northward march, prolonged plum rains will result in the Changjiang River basin. The floods that occurred there in 1931 and 1954 were an outcome of such a weather situation. Conversely, if the plum rain front moves swiftly northward, there will be dry weather and scanty rain in the river basin, because the region is enveloped by a subtropical high pressure. Therefore, plum rains are plentiful in some years, and not so plentiful or even absent in others.

In the Changjiang and Huaihe River basins, the plum rain belt is rather narrow with little south-north swing, but it contains much precipitation. Often a centre of rainstorm is formed and it stays for a rather long period, adding greatly to the total precipitation. According to meteorological statistics from Shanghai, Nanjing, Wuhu, Jiujiang and Hankou, the average plum rain precipitation is 123 mm., roughly 70 per cent of the total registered for June and July at the five places.

Plum rains have an important bearing on agricultural production in the Changjiang and Huaihe River basins, as can be seen from the popular saying: "No plum rains, and we'll go hungry half the year." Ancient Chinese almanacs record calculations for the dates of the beginning and ending of the plum rain season. The advent of plum rains is of great importance to agricultural production in vast areas of eastern China, because it may provide a great deal of water for large tracts of farmland, increase the flow of the rivers and lakes for the benefit of navigation and irrigation, and replenish the reservoirs for use in different seasons. However, prolonged plum rains may bring excessive precipitation to a given area and cause floods and waterlogging. And the resultant lack of sunshine is unfavourable to crop growth.

3) Typhoon

A typhoon is a violent tropical cyclone formed over tropical oceans in the western part of the North Pacific and the South China Sea. As a weather system typhoons have an important influence on China's coasts in both summer and autumn. China customarily classifies the tropical cyclones into three types according to the average maximum wind velocity in their centres: (a) tropical depression, with an average maximum wind velocity of 10.8-17.1 m./sec. (equivalent to wind force 6-7); (b) typhoon, with an average maximum wind velocity of 17.2-32.6 m./sec. (equivalent to wind force 8-11); and (c) violent typhoon, with an average maximum wind velocity exceeding 32.6 m./sec. (equivalent to wind force 12).

After their formation in the general area of the Caroline Islands east of the Philippines, in the West Pacific, typhoons move along vastly different tracks which, however, may be divided essentially into three (Fig. 6): (1) A typhoon moves west to enter the South China Sea via the Philippines and to strike China's coast at Guangdong or Guangxi, or to strike Viet Nam. (2) A typhoon moves northwest past the Bashi Channel to strike Taiwan, Guangdong or Fujian with diminishing force. Then the weakened tropical cyclone may sometimes penetrate as far as Jiangxi, Hunan or Guangxi. (3) A typhoon first moves northwest by west, makes a northeast turn at 20°-30°N. and heads for Japan or the North Pacific. Typhoons that change directions over China's mainland often pass through Korea or China's northeast.

West Pacific typhoons may occur any time of a year, but they mostly occur between May and October, and especially between July and September, a period that experienc-

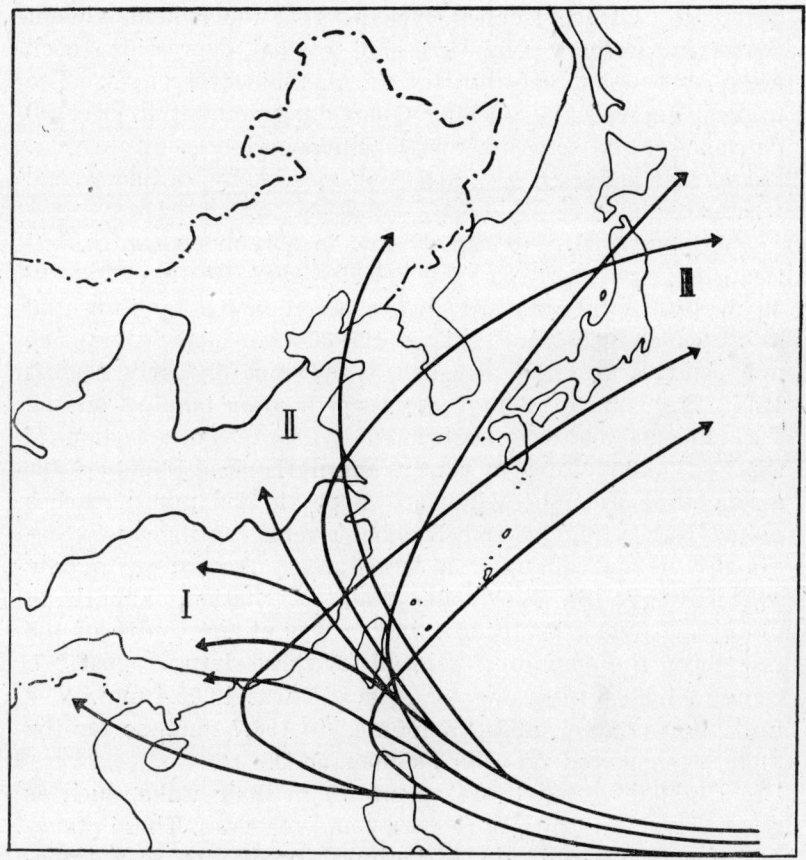

Fig. 6 Typhoon Tracks in China

cs more than 60 per cent of the annual typhoons. They form
in the West Pacific on the average of about 30 a year, but
those that strike the Chinese mainland average only 10. The
areas where they strike the land range from Liaoning in the
north to the Guangdong and Guangxi coasts in the south.
Guangdong Province is the most frequented (about 50 per
cent of the annual occurrences), and next come Taiwan Province (around 20 per cent) and Fujian Province (about 15

per cent). Of the tropical cyclones that reach land, violent typhoons, ordinary typhoons and tropical depressions each make up roughly one-third of the annual occurrences. The tropical depressions reaching Guangdong amount to over 60 per cent of the total number China experiences every year. Taiwan and Fujian are attacked mostly by ordinary and violent typhoons.

Air pressure is extremely low in a typhoon centre, but the wind force is strong, the velocity generally reaching 20-30 m./sec. Typhoons are always accompanied by torrential rains, which generally register 100-300 mm., sometimes 500 mm., and occasionally as much as 900 mm. In early August 1975, Typhoon No. 3 moved up north after landing on the Fujian coast and was obstructed by the eastern section of the Funiu Mountains in southwestern Henan. It stayed for a long time over the windward slopes in the upper reaches of the Ruhe, Honghe and Tangbai rivers, causing an exceptionally heavy rain over a large area. According to data collected by the Linzhuang Rainfall Station, Fangcheng County, Xinyang Prefecture, which was at the centre of the rainstorm, the amount of rainfall for three days, August 5-7, came to 1,628.6 mm., and for August 7 was 1,005.4 mm. The maximum hourly rainfall amounted to 198.7 mm., so far the highest registered on China's mainland.

Typhoons often bring calamities in their wake, such as gales, torrential rains, huge waves and sea tides. These gravely affect industrial and agricultural production, sea transport and fishing operations, and threaten the lives and property of people. But in summer and autumn, when China's southeast coasts are influenced solely by the southeast monsoon, the weather there is clear and hot with little rain. Particularly in areas south of the Changjiang River under the influence of the mid-summer subtropical high pressure, a summer drought may occur. If, at this time, a typhoon or a tropical depression brings not too much rainfall, it will help alleviate or even relieve the dry spell, much to the benefit

of agricultural production.   Since Liberation, China has
greatly intensified its research into typhoons, and improved
typhoon forecasting, the accuracy of which has increased
through the summing up of the experience of fishermen.

3. Characteristics of Temperature Distribution and Thermal Resources

As its land area is large and influenced by monsoons,
China's climate is distinctly continental.   But the annual
range of temperatures in various parts of China is greater
than it is in other parts of the world that are in the same
latitudes.   In winter, the temperature is lower than the
world-wide average value of latitudes, showing a negative
departure.   In summer the temperature is higher than the
world-wide average value of latitudes, showing a positive
departure.   The value of departure is smaller in areas near
the sea and in the lower latitudes.   It increases inland and in
the higher latitudes. Table 2 shows the differences for January and July mean temperatures at different latitudes in
eastern China from north to south.

Table 2.   Value of Departure of January and July Mean Temperatures at Four Representative Stations in Eastern China

Station	January (°C.)	July (°C.)
Aihui	-16.8	+5.2
Beijing	-9.9	+2.3
Hankou	-10.9	+16.0
Qiongshan	-4.0	+0.9

(1) Characteristics of Temperature Distribution

Most parts of China are located in subtropical and temperate zones. Because China has a wide range of latitudes and its terrain undulates markedly, there are wide temperature differences between the south and north, and the terrain exerts notable influences on the distribution of temperature. In terms of annual mean temperature, the difference is more than 30°C. from the South China Sea islands to the northern part of Heilongjiang Province. The basic pattern of temperature distribution is as follows: Temperature decreases gradually from south to north in the eastern part of the country. Orographic influences are greater than latitudinal influences in the western part so that the annual mean temperature for much of the Qinghai-Tibetan Plateau stands below 0°C., whereas that in the centre of the Tarim Basin and Turpan Depression to its north is above 12°C. (Fig. 7). Isothermal lines drawn over plains and huge plateaus are rather sparse while those drawn near plateaus and high mountains tend to be dense.

Because China is widely affected by a monsoon climate, the annual mean temperature is hardly sufficient to illustrate the country's thermal features and cannot show the thermal effect on agriculture and other economic activities. Thus it is necessary to elaborate on the distribution of temperatures in different seasons.

1) Winter Temperature

January is the month when temperatures in different parts of the country fall to their lowest points. So the January temperature can be regarded as representing the winter temperature. It can be seen from the January isotherm distribution chart (Fig. 8) that the temperature in eastern China decreases rapidly with increasing latitudes and that the isothermal lines are densely distributed and roughly parallel with the latitudes. But in western China, the temperature is rather low for the most part, so the isothermal lines are quite sparse-

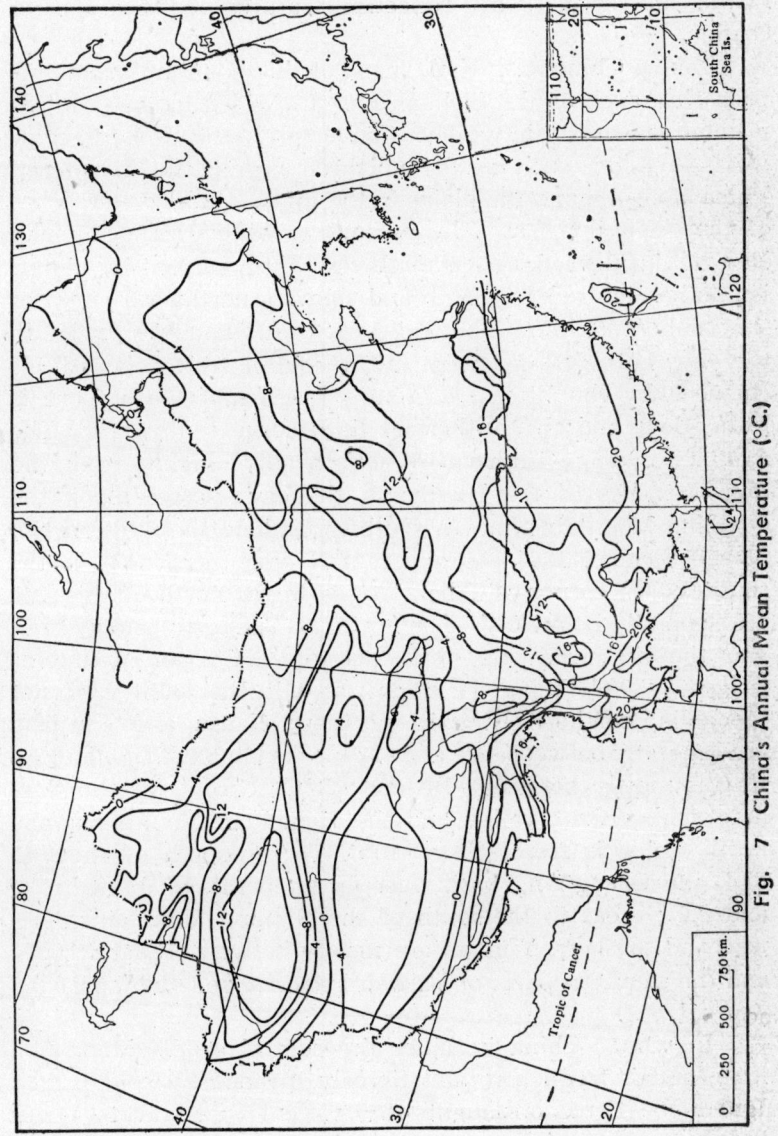

Fig. 7 China's Annual Mean Temperature (°C.)

ly distributed, markedly reflecting features of topographical change.

Taking China as a whole, most of the mountain-surrounded basins, such as the Sichuan and Tarim basins, are centres of relative warmth in winter. Conversely, areas prone to cold-wave invasion, such as the northern part of the northeast, Inner Mongolia and the plains in the middle and lower reaches of the Changjiang, are always cold in winter. The Yunnan Plateau, influenced by the southwest warm current in winter, is another centre of warmth and shows a northward curve of the isothermal lines. The Taiwan Strait, though situated in the low latitudes, is swept by a cold northeaster and influenced by the littoral current. The temperature there is rather low, and the isothermal lines curve southward. The January average isotherm of 0°C. begins roughly from the lower reaches of the Huaihe in the east, passes along the Qingling Mountains, moves southward along the western rim of the Sichuan Basin to about 27°N. and then turns to the southeastern corner of Tibet. Areas to the north of this line are generally below 0°C. The northeast is mostly below -10°C. and the northern part of the Greater Hinggan Mountains is below -30°C., being the coldest area in the country. Inner Mongolia, northern Ningxia, northern Gansu and Xinjiang are generally between -10° and -22°C.; the Qinghai-Tibetan Plateau is mostly between -10° and -20°C., except for the Yarlungzangbo River valley and the Hengduan Mountains; and north China is from -2° to -10°C. To the south of the 0°C. line, the Changjiang basin records temperatures between 0° and 8°C.; areas to the south of the Nanling Mountains, Taiwan and southern Yunnan are mostly between 12° and 20°C.; and the southern parts of Taiwan Province and Hainan Island exceed 20°C.

In winter China is under the control of the Mongolian high, and is frequently and fiercely invaded by cold waves. Under the fierce onslaught of a violent cold wave, various places may report low or extremely low temperatures. Dur-

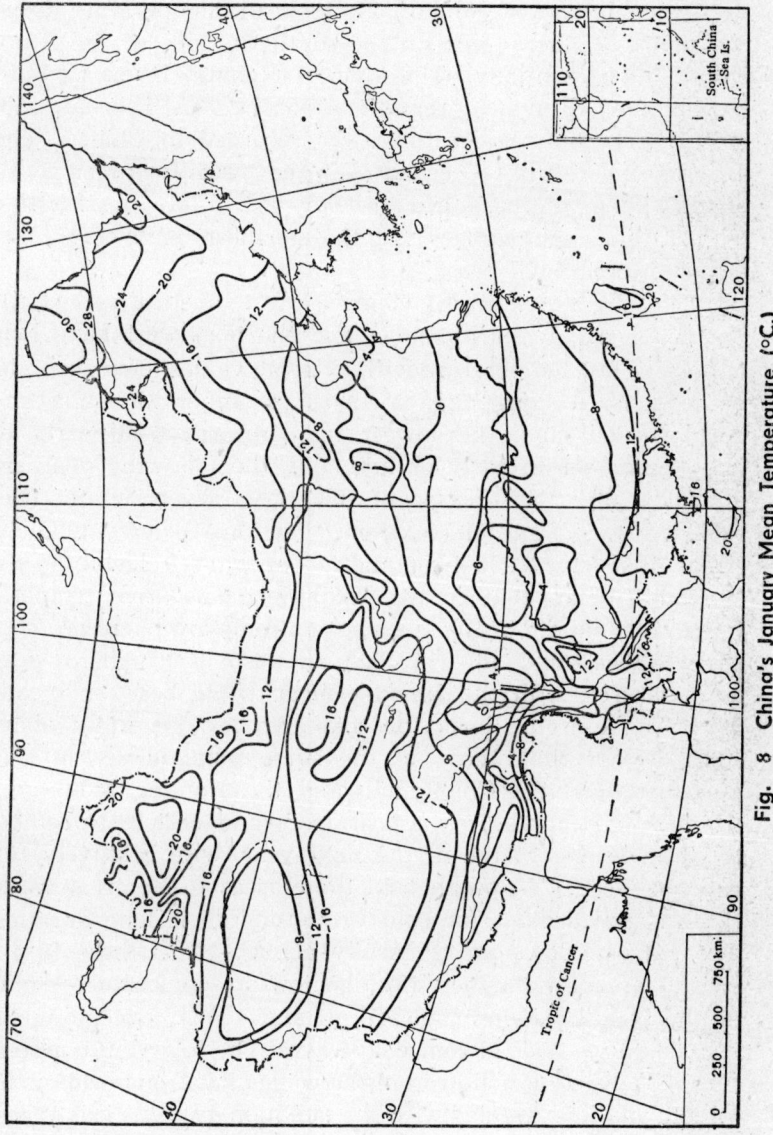

Fig. 8 China's January Mean Temperature (°C.)

ing the cold wave of January 21, 1960, the temperature dropped to -51.5°C. at Fuwen on the southern slope of the Altay Mountains in Xinjiang. The town of Mohe in Huma County, Heilongjiang Province, registered -52.3°C. on February 13, 1969, the lowest temperature ever recorded in China. The lowest temperatures recorded over the years for areas south of the Changjiang basin are all below 0°C. (Table 3). Negative temperatures also appear for the northern part of Hainan Island in occasional years.

The characteristics of China's low temperatures are: (1) The northeast, Inner Mongolia and the northwest have long periods of low temperature with extreme values. For example, in northern Heilongjiang, northeastern Inner Mongolia and northern Xinjiang, the lowest temperatures from early or mid September to early or mid May the following year are all below 0°C. The period of -5°C. lasts seven months (October to April) and the extreme lows are below -30°C. (2) Areas that are 3,000-4,000 metres above sea level on the Qinghai-Tibetan Plateau may experience negative temperatures every month of the year, but extreme lows here are generally above -30°C. (3) The Sichuan Basin has higher winter temperatures, with the January mean being between 0° and 5°C. The extreme lows for this area are generally above -5°C., higher than those in the surrounding areas. (4) For areas between the Changjiang and the Nanling Mountains, the lowest temperatures appear from mid or late November to early or mid March of the next year, with relatively few sub-zero days. Th problem in these areas is the great variation in arrival dates for cold waves and their long duration. The extreme lows are generally above -10°C.; those in the coastal areas are higher. (5) The lowest temperatures south of the Nanling Mountains are all above 0°C., except during occasional years of violent cold waves. The lowering temperatures of advection will drop in the wake of a strong cold-air invasion, and this, coupled with the radiation drop on clear nights, may send the temperature in some areas of northern Hainan

Island into the vicinity of 0°C. and even cause standing water to freeze there for a short time.

**Table 3.   Hottest and Coldest Temperatures in China
(1951-1970)**

Location	Mean temperature in hottest month (°C.)	Extreme high (°C.)	Mean temperature in coldest month (°C.)	Extreme low (°C.)
Nenjiang	20.4	37.4	-25.8	-47.3
Changchun	22.9	38.0	-17.0	-36.5
Hohhot	21.8	37.3	-13.5	-31.2
Beijing	26.0	40.6	-4.7	-27.4
Zhengzhou	27.5	43.0	-0.2	-17.9
Nanchang	29.7	40.6	4.8	-7.7
Guangzhou	28.3	38.7	13.4	0.0
Yulin	23.5	38.6	-10.0	-32.7
Urumqi	24.5	40.9	-15.6	-41.5
Lanzhou	22.4	39.1	-7.4	-21.7
Chongqing	28.6	42.2	7.5	-1.8
Kunming	19.9	31.5	7.9	-5.4
Guiyang	24.0	37.5	4.9	-7.8
Lhasa	15.5	29.4	-2.3	-16.5

2)   Summer Temperature

July is the month when temperatures in all parts of the country rise to their highest and when there are the least dif-

ferences in temperature distribution. The isothermal lines
drawn over the Southeast are sparse and mostly run in a
northeast-southwest direction. In the western regions, however, the isothermal lines become rather dense (Fig. 9) because of a sharp increase in temperature in the inland basins
and because of great vertical changes of temperature in the
high mountains. The July mean temperature for the whole
country is mostly between 20° and 28°C. The Qinghai-Tibetan
Plateau, Tianshan Mountains and Greater and Lesser Hinggan
mountains are under 20°C. owing to their elevation, and the
interior of the Qinghai-Tibetan Plateau is below 8°C. Areas
to the south of the Huaihe have temperatures roughly between 28° and 30°C.; and the Northeast Plain, between 22°
and 24°C. The Sichuan Basin, the Lianghu Basin in the middle reaches of the Changjiang, and the Tarim Basin show a
remarkable foehn effect because topographically they are
low-lying and mostly surrounded by mountains. Some of
these areas are so far inland that they are deeply affected
by the arid climate, and become China's centres of heat in
summer. Among them, the vicinity of the Poyang Lake and
the Turpan Depression are China's two hottest centres. The
Turpan Depression has a July mean temperature of 33.4°C.,
with a daily high that exceeds 40°C. An extreme high of
47.6°C. was registered there on July 4, 1941, the highest temperature ever recorded in China. The average temperature
in south China is rather high because of a longer high-temperature period and long hours of high temperature during each
day. But thanks to frequent cloudy skies and rain in the
afternoon, the extreme highs in this area are lower than they
are in the above-mentioned centres of heat, generally not
exceeding 40°C. The extreme high in Guangzhou, for instance,
was 38.7°C. (Table 3).

3) Spring and Autumn Temperatures

Spring and autumn are transition seasons. In April, most
areas are still controlled by the Mongolian high, but the temperatures generally climb. During the invasion of a cold wave,

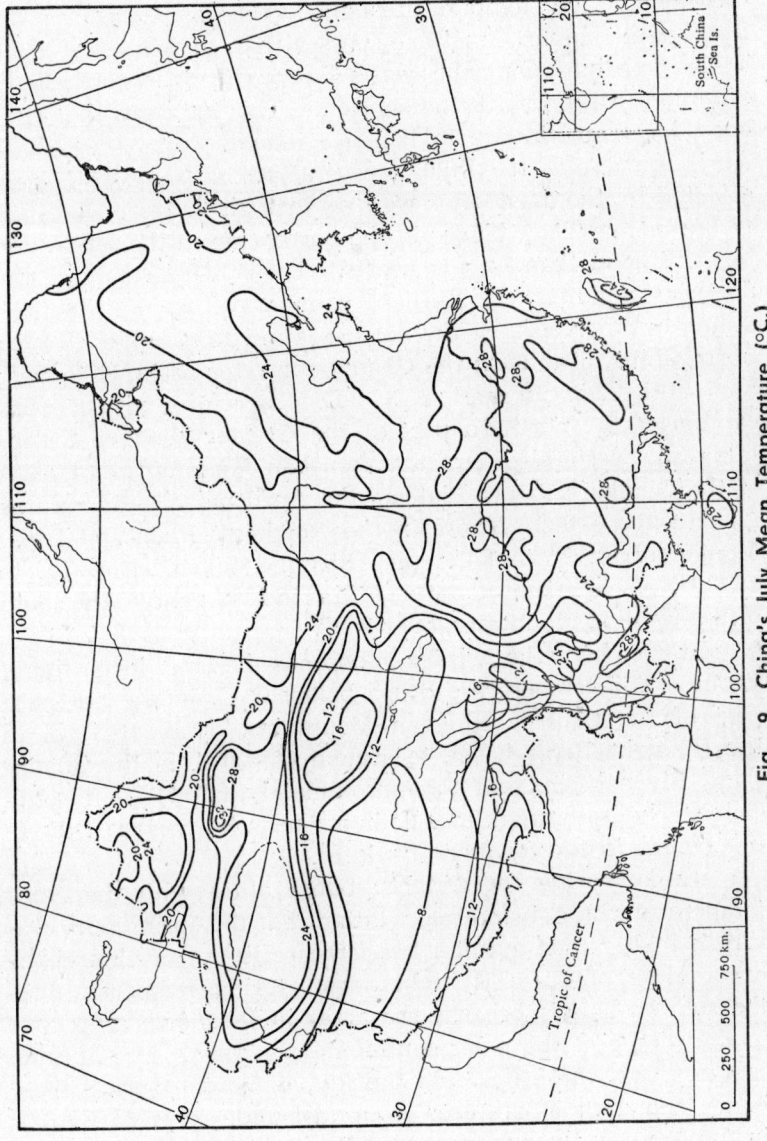

Fig. 9 China's July Mean Temperature (°C.)

occasionally low temperatures may appear. Therefore, the isothermal lines in April are sparser than in winter, and the isothermal lines along the coasts lie roughly in a north-south direction, parallel with the shoreline. This indicates the tendency for temperatures to increase inland. From January to April the extent to which temperature increases is largely affected by the dryness or wetness in a given area. Generally the increases are bigger in the north than in the south, and bigger inland than on the coasts. The northern part of the northeast and northern Xinjiang gain an average of 8° to 10°C. a month; other parts of the northeast and Xinjiang, 6° to 8°C.; north China, 5° to 6°C.; the Changjiang river basin, 3° to 5°C.; and south China, a mere 2° to 3°C. Therefore, with the exception of the northern part of the Greater Hinggan Mountains, the western part of the Tianshan Mountains and parts of the Qinghai-Tibetan Plateau, the April mean temperatures all rise above 0°C. Those in the Northeast Plain and Inner Mongolia rise 2° to 8°C.; the Huanghe River basin, 12° to 16°C., the Changjiang River basin, 14° to 18°C.; and to the south of the Nanling Mountains, over 20°C.

In October, the winter monsoons become increasingly strong. The temperature drops below 0° C. in the northern part of the Greater Hinggan Mountains, to about 12°C. in the Huanghe River basin, to around 16°-20°C. in the Changjiang River basin, and to approximately 22°-24°C. in south China. The isothermal lines lie in a southwest-northeast direction, much in the manner of winter.

By comparing the October temperature with the April temperature in a given area, we find that the spring temperature is higher than autumn temperature in the north and the autumn temperature is higher than spring temperature in the south. This is because the areas in the north are closer to the source of the polar continental air mass. The autumn temperatures there decrease quickly, while the spring there is dry and the temperatures go up fast under sunshine. Areas in the south in the autumn are under the influence of a semi-stationary small high and the weather is fine with clear skies or bright sunshine. But in spring, the confrontation of south and north air currents produces frequent fronts, resulting in cloudy skies and rain.

(2) Annual Temperature Change and Distribution of the Seasons

For most parts of China, January is the coldest month and July the hottest. In the coastal areas, however, because of the ocean's heat-regulating action, the hottest month may be postponed until August (as is the case in Dalian and Qingdao), and the monthly mean temperature will be close to or slightly higher than in July. For areas affected by the southwest monsoons, the hottest month may be May or June because there are so many days of cloudy skies and rain in July, which lowers the temperature.

An analysis of annual temperature variations shows that the annual range of temperatures in various parts of China noticeably amplifies with increasing latitudes. In addition, areas high in elevation, such as the Yunnan-Guizhou Plateau and the Tibetan Plateau, have low summer temperatures and are not easily invaded by cold waves in winter, so that the changes in temperature there are not as sharp as they are on the eastern plains and the annual range of temperature is not large. The distribution of the annual range of temperatures for the whole country is roughly as shown in Fig. 10. The range is over 40°C. in most of Heilongjiang Province, northeastern Inner Mongolia and the Junggar Basin at the northern foot of the Tianshan Mountains in Xinjiang. It is about 30°C. in the Huanghe River basin, the Tarim Basin and the Qaidam Basin, and mostly between 22° and 26°C. in the middle and lower reaches of the Changjiang and the Qinghai-Tibetan Plateau, while only about 18°C. in the Sichuan Basin and the Yarlungzangbo River valley. It averages about 15°C. in most parts of the Zhujiang River basin, the Yunnan Plateau and Taiwan Province. It is less than 10°C. in the southern part of

Hainan Island and in the mountainous areas of Taiwan Province.

When the average temperature for each pentad, or five-day period, is lower than 10°C., it is considered to be winter; when it is higher than 22°C., summer; and when it is between 10° and 22°C., spring or autumn. For example, Beijing's pentad average temperature of 10°C. first appears about April 1, and Nanjing about March 22. So these two dates mark the beginning of spring for Beijing and Nanjing respectively. Phenologically, they roughly correspond to the average dates for the initial blooming of peach flowers. Nanjing's and Shanghai's pentad average temperature falls below 22°C. about September 23, and this is regarded as the date for the end of summer and beginning of autumn. The date roughly coincides phenologically with the average date for swallow's return to the south.

According to this pentad criterion, the area north of a line from Aihui and Nenjiang in the northeast to the Daqing Mountains in Inner Mongolia is a summerless district where winter lasts more than 255 days. The Qinghai-Tibetan Plateau has a high elevation and pentad temperatures in the hottest month rarely exceed 22° C., so there is also no summer there. There is no winter south of the Nanling Mountains. Summer on Hainan Island ranges from late March to mid-November, a period of eight months. For the South China Sea islands, summer remains all year round. The rest of China has distinct contrasts in seasons. It is worth mentioning that the annual variation in the position of the subtropical jet stream axis is an indicator of the natural weather seasons in East Asia. When the axis of the subtropical jet stream moves northward in April, spring begins in East Asia; when the axis moves from 35°N. to the vicinity of 40°N. in July, spring gives way to summer; when the axis retreats from 40°N. to the vicinity of 30°N. in October, summer enters autumn; and when the axis moves south of 30°N. after mid-November we have the arrival of winter.

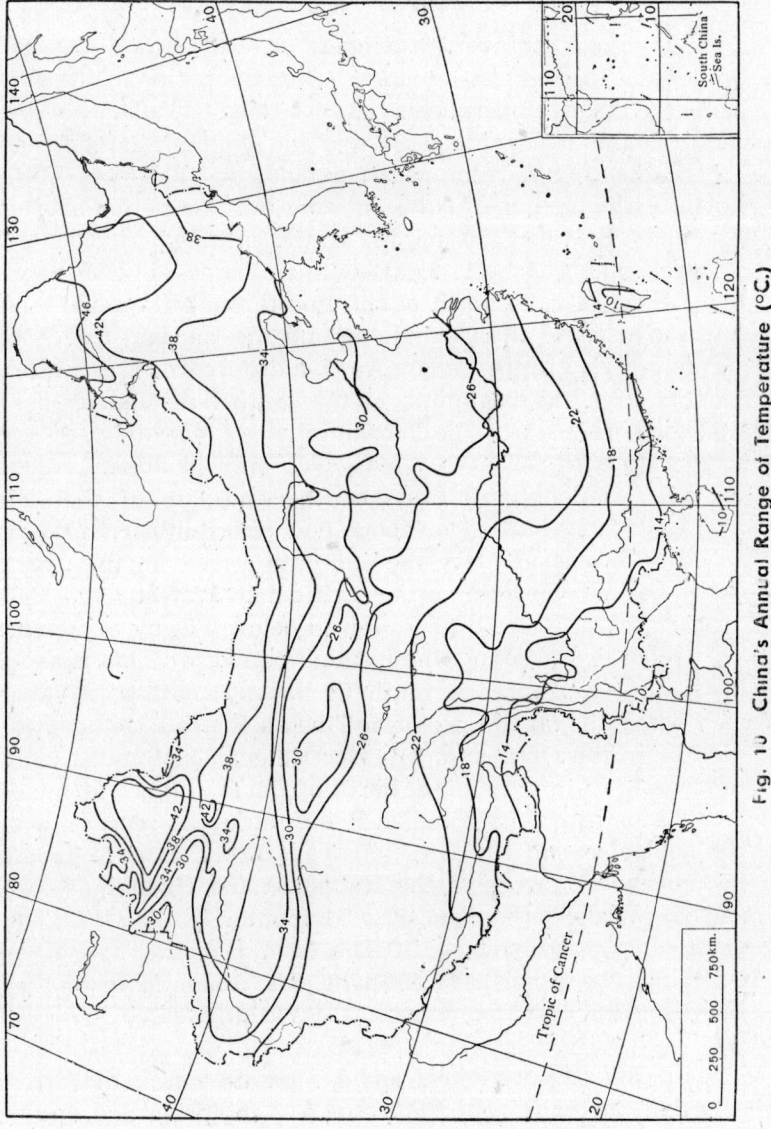

Fig. 10 China's Annual Range of Temperature (°C.)

(3) Growth Period and Frost Period

Whenever the average temperature falls below 0°C., soils freeze and farms must lie fallow. Thus the period of the duration of average temperature above 0°C. may be called the farming period. For most areas south of the Qinling Mountains and the Huaihe, this farming period extends over the year. To the north of the Qinling-Huaihe line, the farming period shortens gradually. Between 110° and 130°E., the farming period generally becomes shorter by 11.2 days with an increase of each degree of latitude. To the north of the line through the middle and lower reaches of the Changjiang and the Hanshui rivers, the farming period begins in late April, a difference of about three months from the beginning in the south (late January). In the northern part of the Tibetan Plateau, the daily average temperature stands at or above 0°C. only in June. And in northern Heilongjiang Province the end-date of the daily average temperature at or above 0°C. comes in early October. In early or mid January the end-date arrives in the Changjiang basin. On the northern Tibetan Plateau, the daily average temperature begins to drop below 0°C. by September.

Generally speaking, the farming period in China is as follows: all year round in south China and southern Yunnan; only 4 months on the northern Tibetan Plateau; about 5 to 7 months in the Greater and Lesser Hinggan mountains in the northeast and in areas to the north of Hetao in Inner Mongolia; 7 to 9 months on the Songliao Plain, the upper reaches of the Haihe, Hetao and the Loess Plateau; about 9 to 11 months in the lower reaches of the Haihe, on the Huanghuai Plain and the Weihe basin; and over 11 months in the Changjiang basin and areas to the south. The farming period spreads for 6 to 7 months in northern Xinjiang, 8 to 9 months in southern Xinjiang, and 9 to 11 months in the Yarlungzangbo River valley.

In China's subtropical and temperate zones, the arrival of a daily average temperature of 5°C. in spring and autumn tallies with the growth period for major crops and trees. Thus the duration of a daily average temperature above 5°C. is called the growth period. The end of the growth period coincides with a daily mean temperature near or at 0°C. China's growth period is distributed in this way: about 130 days for the northern part of northeast China; 150 to 180 days for the Songhua River basin and northern Inner Mongolia; 180 to 210 days for areas extending from the Liaohe River basin to the Yanshan Mountains and the Hetao; 210 to 240 days for the Liaodong Peninsula, the northern part of north China and the Fenhe River basin; 240 to 270 days for the Huanghuai Plain and the upper reaches of the Hanshui River; 270 to 300 days for the middle and lower reaches of the Changjiang; and the whole year for areas south of 25°N. and along the southeast coast south of Wenzhou.

One can see that for eastern China, the growth period roughly gains an average of 9.4 days with each decrease of one degree of latitude, and that there is a difference of as much as seven months between growth period in the south and north. To the west of 110°E., the Sichuan Basin has a growth period of 300 days. There the daily mean temperature is at or above 5°C. all year round south of the Chengdu-Nanchong line. It drops under 200 days on the western Sichuan Plateau, in the Gansu Corridor and in northern Xinjiang. Southern Xinjiang has upwards of 200 days, and the interior of the Turpan Depression and the Tarim Basin may have about 250 days. The Bomi and Zayu areas of the southeastern Tibetan Plateau have as many as 270 growing days, but the northern Tibetan Plateau only has 100, the shortest growth period in the whole country.

The growth of most plants occurs only when the daily mean temperature reaches 10°C. and above. This temperature indicator is usually called the active temperature and its duration is called the active growth period. The length of the active growth period and the accumulated active temperatures are important to agricultural production because they represent, in a relative way, effective heat for the growth of crops. In China, the starting date for daily mean temperatures at or above 10°C. is either half a month or one month later than that of the growth period, but there is not much difference between the ending dates for the two. This reflects the quick replacement of summer monsoons by winter monsoons. In eastern China, the duration of the daily mean temperature of 10°C. or above increases by 1.7 days with a decrease of each degree of latitude. The duration is less than 120 days for the Greater and Lesser Hinggan mountains, 120 to 150 days for the Northeast Plain and northern Inner Mongolia, 150 to 180 days for the Loess Plateau and the Gansu Corridor, 200 to 220 days for the Huanghuai Plain, 220 to 240 days for the middle and lower reaches of the Changjiang, 250 to 280 days for the Sichuan Basin, and over 300 days south of the Nanling Mountains. In the west part of China, it is short of 120 days for the northernmost portion of Xinjiang, and about 200 days for the Turpan Depression and Tarim Basin. The duration is approximately 150 days for the Yarlungzangbo River valley in Tibet, but decreases quickly with an increase in elevation until it is less than 10 days at Nagqu. The accumulated active temperatures for the Qinghai-Tibetan Plateau, northern Xinjiang, northeastern Inner Mongolia and northern Heilongjiang are the least, less than 2,000° to 1,500°C. each. For the northeast and most areas of Inner Mongolia they are less than 3,000°C. They are 3,000° to 4,500C. for north China, and more than 4,500°C. for the Changjiang basin. They rise upwards of 6,500°C. for areas south of 25°N. The accumulated active temperatures are mostly over 3,000°C. for arid regions in the northwest. In the Tarim Basin, a warm centre, they top 4,000°C. Turpan abounds in thermal resources, with an accumulated active temperature of 5,416.9°C. (Fig. 11).

Although the daily mean temperature may be more than 4°C., morning temperatures can still drop under 0°C. when the diurnal range of temperature is larger than 10°C. Therefore frost may occur within the growth period. The initial and final frosts will usually cause damage to crops. In China, the

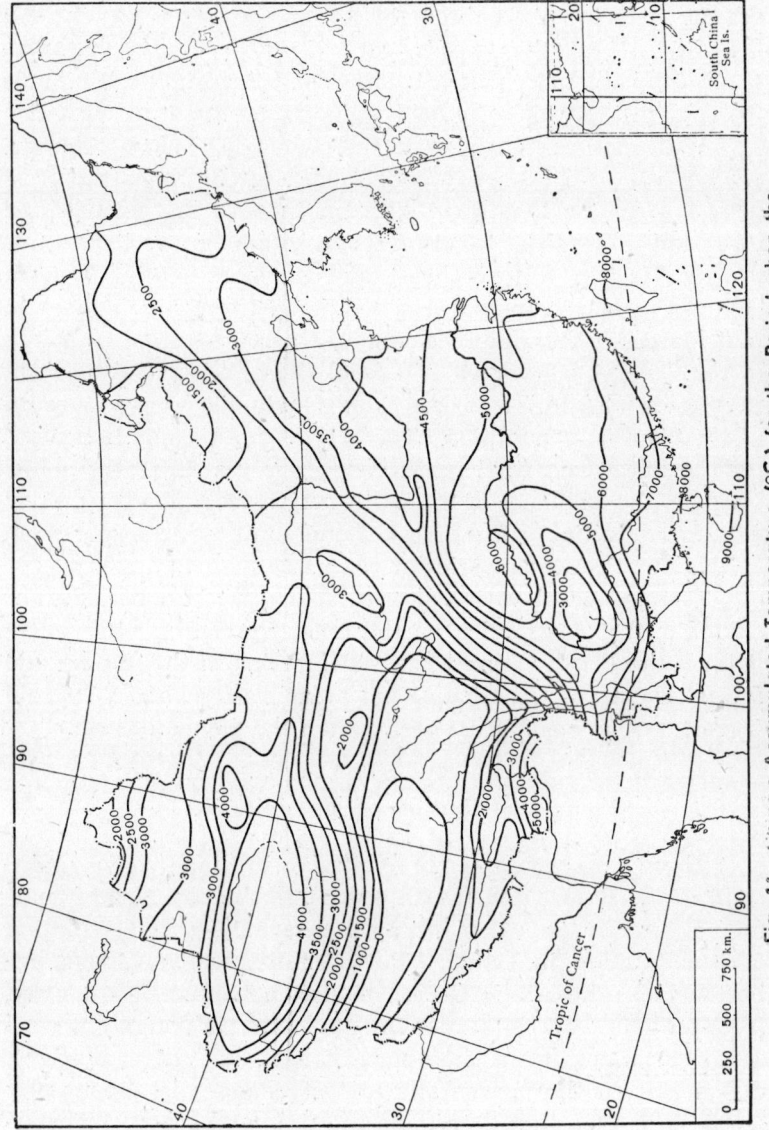

Fig. 11 China's Accumulated Temperature (°C.) for the Period when the Daily Mean Temperature Remains at or Above 10°C.

advection factor plays the main role in forming the early and late frosts. In other words, early frost is closely related to the southward march of a cold wave. Radiation frost tends to occur in the wake of a cold wave in the depth of winter.

With the exception of the Qinghai-Tibetan Plateau, where frost can be seen every month of the year, the frost period in China lengthens with an increase in latitude and elevation. The frost period lasts from September to the following May in the northeast and northern Xinjiang, from October to March in southern Xinjiang, from mid-October to mid-March in the Huanghe valley, from November to March in the Changjiang valley, and from December to February in the Sichuan Basin. Frost occurs only in January in areas south of the Nanling Mountains. The arrival and termination dates for the initial and final frosts vary greatly at different points owing to the influence of the south-moving cold air. The arrival date for an initial or final frost at one point may vary as much as two months over a series of years.

Terrain and elevation also influence the frost period. For example, the frost period on the Loess Plateau is longer than it is on the North China Plain. The plains in the middle and lower reaches of the Changjiang areas, easily visited by cold waves, have a longer frost period than the Sichuan Basin.

4.   Distribution of Precipitation

The water vapour for precipitation in China comes mainly from the Pacific and Indian oceans, so the direction of summer monsoons and their strength determine the distribution of precipitation in China. Furthermore, water vapour imported from the Arctic Ocean, though not much in quantity, is important to precipitation in northern Xinjiang. The seasonal variations in the monsoons of East Asia, their strength, distance from the oceans and abrupt changes in topography are basic factors that determine the time and spatial distribution of precipitation in China.

(1) Spatial Distribution of Precipitation

The pattern of distribution of precipitation in China is of progressive decrease from the southeast coast to the northwest interior, and this decrease becomes increasingly rapid as one moves inland (Fig. 12). If the isohyet of 400 mm. is taken as the boundary line, China can be divided into two parts. To the east of the line is a humid area controlled by the East Asian monsoons, and to the west is the arid section of Central Asia. This line is similar to the dividing line between the interior drainage region and the exterior drainage region in the country, and also it is of important significance in the natural phenomena and agricultural production of the country.

In the humid area, the isohyet runs in a northeast-southwest direction and the amount of precipitation decreases with increasing latitudes. Take the isohyet of 800 mm., which roughly tallies with the Qinling-Huaihe line, as a base. To the south of this is the area with the most active hydrological cycle in China. Precipitation on both banks of the Changjiang is measured at between 1,000 and 1,200 mm., that in the hilly areas south of the river basin and in the Nanling Mountains exceeds 1,400 mm., and that in Guangdong's hilly areas along the coast and in most parts of Taiwan and Hainan islands may reach upwards of 2,000 mm. The latter is China's most rainy region. The Gulf of Tonkin, which is greatly influenced by typhoons, also has a large amount of precipitation during the year, topping 2,000 mm. Western Yunnan and Zayu and Bomi in the southeastern corner of Tibet are influenced by the southwest monsoons, and form a small rainy area with an annual precipitation of over 1,400 mm. Places north of Kunming and Guiyang and the Sichuan Basin form an area of relatively scanty rainfall, the annual amount being between 800 and 1,000 mm. The annual precipitation is 800 to 1,000 mm. for most of the Huaihe River basin and the Qinling Mountains, 500 to 750 mm. for the lower reaches of the Huanghe and the North China Plain, and 400 to 600 mm. for the Northeast

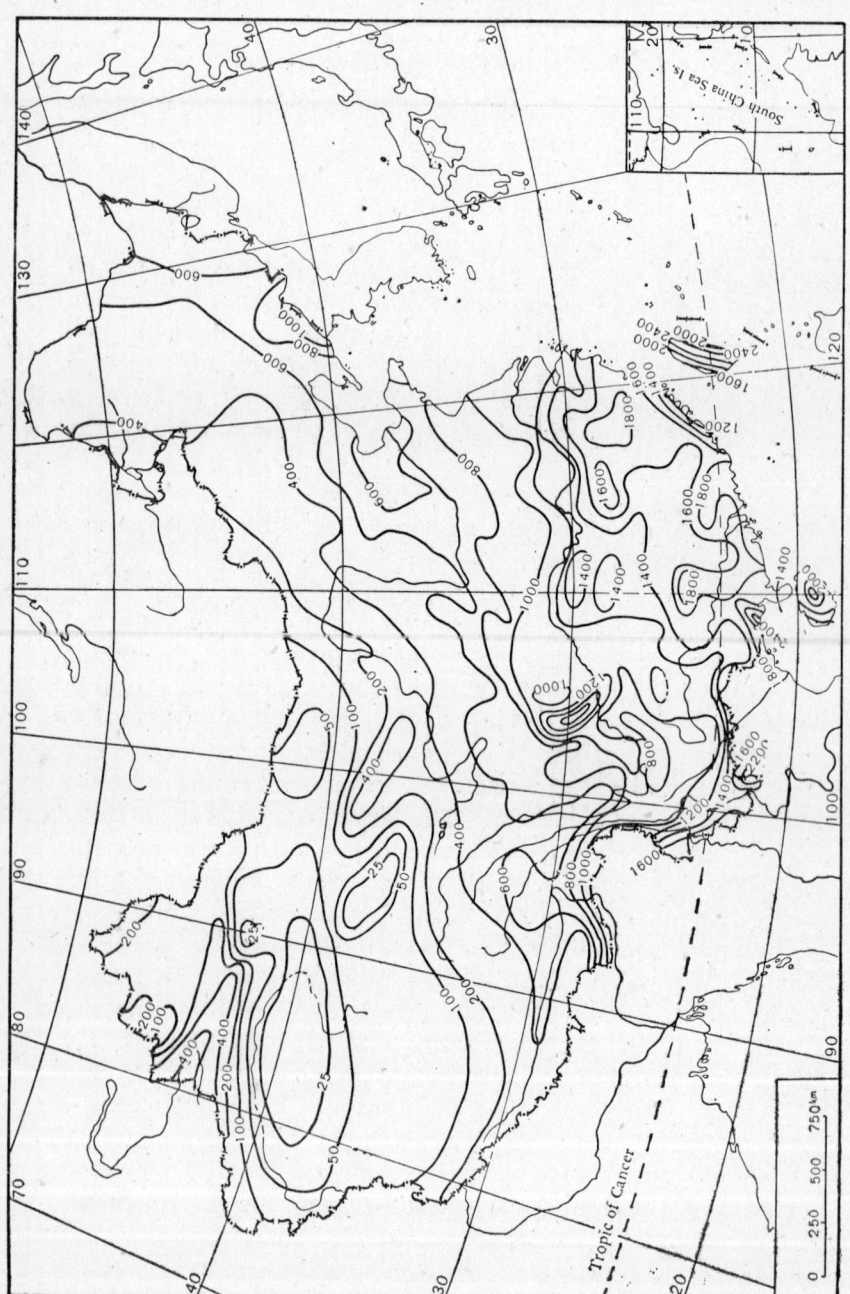

Fig. 12 China's Annual Precipitation (mm.)

Plain. But the amount exceeds 800 mm. for the Changbai Mountains, and it may reach over 1,200 mm. for the Yalu River basin, the region of greatest precipitation in northern China.

In the arid part of China, the annual amount of precipitation is generally 200 to 400 mm. for the western section of the Greater Hinggan Mountains, the Inner Mongolian Plateau and the Loess Plateau. It may reach 400 to 600 mm. at most for the Tianshan and Altay mountains in northwestern Xinjiang, which are influenced by the Atlantic-Arctic moisture system. In other sections of the arid region, annual precipitation is under 200 mm.; it reduces rapidly towards China's driest centres, such as southern Xinjiang, western Gansu and northwestern Qaidam Basin. These dry centres all have less than 50 mm. of rainfall per year. The interior of the Tarim Basin has less than 20 mm., and Qiemo has an average annual precipitation of only 9.2 mm. and no rain in some years, thus making it the place with the least annual rainfall in China. The north Tibetan Plateau, where moisture from the Indian Ocean cannot penetrate because of the surrounding high mountains, is also an area of scanty rainfall. Its annual precipitation is estimated at below 100 mm.

Since mountainous areas generally receive more precipitation than plains and basins and the windward side of a mountain gets more precipitation than the other side, a chart of precipitation distribution in China shows a number of enclosed rainy or rain-deficient centres. The mountains in the middle of Taiwan Island run in a north-south direction. On their east, north and south sides they receive the tropical air masses, equatorial air masses and marine-modified polar air masses from the ocean. Besides, the island is deeply influenced by typhoons. The windward slopes of the mountains get as much as 3,000 mm. of precipitation a year. Huoshaoliao leads, with an average annual rainfall of 6,378 mm. during the years from 1903 to 1945, of which the greatest was 8,507 mm. in 1921, China's highest annual precipitation record. But for the leeward side of the Taiwan Straits, owing to the effect of the mountains, precipitation does not exceed 1,000 mm., it is only 800 mm. in the Penghu Islands. The southeastern slope of the Wuzhi Mountains on Hainan Island has over 2,000 mm. of rainfall each year because of the influence of the tropical marine air mass and equatorial air mass all the year round. But the leeward west coast has only about 1,000 mm., resulting in a savanna-type landscape. The windward slopes of the Nanling Mountains and Wuyi Mountains in Fujian and Zhejiang may have an annual rainfall of over 2,000 mm., about 500 mm. more than that found in the coastal areas between Hangzhou Bay and the Leizhou Peninsula or on the offshore islands, while the Lianghu Basin on the leeward side has no more than 1,500 mm. Mount Emei in the western Sichuan Basin, where the southeast air current is uplifted by the terrain, has an annual rainfall of over 1,400 mm. The greatest annual precipitation recorded there was 7,609 mm., from August 1933 to July 1934, so this mountain is often called the "wet island". Although the Qinling Mountains are far more distant from the sea than the Huaihe River basin and lie farther to the north, they have as much precipitation as the latter. This is because of the effect of high mountains.

In north China, precipitation is plentiful in the hilly areas in Shandong, which have an annual rainfall of 700 to 800 mm. The windward slopes of the Taihang and Yanshan mountains also receive 600 to 700 mm., but the North China Plain receives only about 500 mm. of precipitation. The situation in the northeast is similar to that of north China. The Changbai Mountains in the east receive the greatest amount of precipitation, next comes the windward side of the Greater Hinggan Mountains, and the precipitation in the plains is mostly below 500 mm. The deep valleys between the high mountains of western Yunnan are influenced by the southwest air current and so the western slopes of the mountains have more rainfall than the eastern slopes. This is the opposite of those areas influenced by the southeast air current. In the Hengduan Mountains in the southeastern corner of Tibet, the warm and moist air current from the Indian Ocean and the Bay of Bengal moves along the broad valleys to the eastern sector of the Nyanqentanglha range. Annual precipitation there is more than 1,000 mm. for areas south of Bomi, with the greatest precipitation exceeding 4,000 mm. But the area north of the Himalayas between the Yarlungzangbo River and Kangto Mountain is an area known as the "rain-shadow belt at the northern foot of the Himalayas". It has less than 300 mm. of rainfall a year. The distribution of precipitation in Xinjiang is strictly determined by the macrotopography. In this region there are three rainy centres, the Altay Mountains, the Tianshan Mountains, and the northern foot of the Kunlun Mountains; and three rain-deficient centres, the Junggar Basin, the Tarim Basin and the Turpan Depression.

(2) Seasonal Variations in Precipitation

Monsoons not only control the general trend of precipitation in China but also affect seasonal variations in precipitation for various places. Taking China as a whole, the amount of precipitation is scanty from November to February because of the control by winter monsoons. June through August is a wet season for the whole country because the summer monsoons are at their height. In between are transition periods from dry to wet or from wet to dry. Owing to the varying arrival time and control period of the summer monsoons, the rainy season becomes shorter and rainfall is more concentrated the farther one goes northward.

In the northeast, north China and Inner Mongolia, precipitation is concentrated in summer, with the summer rains comprising 60 to 70 per cent of the annual rainfall. Thus the rainy season in these areas is short and the dry season exceptionally long. In the southern rainy regions, the months between May and October, when the summer monsoons are in effect, are a time for a large amount of rainfall and a long rainy season. But in areas south of the middle reaches of the

Changjiang, an area influenced by the tropical air mass in July, precipitation is relatively less. The Nanling Mountains are the area where the wet season begins earliest in China. This area has more precipitation in March than even the Zhujiang River basin, because of frequent surface cyclonic activity. The month of heaviest rainfall in China can best be discussed with the Changjiang as a boundary line. It occurs mainly from May to June south of this line and from July to August north. The rainfall belt, which advances and retreats along with the summer monsoons, appears south of the Changjiang from April to May, moves to the Huaihe River basin from June to July, and may reach northern portions of north China in August. Beginning in September, it gradually withdraws southward.

The characteristics of China's seasonal precipitation are: (a) Spring precipitation is heaviest in the Lianghu Basin and its surrounding areas and may account for one-third of the year's total in that area. It is over 30 per cent in the Ili valley in Xinjiang; about 20 per cent at the Qinling-Huaihe line and the northwest; 10 to 15 per cent in north China and the northeast; less than 10 per cent on the Tibetan Plateau. (b) Summer has the greatest amount of precipitation for most parts of the country. Except for the areas between the Changjiang and the Nanling Mountains and in the mountainous areas in northwest Xinjiang, where summer precipitation makes up less than 40 per cent of the year's total, the rest of the country has more than 40 per cent. It is over 60 per cent for north China and the northeast, over 70 per cent for the northwest and most parts of the Tibetan Plateau, and as high as 80 per cent and more for the Yarlungzangbo River valley to the west of Lhasa. (c) Autumn precipitation reaches about 30 per cent of the year's total on the Leizhou Peninsula, on Hainan Island, in the Qinling Mountains and in the upper reaches of the Weihe and Hanshui rivers. It is mostly 15 to 20 per cent in other parts of the country. In north China, autumn rains come more often than spring rains, and the spring drought can be quite serious. The Sichuan-Yunnan region and the southeastern part of the Qinghai-Tibetan Plateau are influenced by the southwest monsoons; there the summer and autumn rains, which occur from June to October, account for more than 80 per cent of the year's total. (d) Winter has the least precipitation in most of the country, usually below 10 per cent. Winter precipitation comes to less than 5 per cent in the northeast, north China, Loess Plateau, northwest and Qinghai-Tibetan Plateau. But in northeastern Taiwan, where the northeaster brings with it a large amount of water vapour that turns into rain when it reaches the mountains, the amount of precipitation may reach 30 per cent of the year's total. This gives rise to a peculiar seasonal distribution for China: maximum winter rains, minimum summer rains, and similar rainfall in spring and autumn. Winter rains amount to 20 per cent and more in the Altay Mountains and the Ili valley in northern and western Xinjiang because the winter polar continental air mass brings with it some Arctic water vapour, resulting in a fairly even distribution of precipitation in that area in all four seasons.

The nationwide distribution of rainy days is similar to the distribution of precipitation. Where there is the greatest or least amount of precipitation, there is also the greatest or least number of rainy days. But in the hilly areas along the southeast coast, although there is much precipitation, there are not many rainy days. The Qionglai Mountains on the western rim of the Sichuan Basin and the Dalou Mountains in Guizhou are places with the greatest number of rainy days, 180 to 200 days or more a year. Mount Emei, with 264 rainy days, is a centre for the most rainy days in China. Generally speaking, between Lat. 25° and 30°N. is the belt with most rainy days. The number decreases to 120-140 days southward to the coast of Guangdong and Guangxi. The middle and lower reaches of the Changjiang, north of that belt, also have 120-140 rainy days; areas along the Qinling-Huaihe line, 100-120 days; and north China and the northeast, 75-

100 days. The seasonal distributions of rainy days is also similar to the percentage of precipitation in different seasons.

(3) Precipitation Variability

Another feature of China's precipitation is its great annual variability. This occurs because the precipitation in most parts of the country is formed by the confrontation of cold and warm air masses. In addition, a high percentage of the precipitation is brought on by typhoons in the southeast coastal region, and the autumn and winter precipitation in north China and northern Xinjiang is related to the outbreak of cold waves. So precipitation is one of the most varied of the meteorological elements in China.

The pattern of variability for annual precipitation in different places is as follows: Areas with a great amount of precipitation have a small variability, and vice versa. Areas often visited by cyclonic rain and orographic rain have a smaller variability, while areas visited by less stable typhoon rains and convective rain have a bigger variability. In the eastern part of China to the south of 30°N. is the district with the smallest annual variability, mostly between 10 and 15 per cent. This region is in the low latitudes and near the sea, and experiences tropical or equatorial air masses almost every year in the rainy season. So the rainfall there is plentiful and reliable as well. But the narrow southeast coastal strip, from the estuary of the Qiantang River in Zhejiang through Fujian's coast to the Leizhou Peninsula and the Taiwan Straits, is situated out of the track of cyclonic activity. This area depends on cold waves and typhoons for its winter and summer precipitation. The annual relative variability here is above 15 per cent. North of 30°N., the annual variability increases with increasing latitudes, reaching its maximum in north China. The area from Jinan, Tianjin, Beijing and Zhangjiakou to Hohhot forms a centre of high variability, coming to 30-35 per cent, because rainfall here in seasons other than summer is unreliable and rainfall intensity in summer is exceptionally high. The northeast is in a higher latitude, but it is also close to the ocean and therefore has more water vapour and frequent cyclonic activity. Thus the precipitation is rather stable. The variability for the plains is 15-20 per cent, dropping to 10-15 per cent or less in the Changbai Mountains and the Lesser Hinggan Mountains.

The southwest monsoons are more stable in character, so areas under their influence generally have less precipitation variability than eastern areas in the same latitude. West of the Hengduan range and the Ailao Mountains is the area with the smallest variability in China, under 10 per cent a year. It is about 10-20 per cent for the Tibetan Plateau as a whole. The interior drainage area in Xinjiang has the greatest precipitation variability, generally 30 to 40 per cent. Its annual variability is distributed in this order: (a) Areas with less precipitation have greater variability, and vice versa. Tacheng has the lowest variability, 9 per cent, while Turpan has 62 per cent, the highest. (b) The desert area is visited by sporadic rainfalls, which are highly variable. For example, the Tarim Basin generally has a variability rate of about 50 per cent. But the central part of the desert area is estimated at 70 per cent. The variability rate in the Junggar Basin is generally over 30 per cent while that in its central part is about 40 to 50 per cent. (c) The variability for northern Xinjiang is 20 to 30 per cent, and that for southern Xinjiang, 30 to 50 per cent. Obviously these differences are due to the sources of water vapour.

(4) Intensity of Precipitation

Both the intensity of precipitation and the variability determine the utilization value of precipitation. In China, the south generally receives greater precipitation intensities than the north. The lower the latitude, the richer the water vapour, the higher the temperature, the bigger the influence of tropical air masses and equatorial marine air masses, the more the chance of thunderstorms, and the greater the precipitation intensity. Precipitation intensities are also greater along the southeast coast, where typhoons have the most influence and where the terrain tends to uplift the air currents.

The greatest precipitation intensities generally occur in the summer in China. Often the precipitation in a single month can account for one-fourth or even half of an area's annual total. What's more, that month's precipitation is often the result of a few heavy rainfalls. In eastern and southern China, the greatest daily precipitation always exceeds 100 mm., and in some places it may top 200 mm. For example, Changchun recorded a daily precipitation of 126.8 mm. on July 11, 1967; Beijing, 244.2 mm. on July 31, 1959; Hangzhou, 189.3 mm. on September 12, 1963; and Guangzhou, 284.9 mm. on June 6, 1955. Exceptional torrential rains, caused by typhoons, occur over the south China coast, the Changjiang and Huaihe valleys and in north China. The greatest rainfalls recorded in these areas for a single day were 619 mm. at Puning along the coast in eastern Guangdong; 582 mm. at Gongping in northern Haifeng; 437 mm. at Liuza in Yangzhou City, Jiangsu; 307 mm. at Xingtai; and 264 mm. at Anyang on the eastern foot of the Taihang Mountains. On August 7, 1975, a daily rainfall of 1,005.4 mm. was measured at the Linzhuang rainfall station of Fangcheng in Henan Province, the maximum hourly rate being 198.7 mm. Taiwan has the greatest precipitation intensity of all China. Many places on this island record a daily precipitation rate of more than 500 mm. Among them, Xinliao has a rate of 1,672 mm. and Baixin, 1,248 mm.

Generally speaking, the greatest precipitation in June occurs chiefly south of the Changjiang. The Poyang Basin and the surrounding hilly areas are torrential rain centres that cover a wide area. The Qingjiang River in Hubei, the Lishui River in Hunan, the upper reaches of the Beijiang River and the mountainous area in northern Guangxi are also centres of torrential rain. In these places there are many cyclones be-

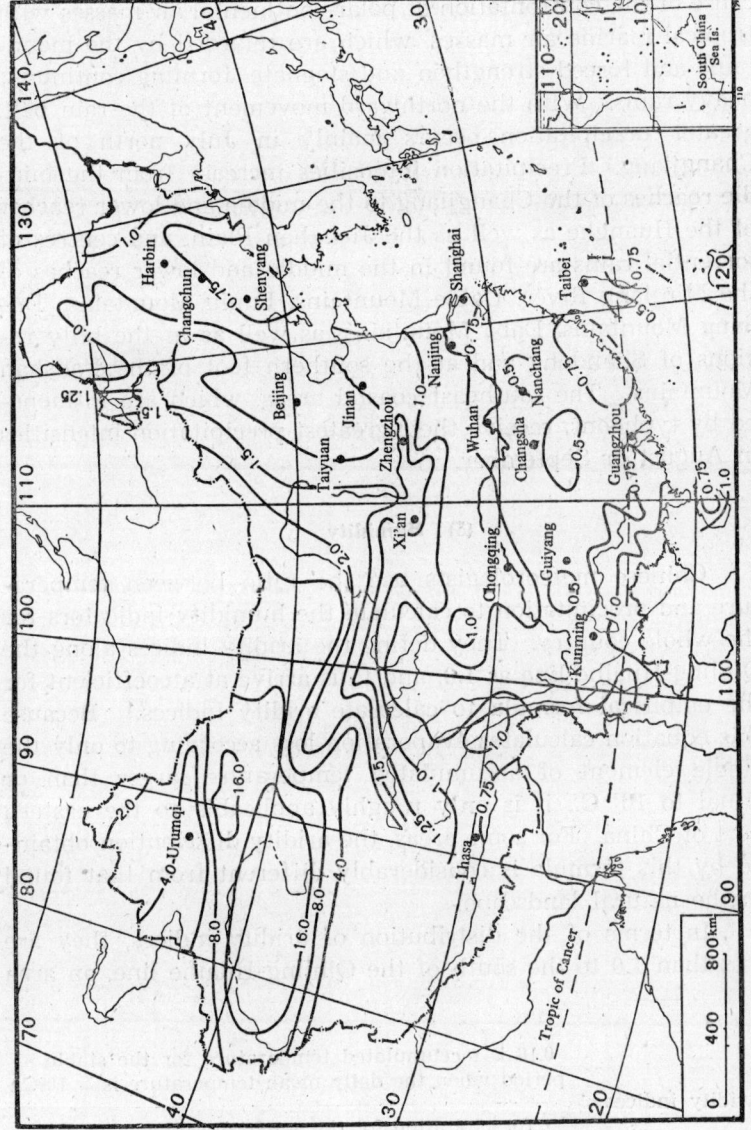

Fig. 13   Chart Showing the Distribution of Aridity in China

cause of the confrontation of polar continental air masses with tropical marine air masses, which are retarded by the mountains and forced strengthen and stagnate, forming continuous heavy rains. With the northward movement of the rain belt, greater precipitation occurs mainly in July north of the Changjiang. Precipitation intensities increase from the middle reaches of the Changjiang to the middle and lower reaches of the Huanghe as well as the Jianghan Plain, and centres of torrential rains are found in the middle and lower reaches of the Minjiang River, Dabie Mountains, Funiu Mountains, Taihang Mountains, Daba Mountains, as well as in the hilly regions of Shandong and at the southern foot of the Yanshan Mountains. The southeast coastal areas, which are influenced by typhoons, receive their greatest precipitation intensities in August or September.

(5) Humidity

Chinese meteorologists use the ratio between temperature and precipitation to calculate the humidity indicators for the whole country. They define the aridity indices along the Qinling-Huaihe line as 1.0, and thus arrive at a coefficient for the empirical formula to calculate aridity indices.[1] Because this equation calculates evaporation loss according to only the single element of accumulated temperature larger than or equal to 10° C., it is only roughly applicable to the eastern part of China. For some areas, the aridity distribution obtained by this formula is considerably different from that found in the natural landscape.

In terms of the distribution of aridity indices, they are less than 1.0 to the south of the Qinling-Huaihe line, an area

---

[1]

$$\text{Aridity indices} = \frac{0.16\ \Sigma\ \text{(accumulated temperature for the stable period when the daily mean temperature is} \geq 10°\text{C.)}}{r\ \text{(precipitation for the stable duration when the daily mean temperature is} \geq 10°\text{C.)}}$$

belonging to a humid climate. Aridity indices increase gradually to the north of this line. The northeast and north of
China, between 1.0 and 1.5, belong to a semi-humid climate.
Inner Mongolia, between 1.5 and 4.0, belongs to a semi-arid
and arid climate. Areas to the west of the Helan Mountains
exceed 4.0 and belong to a desert climate (Fig 13).

5. The Role of China's Climate in the Formation of the Natural Landscape and Its Relation to Agricultural Production

Climate is one of the most important factors in the study
of physical geography and it has a direct bearing on hydrological conditions, the exogenetic force for the development of
landforms, and the formation and distribution of soil and
vegetation. Climate has thus played an important role in the
formation and development of China's natural landscape, as
well as its utilization and transformation.

1) China's climate is complex and varied, but the distribution of water and heat in this country can be divided into
specific zones.

Eastern China, because of differences in heat distribution from north to south, can be divided into frigid-temperate,
temperate, warm-temperate, subtropical and tropical zones.
From east to west, with the increasing distance from the
ocean and varying water conditions, we find first a humid
climate, then a semi-humid climate, then a semi-arid climate
and finally an arid climate. All the mountains in the country
show vertical zones. As a rule, the mountains with a high
relative altitude or lower latitude have a more complex structure of vertical zones.

Owing to the progressive variation in climatic belts, China's soil and vegetation also can be divided into zones. The
monsoon region in the southeast mainly has forest vegetation,
whereas the non-monsoon region in the northwest mainly
has steppes and deserts. To the south of the Qinling-Huaihe

line, in eastern China, the differences in heat are most pronounced and the natural landscape changes in latitudinal zones. But in the temperature region to the north, because of decrease in available water, the natural landscape shows a marked pattern of longitudinal zones, from forest to forest grassland to steppe to desert.

2) China is rich in climatic resources that are favourable to agriculture.

China's climate is characterized by monsoons, with rainfall concentrated in the high temperature period of summer. Both the solar radiation and heat and water conditions are highly favourable to agricultural production. The plains in the east are suitable for growing rice, wheat, cotton and other important crops. The tropical areas in the south are suitable for growing tropical industrial crops. And the vast temperate grasslands in the north are livestock breeding centres. Farming and livestock breeding is also conducted on the Qinghai-Tibetan Plateau, over 4,500 metres above sea level.

Summer in China witnesses high temperatures and much rain, which is favourable for rice growing. Judging by a rice paddy's initial growth period (dekan mean temperature >10°C.) and safe earing period (pentad mean temperature above 23-24°C.), the growth period of rice in China is about 100 to 130 days in northern Heilongjiang Province, 150 to 170 days in the southern part of the northeast, 160 to 220 days in north China, 200 to 260 days in the Changjiang basin, and over 260 days in south China. Although southern China has a relatively short duration of sunshine during the day, this is compensated for by its great photo intensity. Northern China has longer hours of sunshine and a high insolation, ideal conditions for photosynthesis during the growing period of rice. Thus the fructification rate and plumpness of the rice there is greater than it is in the south. The differences in water and heat conditions in China provide potentials for the development of agriculture in varied zones.

3)   China's climate also produces drought and waterlogging.

There are many unfavourable conditions caused by China's climate. The unfavourable aspects of this climate are an uneven distribution of precipitation in regions and throughout the year, a great variation in precipitation from year to year and the instability of rainfall. Spring drought is frequent in the north. Furthermore, the height of summer is often accompanied by torrential rains, floods and waterlogging. There are many instances in which a summer drought appears because of the lack of rain over a long time during the rainy season. Prolonged torrential rains often visit the Changjiang basin during the plum-rain period, while dry spells of varying degree occur at the height of summer. The southwest and south of China have little precipitation in winter and early spring, which usually leads to a winter dry spell and a spring drought. The coastal areas of the southeast are visited by windstorms or rainstorms every year in the summer and autumn, when typhoon activity is at its height.

Many water conservancy projects were undertaken in China after Liberation. These have helped to alleviate the traditional damage caused by natural calamities. They have also aided the development of agriculture. More water conservancy works are being planned and constructed in various localities in an effort to transform nature in accordance with local conditions. At the same time, there is a stress on raising the accuracy of weather forecasts in the hope of overcoming the problems of drought and waterlogging.

CHAPTER IV
TERRESTRIAL WATER

According to statistics, China has over 50,000 rivers, with a drainage area upwards of 100 sq. km. each. Of these, 1,580 have a drainage area of more than 1,000 sq. km. each, and 79 have a drainage area of over 10,000 sq. km. each. The total volume of annual runoff in China is nearly 2,600,000 million cu. m., accounting for 6.6 per cent of the runoff for all the rivers in the world (39,700,000 million cu. m.). This volume is 19.3 per cent of the total for Asia, and it is almost equivalent to the total for Europe. The numerous rivers and their extensive drainage areas provide favourable conditions for developing production and transforming nature.

1. Drainage Basins and Drainage Systems

(1) General Situation of Drainage Basins

China's rivers can be classified into two main categories: exterior drainage basins and interior drainage basins. The exterior drainage basins include rivers linked to the Pacific, Indian and Arctic oceans. Situated in the eastern and southern parts of China and in the northwestern corner of Xinjiang, the exterior drainage basins cover a total of 6.12 million sq. km., or 63.8 per cent of China's territory. The interior drainage basins are situated in the eastern part of the Eurasian interior, an area that includes the Mongolian-Xinjiang area and the Qinghai-Tibetan Plateau. They cover 3.47 million sq. km., or 36.2 per cent of China's territory. The dividing line between the interior and exterior drainage basins runs in a

northeast-southwest direction from the western foot of the
Greater Hinggan Mountains at the Sino-Soviet border along
the southern rim of the Inner Mongolian Plateau, the Yinshan,
Helan, Qilian, Reyue, Bayanhar, Nyainqentanglha and Gandise mountains to China's western border.   To the east of
this line, the drainage basins are all exterior basins, except
for some interior drainage basins in the Ordos Highlands and
the Songnen Plain. To the west of this line, the drainage basins are all interior ones, except for the Ertix (Irtish) River
basin in the northwestern corner of Xinjiang.

Among the exterior drainage basins, the Pacific drainage basins are the biggest in area.   They cover an area of
5.4 million sq. km., or 56.8 per cent of China's territory, and
account for 88.9 per cent of all the area covered by China's
exterior drainage basins.   China's most important rivers, including the Changjiang, the Huanghe, the Heilong and the
Zhujiang, all belong to this category.   Since these rivers
empty into different seas individually, the Pacific drainage
basin can be further divided into the Okhotsk Sea drainage
basin (consisting chiefly of the Heilong River valley), the
Japan Sea drainage basin (including the Tumen and Suifen
River valleys), the Bohai Sea and Yellow Sea drainage basins
(including the Yalu, Liaohe, Luanhe, Huanghe and Huaihe
River valleys), the East China Sea drainage basin (including
the Changjiang, Qiantang, Oujiang and Minjiang basins) and
the South China Sea drainage basin (including the Hanjiang,
Zhujiang, Yuanjiang, Lancang and other river valleys).   The
rivers in eastern Taiwan pour directly into the Pacific.

The Indian Ocean drainage basin does not occupy a big
area in China, only about 620,000 sq. km., or 6.5 per cent of
the country's territory. Rivers belonging to the Indian Ocean
drainage basin are all located in the southern part of the Qinghai-Tibetan Plateau.   They consist chiefly of the Nujiang,
Yarlungzangbo, Shiquan and Xiangquan rivers.   The lower
reaches of these rivers flow across other countries to pour into
the Indian Ocean.   The Nujiang, which is named the Salween

after flowing into Burma, empties into the Andaman Sea. The Yarlungzangbo, which is named the Brahmaputra after flowing into India, crosses Bangladesh before emptying into the Bay of Bengal. Many small rivers in the Himalayan area on Tibet's southwestern border flow south across Bhutan and Nepal into India to join the Ganges, which empties into the Bay of Bengal. The Shiquan is the main source of this Indian river; and the Xiangquan, which is named the Sutlej after flowing into India, joins the Ganges in Pakistan before the latter pours into the Arabian Sea.

The Arctic drainage basin covers the smallest area of all. In this area, there is only one river, the Ertix, which is situated in the northwestern corner of Xinjiang. Its basin covers only about 50,000 sq. km., or 0.5 per cent of China's territory. The Ertix is the upper course of the Ob River. After flowing out of China, it makes its way across Kazakhstan and western Siberia to reach the Kara Sea of the Arctic Ocean.

The interior drainage basins cover a large area, including the Inner Mongolian, northwest China, Tibet and Songnen interior drainage basins. Among these, the northwest interior drainage basin occupies the largest area. It covers 2,370,000 sq. km., and accounts for two-thirds of the total area of interior drainage basins. All the rivers in this area begin in high mountains and flow across desert basins. Fed by ice and snow, the rivers have ample sources of water in the mountain areas. However, after descending from the mountains, they diffuse over sandy and gravel lands and are subject to extensive seepage. The Aksu and Urumqi rivers, for example, are like this. The inland rivers in Tibet also have short courses across flat and broad valleys. They empty into local lakes separately and have little connection with each other. Wihin the Inner Mongolian interior drainage basin, there are a few scattered rivers with very short courses, and quite extensive areism.

(2) General Characteristics of Drainage System

1) The Distribution of Drainage Systems

The distribution of China's drainage systems is extremely uneven. Whereas most of the rivers lie in the external drainage basins of the eastern and southern parts of the country, a small number lie in the internal drainage basins of the west. Such uneven distribution is mainly caused by climatic and topographical conditions.

The rivers that empty into the sea originate chiefly in three areas: (a) The eastern and southern borders of the Qinghai-Tibetan Plateau; (b) The line extending from the Greater Hinggan Mountains to the Hebei-Shanxi mountain area, the mountain area in western Henan, and the Yunnan-Guizhou Plateau; (c) The line extending from the Changbai Mountains to the Shandong Hills and the hilly lands near the southeastern coast.

Since the rivers that have their sources on the southeastern border of the Qinghai-Tibetan Plateau arise far from the ocean, most of them, such as the Changjiang, Huanghe, Lancang, Nujiang and Yarlungzangbo, travel great distances and rank among the famous rivers of the world. These rivers constitute the backbone of the drainage network in Southeast Asia. The rivers originating in the second area, from the Greater Hinggan Mountains to the Yunnan-Guizhou Plateau, include the Ergunhe on the upper reaches of the Heilong River and the Nenjiang, Liaohe, Luanhe, Haihe, Huaihe, Xijiang and Yuanjiang rivers. These rivers also rank among the great rivers in China, yet they have shorter lengths than the first group. As for the rivers originating in the third area, from the Changbai Mountains to the Shandong Hills and near the southeastern coast, these include the Tumen, Yalu, Yishui, Shushui, Qiantang, Oujiang, Minjiang, Hanjiang, Dongjiang and Beijiang rivers. Their sources lie near the ocean and most of them flow into the sea on direct course. They form many short and steep streams, yet have ample flows.

The direction of the rivers that flow into the sea is determined by the general features of China's terrain. Their main courses, except for some rivers in the northeast and southwest, flow from west to east. Such a direction of flow has an important bearing on China's hydrography. Due to the fact that China's rain belt often extends roughly in an east-west direction and the amount of rainfall gradually decreases as the rain belt shifts from the south to the north, the basic tendency of China's rivers in their discharge is to show a decrease from the southern to northern parts of the country. Furthermore, because the rain belt is parallel to the course of most rivers, when the rain belt lingers over the basin of a certain river, heavy rainfall often occurs in its upper, middle and lower reaches simultaneously. This rapidly swells the flow of the river and results in excessive flooding. After the rain belt moves away, the runoff for the entire river basin decreases simultaneously.

2) Patterns and Densities of Drainage Networks

There are different patterns of drainage networks in China, since it has complex physical geography and rivers flow across areas with different environments. Generally speaking, in mountainous regions dentritic drainage networks are well developed. The upper and middle reaches of such great rivers as the Changjiang and the Xijiang, as well as a number of rivers in mountainous areas, have this pattern. In the Changbai Mountains, the southeastern coastal hills and the Hengduan Mountain area, the tributaries of a number of rivers, influenced by fault lines, meet the main course at right angles to form drainage networks with a trellis pattern. The Yalu, Oujiang and Minjiang and some rivers in western Sichuan and northern Yunnan have this pattern. On the deltas of great rivers, such as the Changjiang and Zhujiang, waterways intersect one another to form reticulate drainage networks. Rivers in northeast and north China have a small number of tributaries and form linear drainage patterns. Rivers on Taiwan and Hainan islands originate in the mountains in the central parts of these islands, have short courses and a torrential flow and form radial drainage patterns. As for the Haihe and Jialing rivers, their tributaries flow into the main course after going only a short distance and form fan-shaped networks. The tributaries of the Wusuli, Luanhe, Xiangjiang and Wujiang rivers are evenly distributed on both sides of the main course to form feather-shaped networks. The tributaries of the Ertix and some other rivers are situated on one side of the main course and form comb-shaped networks. The upper course of the Xijiang flows across the karst area of southwest China, and some of its tributaries have subterranean streams that do not become a part of the surface drainage.

China's internal rivers are thinly scattered and have only a small number of tributaries. Due to the arid climate, seepage in their beds, and use of their water for irrigation, their flow decreases as they reach their lower courses until they disappear into desert or semi-desert areas. Among these rivers, the larger ones have broad channels and flow only for short periods in the summer. At their origin, in mountainous areas, the rivers are densely distributed and form comb-shaped networks. Due to their high altitude and small rate of evaporation, the internal rivers of Tibet have a specific type of drainage network, in which most of the small, short rivers are connected to lakes on low-lying land that is dissected into numerous small drainage basins.

The density of drainage networks varies greatly from one area to another. Broadly speaking, the density gradually decreases from the southeast to the northwest, and the density in the mountain areas is relatively greater than elsewhere.

For the exterior river basins, the density of drainage networks is greatest to the south of the Huaihe and east of the Yunnan-Guizhou Plateau, reaching over 0.5 km. per sq. km. in most areas and 0.7 km. per sq. km. in mountain regions. The Changjiang and Zhujiang deltas have the densest drainage networks, reaching densities of one to two km. per sq. km. In the Yunnan-Guizhou Plateau and Sichuan Basin, because of less rainfall and the widespread distribution of limestone, the density of drainage networks is less than 0.5 km. per sq. km. in most places, except on the Chengdu Plain. To the north of the Huaihe and the Qinling Mountains, the density of drainage networks ranges between 0.3 and 0.5 km. per sq. km. on the Shanxi Plateau, the coastal lowlands along the Bohai Bay and in the Sanjiang Plains (Songhua-Wusuli-Heilong River Plains). But in most of the other areas, the density is less than 0.3 km. per sq. km. Among these, the Greater and Lesser Hinggan Mountains, the Changbai Mountains and the Shandong Hills have drainage networks with densities of 0.2 to 0.3 km. per sq. km.; the Northeast and North China plains and the Loess Plateau record a density of 0.1 to 0.2 km. per sq. km., and the density in the lower reaches of the Nenjiang River on the Northeast China Plain is less than 0.05 km. per sq. km. A few exterior basin areas have no runoff at all.

As for the density of drainage networks for China's interior drainage basins, this often reaches 0.1 to 0.5 km. per sq. km. only in mountainous and hilly areas, but the density decreases abruptly in piedmont areas. Most parts of the Inner Mongolian Plateau, Tarim Basin, Junggar Basin and Caidam Basin are areisms where the density of drainage networks is less than 0.05 km. per sq. km., the smallest in China. The pattern of distribution for the interior drainage networks in Tibet is relatively simple. Their density in the eastern part of Tibet is 0.2 to 0.3 km. per sq. km., while it is 0.1 to 0.2 km. per sq. km. in the western part.

2.   Main Characteristics of River Flow

The formation, distribution and variation of surface runoff in China is chiefly influenced by climate and topography, although the activities of human beings in transforming nature are also important. River flow in various parts of the country has specific regional characteristics. However, the general characteristics are: (a) Rivers in China have rich water resources, but their distribution is extremely uneven from one area to another. (b) The distribution of river flow varies greatly from season to season and from year to year, primarily because of the monsoon climate of East Asia. (c) The surface runoff results in strong erosion so that the rivers have a large amount of solid runoff.

(1) The Resources of River Flow

It is estimated that China's rivers produce an average annual runoff of about 2,600,000 million cu. m., ranking them third in the world in terms of runoff resources, next only to those of the Soviet Union and Brazil. But these runoff resources are quite unevenly distributed throughout the country. While the exterior drainage basins have a total annual runoff accounting for 96 per cent of the national total, the interior drainage basins account for only 4 per cent.

The Pacific drainage basin has a total annual runoff of 2,140,000 million cu. m., accounting for 82.5 per cent of the total for all China. Among these the Changjiang basin has the most, coming to 979,350 million cu. m., or 37.8 per cent of the national total. The Zhujiang and other rivers along the coast of Guangdong Province also have rich runoff resources, making up 17.3 per cent of the national total. The external drainage basins in Zhejiang and Fujian provinces, in southwest China and southern Tibet account for 8 to 8.5 per cent of the national total each. The runoff resources in other parts of the country are much smaller.

The rivers in north China and the northeast, and the interior drainage basins of northwest China account for only 13.8 per cent of the national total. Among these the Huanghe basin, which covers 7.8 per cent of the total area in China, has an annual runoff of only 2.2 per cent. Of the interior drainage basins, those in Gansu and Xinjiang have the largest runoff, roughly 2.7 per cent of the national total.

According to data compiled by the Huanghe River Conservancy Committee, the runoff in southern China accounts for 75 per cent of the national total, while cultivated acreage in this area makes up only 38 per cent of the national total. The runoff in the vast area of northern China (excluding the northeast) accounts for only 17 per cent of the national total, yet its farming area composes 50 per cent. Therefore, the fundamental aim in the utilization of water resources in China is to divert surplus water from the south to the north so as to balance the distribution and utilization of surface water and to transform the physical features of semi-arid and arid areas.

Apart from the marked differences in the regional distribution of China's surface runoff, there are also great differences in the flow of the rivers. Calculated on the basis of the annual average flow of the major rivers (flow of those rivers that cross the national boundary are calculated at the points where they cross), the annual average flow of the Changjiang is the greatest, reaching 31,055 cu. m. per second. It thus ranks fourth among the great rivers of the world, next only to the Amazon in South America (100,000 cu. m. per second), the Congo in Africa (43,000 cu. m. per second), and the Ganges in Asia (38,000 cu. m. per second).

The Zhujiang is situated in an area with abundant rainfall. Although its drainage area is less than one-fourth that of the Changjiang, its annual average flow comes to 11,075 cu. m. per second, roughly equivalent to one-third of the Changjiang. The Zhujiang's annual average flow ranks second among China's rivers, thus placing it 17th among the great rivers in the world. The section of the Heilong River upstream from its confluence with the Wusuli covers a drainage area of 1.62 million sq. km., including the drainage area in both China and the Soviet Union. The annual average flow of the Heilong is 8,600 cu. m. per second, ranking it third in China.

As for the other rivers, eight have annual average flows of 1,000-3,000 cu. m. per second, four 500-1,000 cu. m. per second and seventeen 200-500 cu. m. per second. This shows that

Table 4.   Volume of Flow of China's Major Rivers

Name of River	Sea or lake they empty into	Drainage area (sq. km.)	Length (km.)	Average flow (cu. m. sec.)	Total volume of flow (billion cu. m.)	Depth runoff (mm.)
Changjiang	East China Sea	1,807,199	6,380	31,055	979.350	542
Zhujiang	South China Sea	452,616	2,197	11,075	349.200	772
Heilong	Okhotsk Sea	1,620,170	3,420	8,600	270.900	167
Yarlung-zangbo	Bay of Bengal	246,000	1,940	3,699	116.652	474
Lancang	South China Sea	164,799	1,612	2,354	74.248	412
Nujiang	Bay of Bengal	142,681	1,540	2,222	70.088	469
Minjiang	Taiwan Straits	60,924	577	1,978	62.366	1,024
Huanghe	Bohai Bay	752,443	5,464	1,820	57.450	76
Qiantang	East China Sea	54,349	494	1,484	46.799	861
Huaihe	Huanghai Sea	185,700	1,000	1,113	35.097	189
Yalu	Huanghai Sea	62,630	773	1,040	32.760	541
Hanjiang	South China Sea	34,314	325	942	29.710	866
Haihe	Bohai Bay	264,617	1,090	717	22.600	85
Jiulong	Taiwan Straits	14,689	258	445	14.018	954
Yuanjiang	Beibu Bay	34,917	772	410	12.917	370
Ili	Balkhash Lake	56,700	375	374	11.790	208
Ertix	Kara Sea	50,862	442	348	10.985	216
Liaohe	Bohai Bay	164,104	1,430	302	9.526	58

i) The figures for Heilong and Yalu rivers include the sections of their courses outside China. The Heilong is calculated up to the point where it meets the Wusuli River.

ii) The Liaohe includes the Hunhe and Taize rivers, its two tributaries.

the annual average flow for most of China's major rivers is below 500 cu. m. per second (Table 4). The Huanghe River, the fifth longest in the world with a length of 5,464 km., flows across arid and semi-arid areas where there is no ample surface runoff. Its flow is not heavy, averaging 1,820 cu. m. per second, even less than that of the Minjiang with a length of only 577 km.

(2) Water Balance

The annual rainfall in China averages 6,032,000 million cu. m., which is equivalent to a precipitation depth of 630 mm. The average amount of annual runoff is 2,600,000 million cu. m., equivalent to a runoff depth of 270 mm. This means that the total amount of evaporation is 3,432,000 million cu. m., which is equivalent to a nationwide water depth of 360 mm. Therefore, the annual runoff accounts for 43 per cent of the total annual precipitation in China.

Because the amount of evaporation (57 per cent) is larger than the annual runoff (43 per cent) the water balance is unfavourable to agricultural production. But the water balance varies greatly in different parts of the country. A chart of the water balance of river basins in different areas (Table 5) shows that in the middle and lower reaches of the Changjiang, located around 30° N., the annual runoff and annual evaporation each account for about half the annual rainfall. In areas south of the Changjiang, runoff exceeds evaporation, especially in the mountain areas. North of the Changjiang, evaporation is greater than runoff. And the farther inland, the greater the evaporation. To the north of the Great Wall and west of the Helan Mountains, almost all the precipitation is lost through evaporation so that surface runoff there is very small. In the Tarim and other extremely arid inland basins, the surface runoff is nearly equivalent to zero and all the precipitation is lost through evaporation. Although the amount of rainfall in the mountainous regions of the inland arid areas is relatively heavier and the temperatures lower, the amount of evaporation there is still greater than the total amount of runoff. This is markedly different from mountainous regions in humid areas. The Kunlun, the Altun and other arid mountain areas, therefore, are almost without exception covered by steppes and have few forests.

The development and extension of irrigation projects has brought about great changes in the runoff. In many parts of northern China and large areas in the arid regions, river and underground waters are now diverted to irrigate farmland, and there are large areas of irrigated rice fields in southern China. If we take the area of China's irrigated farmland as 33.3 million hectares, and the consumption of water for every hectare as 7,500 cu. m., then a total of 250,000 million cu. m. of water are needed, or an amount equivalent to one-fourth of the annual flow of the Changjiang.

(3) Geographical Distribution of Annual Runoff

Since the formation of surface runoff is in the main determined by the atmospheric precipitation, the general pattern of the geographic distribution of annual runoff is by and large similar to the pattern of precipitation. The runoff in the south is greater than it is in the north; the runoff in areas near the ocean, greater than in inland areas; and the runoff in mountainous and hilly regions, greater than on the plains. During the process in which atmospheric precipitation turns into runoff, the landform, mantle, soil, vegetation and economic activities of human beings all play a part in the re-distribution of water. Therefore, the geographical distribution of annual

Table 5. Water Balance in Typical River Basins for Different Parts of China

Drain-age system	Name of river	Name of station	Control area (sq. km.)	Annual runoff (mm.)	Annual precipi-tation (mm.)	Annual evapora-tion (mm.)	Runoff coeffi-cient (%)
Heilong	Nen-jiang	Kumo-tun	31,693	196.5	525.0	328.5	37.5
Haihe	Chaohe	Daiying	4,266	86.7	530.0	443.3	16.7
Haihe	Juma	Zijing-guan	1,760	227.0	670.0	443.0	33.9
Huang-he	Taohe	Lijia-cun	23,500	199.5	575.0	375.5	34.7
Huang-he	Fenhe	Lancun	7,600	82.6	485.0	402.4	17.0
Huaihe	Yishui	Gegou	5,565	337.0	840.0	503.0	40.3
Chang-jiang	Nan-jiang	Ba-zhong	3,211	653.5	1,150.0	496.5	56.9
Chang-jiang	Jushui	Ma-cheng	888	524.6	1,232.4	707.8	42.5
Chang-jiang	Baihe	Nan-yang	3,363	363.5	910.0	546.5	40.0
Chang-jiang	Qingye	Chen-cun	2,840	936.0	1,676.0	740.0	55.9
Qian-tang	Cao'e	Dong-shabu	3,362	731.0	1,499.0	718.0	50.5
Min-jiang	Jianxi	Yefang	9,497	1,097.1	1,850.0	752.9	59.2

Zhu-jiang	Gui-jiang	Guilin	2,860	1,481.8	2,000.0	518.2	74.0
Zhu-jiang	Dong-jiang	Long-chuan	7,285	804.0	1,590.0	816.0	50.7
Honghe	Lixian	Lixian-du	17,273	746.7	1,650.0	903.7	45.2
Inland River	Chang-ma	Chang-mabao	11,600	67.7	285.0	217.3	23.7
Inland River	Golmud	Golmud	19,332	35.1	145.0	109.9	24.2
Inland River	Ili	Yamadu	48,421	257.9	450.0	192.1	57.3

runoff in China is more complex than the distribution of rainfall.

On a map showing depths of the annual averages of runoff in China (Fig. 14), the isolines of runoff depth of 50 and 200 mm. are the two important demarcation lines for the country's hydrogeography. The isoline of runoff depth of 50 mm. extends close to the isohyet showing 400 mm. of annual rainfall. It runs from Hailar in Inner Mongolia southwestward across the country, passing through Harbin, Zhangjiakou, Yanan, Lanzhou and Huangheyan to end in southern Tibet. This can also be viewed as a demarcation line between the agricultural areas in the eastern part of China and the stockbreeding areas in the western part of the country. The isoline of runoff depth of 200 mm. roughly coincides with the isohyet showing 800 mm. of annual rainfall, which extends along the Huaihe River and the Qinling range to divide China's agricultural areas into two, one south and one north. The south is devoted chiefly to rice growing, and the north, to dry cropping.

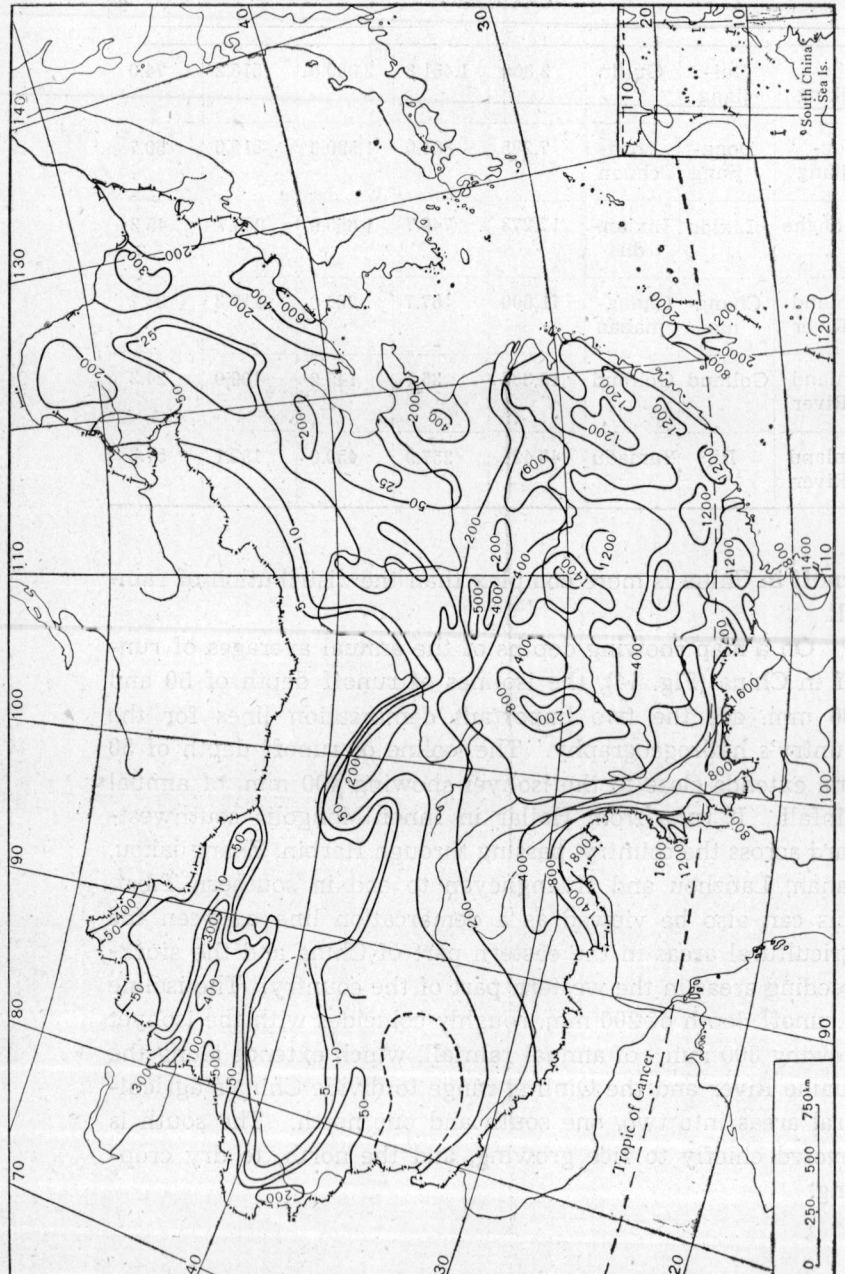

Fig. 14 Depths of the Annual Averages of Runoff in China (mm.)

In the geographical distribution of annual runoff, the
hilly areas along the southeastern coast and the mountainous
areas of Taiwan have the most abundant surface runoff, exceeding 1,000 mm. in most areas. The windward slopes of the
coastal hills and mountains in Zhejiang and Fujian provinces
are centres of heavy runoff. There the annual runoff depth
generally ranges between 1,200 and 1,400 mm., and it reaches
as much as 1,600 mm. in the Yandang Mountains. The annual
runoff depth in Taiwan is generally over 2,000 mm., since it
is directly influenced by moist air from the ocean and the
height of the mountains through which the rivers flow. The
Tatun Mountain area in Taiwan has over 4,000 mm. of runoff,
ranking as the heaviest runoff area in China. But the terrain
of plains in the southeastern coastal areas is not favourable
to the formation of rainfall, and so the annual runoff depth
there is only 700-800 mm.

There is also abundant surface runoff in areas south of
the Nanling Mountains and on Hainan Island. The runoff
depth in mountain areas there ranges between 1,400 and 1,600
mm., and in the central parts of the Shiwandashan area, it
reaches as much as 2,000 mm. But runoff is relatively less on
the coastal plains, the Zhujiang River delta, the Leizhou
Peninsula and the northwestern parts of Hainan Island, generally smaller than 800 mm.

The rugged terrain in the hills south of the Changjiang
basin is favourable to the formation of precipitation. Moreover, the red and yellow earths in this area are sticky and lumpy,
with poor permeability, which helps increase runoff. Although
the runoff here is less than that in the hills along the southeastern coast, it is fairly ample in the mountainous areas. In the
Wuling, Xuefeng, Jiuling, Mufu and Jinggang mountains
which are centres of heavy rainfall, the runoff depth is between 1,000 and 1,200 mm. The plains and basins among the
mountains are areas of fairly shallow runoff. The runoff
depth in the Dongting Lake basin and on the plains of the
middle and lower reaches of the Xiangjiang is between 400

and 500 mm. It is slightly larger in the Boyang Lake basin and on the plains of the middle and lower reaches of the Ganjiang River, but still less than 700 mm.

The distribution of runoff varies greatly in the Sichuan Basin. The runoff depth in the eastern part of the basin, where there are parallel ranges and valleys, exceeds 600 mm. while it is only 300 mm. in the central part of the basin. And it is less than 500 mm. in the rest of the basin. The mountains surrounding this basin are areas with heavy runoff, where the runoff depth may exceed 1,000-1,200 mm. In the vicinity of Mount Emei and in Ya'an, the depth is particularly great, reaching over 1,600 mm.

The mountainous areas along the western and southern borders of the Yunnan-Guizhou Plateau are areas of heavy runoff, reaching 1,000-1,800 mm. in depth. But the depth is only 300-400 mm. in the valleys on the leeward side. The runoff depth on the Guizhou Plateau, except for the Panxian area in its western part, may exceed 1,000 mm. However, the limestone areas in the central and eastern parts of the Yunnan Plateau are regions with low runoff, the depth being under 200 mm., the least for areas south of the Changjiang.

The Changjiang delta, low-lying and flat and having loose surficial materials, is criss-crossed by waterways. A large amount of its surface runoff is intercepted for irrigation of farmlands. The runoff depth in this delta is less than it is for other parts of the middle and lower reaches of the Changjiang basin, around 300 mm.

The runoff in north China is markedly distributed in a longitudinal pattern. The runoff depth for the coastal hills of Shandong Province is between 200 and 300 mm. The North China Plain, which is low-lying, has scanty rainfall and high evaporation. The river beds there are choked by large deposits of sediment which have gradually raised them higher than the surrounding land. This makes it impossible for the rivers to receive water from land beyond the sediment dykes, and the runoff outside these dykes often accumulates in low-lying areas between the rivers to cause waterlogging and greater evaporation. Furthermore, the thick, loose alluvial deposits of the rivers result in seepage and the formation of underground water. As a result, surface runoff decreases sharply from the Huanghuai Plain to the Haihe Plain and the runoff depth also decreases from 200 to less than 50 mm. It is even less than 25 mm. in the area from Suning to Zaoqiang.

The orographic conditions of the Yanshan Mountain area are conducive to the formation of rainfall. The mountains are composed of hard, crystalline rock, and the permeability of their soils is poor. In addition, the mountains have been long ago stripped bare of vegetation by timber felling, and so heavy runoff occurs after each heavy rainfall, with the runoff depth exceeding 100 mm. in most areas and as great a depth as 300 to 400 mm. on the windward sides. The Loess Plateau, situated farther from the ocean, on the other hand, has scanty rainfall and a high rate of evaporation. The loess is loose, highly porous and has a high rate of permeability. The land surface has little vegetation, and the runoff depth in most areas of the plateau is below 50 mm. The Muus Desert in the Ordos area is the region in northern China with the least runoff, with a runoff depth of less than 10 mm.

The distribution of runoff in the northeast is similar to that in north China. Since precipitation in the mountains of the northeast is greater than it is in north China and large areas of forests in the northeast have been preserved, the surface runoff is greater and readily replenished. The runoff depth in most parts of the mountain areas in northeast China is above 100 mm. In the Changbai Mountains it is generally 300-500 mm., while in the middle and lower reaches of the Yalu River, it is as great as 700 mm. Precipitation in the Lesser Hinggan Mountains is relatively small, with the runoff depth there dropping to around 200 mm. There is a great difference in the amount of surface runoff in the Greater Hinggan Mountains. The northern part of the Greater Hinggan range has relatively heavier rains and evaporation in this area is not

great.   There are also island-shaped areas of frozen earth
where the soil is impervious to water, preventing seepage into
the ground. This increases the amount of surface water. The
runoff depth here is about 150 to 200 mm. The southern part
of the Greater Hinggan range, belonging to the semi-arid area
of Inner Mongolia, has scanty rainfall and a high rate of evaporation. The runoff depth is only about 50 mm. Bogs cover
a large area of the Northeast Plain, and they are especially
evident in the lower reaches of the Nenjiang River and on the
Sanjiang Plains. In these areas most of the surface runoff
disappears into the bogs and marshes. This increases the
amount of evaporation. The runoff depth is generally less
than 25 mm., and it is less than 10 mm. on the Hulunbuir
Grasslands to the west of the Greater Hinggan Mountains.

The Inner Mongolian Plateau, which is situated far from
the ocean, has a dry climate. There are no high mountains
there and the supply of water from ice and snow is inadequate. Grasslands spread widely over a large area, which increases the roughness of land surface and retards surface
runoff. This results in a great deal of evaporation in the
drainage areas. Moreover, the herbs that grow among the
grasses absorb water from the soil and transpire it through
their leaves. This reduces potential underground runoff.
Therefore, the runoff depth on the Inner Mongolian Plateau
is below 25 mm., and there are large areas where there is no
runoff.

Xinjiang, situated in the heart of the Eurasian Continent,
has a dry climate and little runoff. Precipitation there is ex-
tremly scanty. In the semi-desert and desert areas, the land
is covered by loose sand or gravel. Almost all rainfall is lost
through evaporation, and the runoff depth in most areas of
Xinjiang is under 10 mm. The average rainfall in the Hami
Basin is only 8.5 mm., and rainfall does not form surface
runoff except in times of exceptionally heavy rains. In the
desert areas, there is no runoff all year round. The topography
in the Ili River basin is favourable to the penetration of moist

air from the west, and the runoff depth there reaches 343 mm.

Northern Xinjiang is influenced by the westerly circulation and is subject to frequent cyclones. The runoff depth in the Junggar Basin is 58.5 mm. Southern Xinjiang is influenced by subtropical anticyclones so that rainfall there is scanty. The runoff depth in the Tarim Basin is only 40 mm. In the mountains, such as the Altay and Tianshan, conditions are favourable for precipitation and permanent snow and glaciers provide supplements of water so that the runoff is abundant. The Altay Mountain area, with relatively greater rainfall, has a maximum runoff depth of 750 mm. The annual runoff in the Tianshan Mountains is generally 200-300 mm., while it is over 500 mm. on Mount Hantengri and an estimated 700 mm. in the glacier areas of its upper reaches. The Kunlun Mountain area is relatively dry and the mountain slopes there are covered mainly by steppes. The annual runoff depth there is about 50 to 100 mm. The transitional areas between the mountains and plains consist of vast expanses of piedmont alluvial and diluvial fans, covered by a layer of coarse gravel. Much of the surface runoff seeps underground, oozing out at the front of the alluvial and diluvial fans to turn these areas into desert oases. The runoff depth in these areas is generally between 10 and 25 mm.

Since river flow in the Xinjiang region relies mainly on glaciers to supplement water, the volume of flow is somewhat dependent on the average elevation of the drainage basin. Generally speaking, the higher the drainage basin, the greater the flow. The areas situated at altitudes of between 2,000 and 4,000 m. have the greatest amount of rainfall and, moreover, are transitional areas between liquid precipitation and solid precipitation. Consequently the increase in runoff depth there is greatest.

Runoff in the valleys of the Yarlungzangbo River results from rainfall caused by moist air coming from the Indian Ocean. However the runoff depth, influenced by the rain shadow belt of the Himalayas, decreases from 300 mm. in the lower reaches to less than 100 mm. in the upper reaches. In Zayu and other areas in the lower reaches, the southwest monsoons bring a great volume of rainfall and the valleys are deeply cut. The runoff depth here may reach over 1,000 mm.

The northern Tibetan Plateau, over 4,500 metres above sea level, has a dry and cold climate. The glaciers in nearby mountains are not large in size. The rivers have flat and shallow beds, and their water accumulates to form lakes in some low-lying areas. Such conditions are unfavourable for the formation of runoff. Although the land is covered by a thick layer of frozen earth, which prevents surface runoff from sinking into the ground, the low temperatures reduce the rate of evaporation and so runoff depth is greater here than it is in the arid basins in the northwest. It is estimated at below 50 mm.

As described above, the distribution of annual runoff in China is different from one region to another with changes in physical geography, and these differences are particularly marked in some relatively small areas. Yet the distribution of annual runoff in China still has geographical and regional characteristics corresponding with the distribution of landscapes. In general, areas with a runoff depth less than 10 mm. correspond to desert areas; areas with a runoff depth of 10-25 mm. correspond to semi-desert areas; 25-50 mm., to grassland areas; 50-200 mm., to deciduous broad-leaved forests and forest-grassland areas; 200-600 mm., to evergreen and deciduous broad-leaved forest belts in the northern sub-tropical zone; 600-1,000 mm., to evergreen broad-leaved forest belts in southern sub-tropical zone; and over 1,000 mm., to tropical rain forest belts and sub-tropical evergreen mountain forests.

(4) Seasonal Distribution and Variation of Annual Runoff

Influenced to a great extent by the East Asian monsoon climate, the seasonal distribution of runoff in China varies greatly as does the interannual runoff. The supply of rain water accounts for 80 to 90 per cent of the annual runoff in hills and mountains along the southeastern coast and on the North China Plain, 70 to 80 per cent in rivers south of the Changjiang and over 80 per cent in Inner Mongolia. It generally makes up 50 to 60 per cent of the annual runoff in northeast China, 60 to 70 per cent in southwest China, less than 40 per cent on the northern Tibetan Plateau and only 5 to 25 per cent in arid areas in northwest China.

In the case of the rivers that get their supply of water from rainfall, the yearly distribution of river flow is closely related to the volume of rainfall and to the seasonal changes in rainfall. The flood season in most areas influenced by the East Asian monsoons occurs between May and October. The dry or low water season occurs between January and February. The seasonal distribution of river flow is quite uneven, and there is a great difference in the volume of flow between high and low water seasons.

The supply of water from melted ice and snow is important for rivers in northeast and northwest China and the northern Tibetan Plateau. In general, rivers south of the Changjiang are not supplied by snowfall. In north China, the volume of snow runoff is quite small. The seasonal supply of melted snow accounts for only 10 to 15 per cent of the total annual river flow in northeast China, but it is over 60 per cent in some rivers on the northern Tibetan Plateau, and generally 40 to 50 per cent in rivers in northwest China. In the case of rivers supplied mainly by melted ice and snow, the fluctuation in their flow is closely related to the temperature in their basins. Their flood season occurs in warm months and their low water season in the winter. The change in river flow fed by ice and snow, both within a year and from year to year, is generally smaller than that recorded for rivers replenished by rain water. And since both the rainy season and the hot season in China fall in summer, summer is the period with heaviest river flows and winter is the low water season.

Almost all the rivers in China are also supplied by groundwater, but variations in the amount of water supplied by this source are great. The amount of groundwater entering rivers south of the Changjiang, except those in the Sichuan Basin and the coastal hills of Zhejiang and Fujian provinces with less than 10 to 20 per cent of the annual flow, accounts for 20 to 30 per cent of the annual flow. Such a supply accounts for less than 20 per cent of the annual flow in the rivers on the Huanghe, Huaihe and Haihe plains, 20 to 30 per cent in the Shandong Hills, as high as 50 to 60 per cent on the Loess Plateau, 60 per cent in the southern part of the Ordos Desert, generally less than 20 per cent in Inner Mongolia, 30 to 40 per cent in the karst areas of southwest China and 50 to 60 per cent in the broad valleys and basins in northern Tibet. In the piedmont alluvial fans in northwest China, the proportion of groundwater flowing in rivers is markedly greater, generally 50 to 60 per cent. And the rivers flowing down from the piedmont diluvial fans are almost entirely supplied by groundwater. The fluctuation of flow both within a year and from year to year is relatively stable in such rivers totally replenished by groundwater.

Most of the floods caused by China's rivers are formed by heavy rainstorms, and the occurrence of a flood coincides with a period of heavy rainstorms. The rise and fall of flood waters are related to the rainstorm system, the size of a river basin and a river's capacity to regulate a flood. The floods of medium and small-sized rivers often rise and decline abruptly. In southern China, heavy rainstorms occur frequently with short intervals between them, and this leads to the formation of continuous flood peaks, one immediately following another. In northern China, floods occur less frequently and the duration of each one is shorter. In big rivers, the rise and decline of floods is a relatively slow process, but they last longer because the floods are formed by the convergence of water from their tributaries. Most of the floods that originate in high mountains in northwest China are formed by water from both

melted ice and snow and from rainstorms. Flood peaks formed by melted ice and snow alone do not generally result in a
large volume of flow, and such floods rise and decline with
the changes of temperature between day and night. Flood
peaks caused by both melted snow and rainstorms have
heavier flows.

The seasonal distribution of runoff in China is characterized by the fact that as the front of plum rain moves northward, the period of peak flow from south to north is delay-
ed and the duration of the peak flood season also becomes
shorter. The proportion of the annual peak flow for the four
months between April and July increases from south to north.
The proportion is 60 to 65 per cent in the southeastern coastal
areas and as high as 80 per cent in north China and Inner
Mongolia.

Winter is the season with the smallest flow, generally accounting for less than 10 per cent of the annual total. Northern
Taiwan is the only area where there is a great deal of precipitation in winter, and there the runoff in this season accounts
for 28 per cent of the annual total. The flow of rivers in China
generally increases in the spring accounting for 10 to 20 per
cent of the annual total in most areas. But in southwest China,
influenced by the Indian monsoons, it is only 5 to 10 per cent
in the spring. An exception is the hilly regions south of the
Changjiang and the Nanling Mountain area, where the spring
flow accounts for about 40 per cent of the annual total. The
flow of China's rivers is the heaviest in summer, accounting
for 50 to 60 per cent of the annual total in most areas. Yet in
the hills south of the Changjiang, the flow decreases to 30-40
per cent as the summer monsoons move northward. The flow
everywhere generally decreases in autumn, accounting for
15 to 25 per cent of the annual total in most areas. Influenced by the shifting of the low pressure trough, the autumn river
flow in areas south of the Qinling Mountains accounts for
about 40 per cent of the annual total. In southwest China, the
Indian monsoons retreat later, and river flow in autumn may

account for 30 to 35 per cent of the annual total. In the Xi-shuangbanna area, the autumn flow amounts to 40-45 per cent of the annual total. The coastal provinces are influenced by typhoons which often cause a heavy flood flow. On Hainan Island, autumn floods account for over 50 per cent of the annual total discharge of rivers.

In the monsoon-swept areas of eastern China, where rivers are mainly supplied by rainfall, the coefficient of variation of annual runoff increases from the south to the north and is smaller in hilly areas than on the plains. This corresponds to the general distribution pattern of rainfall. The coefficient is generally 0.2 to 0.4 in areas south of the Changjiang, over 0.3 in the coastal areas in southeast China, 0.4 in coastal areas in Zhejiang and Fujian provinces and as high as 0.6 on Hainan Island. The coefficient is roughly 0.2 to 0.3 in southern Yunnan, the karst areas of southwest China and the hilly areas in western Sichuan Province. This indicates that the source of water supply there is more stable. The coefficient north of the Changjiang is generally 0.6 to 0.8, and as high as 1 for the Douhai and Majia rivers. The Huanghe, Huaihe and Haihe River valleys were therefore the areas hit by the most disastrous droughts and floods in the past. The coefficient in most of the other areas of northeast China is 0.4 to 0.6, and even below 0.3 in the Changbai Mountain area. On the Loess Plateau, where groundwater accounts for a large proportion of the annual flow, the coefficient is below 0.4, and only 0.2 to 0.3 in the tributaries of the upper reaches of the Wuding River.

The coefficient is relatively small on the plateaus and in areas covered by high mountains in the western part of China, where the rivers are supplied by melted ice and snow or by groundwater. The coefficient in the Tianshan and Qilian Mountain areas is only 0.1 to 0.2, and does not exceed 0.3 in the Altay Mountains. On the Tibetan Plateau it is roughly 0.3 to 0.4.

The coefficient increases markedly in arid areas where the rivers are supplied by rainstorms. For example, it reaches over

0.8 in Inner Mongolia and in the arid basins in northwest China.

Based on observations made over many years, fluctuations are smaller in the annual flow of the main courses of big rivers than in their tributaries. This is because the big rivers gather water from a large number of tributaries that flow through different regions where the rainy and dry seasons do not occur simultaneously. Thus the runoff from different regions is regulated by the river channels. The coefficient in the tributaries of the Changjiang in the section from the Jinsha to the Datong River is above 0.2, while it is below 0.2 in the main course of the Changjiang. The coefficient registered at all the hydrological stations along the main course of the Huanghe, downstream from Lanzhou, is between 0.2 and 0.25, but it is over 0.3 in tributaries flowing into this section of the river.

(5) River Silt

China has an undulating terrain, concentrated rainfall and heavy rainstorms, and because of the destruction of the natural vegetative cover in the past, the surface runoff results in a great deal of erosion. According to statistics, the total volume of silt transported into the oceans by China's rivers reaches 2,600 million tons a year. This figure is calculated on the basis of suspended sediment alone (Table 6). Of this amount, the annual silt discharge of the Huanghe is 1,593 million tons, or 60.6 per cent of the national total. The silt content carried in all the rivers of north China ranks second to the Huanghe, but the total silt discharge there is only 150 million tons, since the rivers do not have abundant runoff. The average silt content of the Changjiang is somewhat less than the combined total for the north China rivers, but since the Changjiang has ample flow, its total silt discharge reaches 502 million tons a year, or 19.1 per cent of the national total.

The Loess Plateau suffers from serious soil erosion. All the rivers that originate in or flow across the loess area have a high silt content. The section of the Huanghe River in Shan-xi and Shaanxi provinces and the basins of its three tribu-taries — the Jinhe, Luohe and Weihe — are centres of heavy rainstorms. The land in this area is carpeted by a thick layer of loess and there is scanty vegetative cover, so that the land surface is dissected by numerous gullies. The area is subject to serious soil erosion and is the major source of the sediment load in the Huanghe. The average silt content of the Huanghe is 38 kg. per cu. m., ranking it as the most silt-filled major river in the world. The silt content of a number of its smaller trib-utaries is even greater. For instance, the silt content of the Jinhe River is 171 kg. per cu. m. and that of the Zuli River is 457 kg. per cu. m.

The upper reaches of the Xiliao and other rivers in north China also have a high silt content, generally over 10 kg. per cu. m. The silt content of the Laohe River, a tributary of the upper Xiliao River, reaches as high as 90 kg. per cu. m. and that of the Yongding River, 43.5 kg. per cu. m. The silt content of most of rivers in the Changjiang basin is below 1.0 kg. per cu. m. The tributaries in the river's upper reaches have a silt content of 0.5-1.0 kg. per cu. m., while the tributaries in the middle and lower reaches have a silt content of around 0.2 kg. per cu. m. The only exceptions are the middle reaches of the Jinsha River, the upper and middle reaches of the Jialing River, and the Hanjiang River where the silt content reaches 1-10 kg. per cu. m. The silt content is quite small in the rivers of the Zhejiang and Fujian coastal areas, in the Zhu-jiang River basin and in southwest China, where it is generally below 0.3 kg. per cu. m. The silt content of the Yuanjiang River exceeds 1.0 kg. per cu. m. because the slope of the river basin is quite steep The Hongshui River basin on the upper reaches of the Xijiang River is carpeted by weathered red soil and has a silt content of over 1.0 kg. per cu. m. The northeast China area has dense forests and grasslands so that the silt content of the rivers there is quite low. The figure for the

Table 6. River Silt of China's Exterior Drainage Basin

River basin	Average silt content (kg./cu. m.)	Silt discharge	
		Million tons	Per cent of total
Rivers in northeast China	0.51	86	3.2
Rivers in north China	8.72	150	5.7
Huanghe (Shaanxian)	37.7	1,593	60.6
Huaihe, Yihe and Shehe rivers	0.25	15	0.6
Changjiang (Datong)	0.54	502	19.1
Rivers in the Zhejiang and Fujian coastal areas	0.11	26	1.0
Zhujiang and other rivers in south China	0.20	95	3.6
Rivers in southwest China	0.08	162	6.2
Total	6.01	2,629	100

Songhua River is 0.16 kg. per cu. m., and that for the Huma River, only 0.02 kg.

The rivers in the arid areas of northwest China generally have a sediment content of 0.1 to 0.5 kg. per cu. m. The lowest silt content is registered in rivers supplied mainly by groundwater; rivers supplied by melted ice and snow rank next lowest. Temporary rivers formed by heavy rainstorms have the heaviest silt content, sometimes even containing mud and rock flows.

The distribution of the fluvial erosion modulus in China coincides with the river silt content. The Huanghe basin has the greatest fluvial erosion modulus. The fluvial erosion modulus of its tributaries between Shanxi and Shaanxi provinces reaches as much as 10,000-30,000 tn./sq. km., and that registered along the main course of the river at Shaanxian is 2,322 tn./sq. km. The figure for the Xiliao River basin and the upper tributaries of the Haihe River is about 1,000-5,000 tn./sq. km., while that for the southeastern coastal area and southwest China is below 500 tn./sq. km.

In general, Yichang in Hubei Province can be taken as the dividing point in the Changjiang River basin. The fluvial erosion modulus upstream from Yichang is mostly above 200 tn./sq. km., and in the upper Jinsha River and the basin of the Jialing River, the figure reaches 1,000 tn./sq. km. Downstream from Yichang, the figure is generally below 200 tn./sq. km., yet in the basin of the Hanjiang River it may reach as high as 784 tn./sq. km. The figure for most of the northeast China rivers is below 50 tn./sq. km. This is the area where soil erosion is smallest. The arid basins in northwest China suffer mainly from wind erosion, and the fluvial erosion modulus there is generally below 200 tn./sq. km.

The rivers in the northern parts of the country have a high silt content but relatively less runoff, while the rivers in southern China have a lower silt content but abundant runoff. All China's rivers, therefore, carry a considerable silt discharge. This silt supplies alluvial sediment to the plains formed by the lower reaches of the rivers and to river deltas. According to historical records, the Huanghe delta has advanced seaward at an average rate of 46 m. per year, while the coast of the Changjiang River delta has extended seaward at an average rate of 25 m. per year. Nearly 40,000 cu. m. of sediment is deposited each year at Tianjin's Xingang Harbour, the location of the Haihe estuary.

3. General Description of the Hydrological
Features of Major Rivers

The Zhujiang, Changjiang, Huanghe and the Heilong are the four major rivers of China. They all flow from west to east through the different latitudinal zones into the Pacific Ocean. Their basic features are described in the following table.

The Changjiang has the widest drainage area and the biggest water flow. Both the drainage area and length of the Zhujiang are only half that of the Huanghe, yet its flow is eight times that of the latter. The runoff modulus values of these four rivers fully reflects the latitudinal features in China under its monsoon climate.

The Changjiang is the longest river in China, having many tributaries that form a vast drainage system. Ten tributaries each have an annual mean flow of more than 1,000 cu. m. per sec. The Changjiang basin lies in the subtropical monsoon region of China. With a great deal of precipitation, the area has abundant water resources. The annual mean flow at Batang on the Jinsha River, a tributary on the upper reaches of the Changjiang, is three times that of the Haihe River. The annual average flow of the Changjiang at Yibin is four times that of the Huanghe, and at its mouth it is 17 times that of the latter. The water in the Changjiang comes mainly from its upper and middle reaches, which account for more than 90 per cent of its total runoff (46.4 per cent from the upper reaches and 47.3 per cent from the middle reaches). The water entering this river in the lower reaches accounts for only 6.3 per cent of the total.

The seasonal distribution of runoff in different sections of the Changjiang is as follows: about 40 per cent of the annual total on the upper reaches and 50 per cent on the lower reaches in summer; 32 to 33 per cent in autumn; less in spring, and the least in winter. Compared with rivers in the north, this

Table 7. Main Features of China's Four Major Rivers

Name	Drainage area (sq. km.)	Length (km.)	Mean flow (cu. m./sec.)	Runoff modulus l./sec. sq. km.)
Zhujiang	452,616	2,197	11,075	24.5
Changjiang	1,807,199	6,380	31,055	17.2
Huanghe	752,443	5,464	1,820	2.4
Heilong	1,620,170	3,420	8,600	5.3

yearly variation of flow is relatively even. The biggest flow occurs in summer, sometimes early and sometimes late, depending on when the summer monsoons move northward. Roughly speaking, the earliest flood comes from the Dongting Lake drainage system, then from the main stream of the Changjiang west of Yichang and last from the Hanjiang River. If high water from the main stream and its tributaries arrives at the same time, the flood may last for a long period, presenting a big menace to land areas along the middle reaches of the Changjiang. For example, the flow at Yichang in 1954 was measured at 69,000 cu. m. per sec., producing the worst flood in a century. In flood years, about 60 per cent of the total flow at Hankou comes from the main stream west of Yichang, 20 to 30 per cent from the Dongting Lake system and 7 to 9 per cent from the Hanjiang River.

In order to relieve the Changjiang flood menace, large-scale work has been done since Liberation to control the river. Great achievements have been made along its course in flood prevention, irrigation, power generation and navigation. Dykes along its main stream and its main tributaries have been repaired, raised or strengthened. The Jingjiang flood-diversion project, the Hanjiang flood-diversion project and other flood-storage projects have been built along its middle reaches, the area often hit by unusual floods. Many lakes have been dredged, and some bending in the river course has been straightened. All this has increased the capability of the Changjiang to prevent floods.

More than 40,000 small reservoirs, mainly for irrigation, and over 500 big and medium-sized reservoirs for multi-purpose utilization have also been built. The farm area now irrigated is three and a half times the total before Liberation, and the area of farmland that promises good harvests in all weather has increased to over one quarter of the total cultivated land in the river basin. Agriculture, forestry, livestock breeding, sideline production and fishery have all grown rapidly. The Changjiang is not only China's main artery for inland river navigation, it also provides abundant water power resources, and some of its huge water flow has been diverted to the northern parts of the country. It is therefore of great importance to the development of China's national economy.

The Huanghe is the second longest river in China. Compared with the other three rivers, however, its mean runoff is quite small. Its annual mean flow at Shaanxian is only 1,350 cu. m. per sec., far from enough to meet the needs of the growing industry and agriculture in its catchment area. Statistics show that most of the runoff of this river comes from its upper and middle reaches, with more than 50 per cent of the water coming from its upper reaches west of Lanzhou. The Weihe River, the largest tributary on the middle reaches of the Huanghe, supplies about 20 per cent of the water and the Yiluo and Qinhe rivers provide only 10 per cent. The other tributaries provide very little. The water flow of the Huanghe from Lanzhou down does not increase as its catchment area enlarges, but decreases gradually as it flows into its lower reaches. For example, the drainage area of the river between

Lanzhou and Baotou increases by nearly 20 per cent, but its runoff drops by 6,000 million cu. m. Many tributaries join the main stream as the river runs through the Loess Plateau between Baotou and Shaanxian, with the drainage area becoming 44 per cent bigger, but the water flow increases only 32 per cent. Because the river bed is higher than the ground surface in the section from Shaanxian downward, not only do no major tributaries flow into the main stream but the river water percolates through the banks and gradually decreases.

The water flow in the main stream of the Huanghe increases in summer and autumn. Along the upper reaches of the river west of Lanzhou, the biggest flow comes in summer, accounting for 43.2 per cent of the annual runoff. Floods in the Huanghe result mainly from rainstorms, especially those over the Weihe, Yiluo and Qinhe rivers in Shanxi and Shaanxi provinces. For example, the peak flow of the river in 1958 at Huayuankou north of Zhengzhou, capital of Henan Province, reached 22,300 cu. m. per sec. About 30 per cent of the water in that peak flow came from the Yiluo River. The biggest flow at Shaanxian in 1933 was 22,000 cu. m. per sec., 80 per cent of which came from the Jinghe, Luohe and Weihe rivers.

The Huanghe is well-known for its abundant silt. The average silt content at Shaanxian is 37.7 kg. per sec., and the average silt discharge of the river as a whole is 1,590 million tons. An analysis of the silt content at Lanzhou shows that it is 7 per cent of the total volume, and 90.9 per cent of this silt comes from the loess highlands between Shaanxi and Shanxi provinces. About 63 per cent of the silt comes from the main stream of the Huanghe and 25.3 per cent from the Weihe, Jinghe and Fenhe rivers. The rest comes from the banks of the Huanghe channel.

After Shaanxian, the Huanghe enters a plain and the river course is relatively flat. Not all the silt can be discharged into the sea and large quantities have been deposited in the river bed, until it has risen higher than the ground surface on both sides of the river. It is thus a "river above the ground" in the sections where this has happened.   The mouth of the river was also silted so that it has often changed its course to the sea.   In the past, whenever torrential rains occurred in summer or autumn and the river banks failed to control the high water, floods broke out, dykes were breached and the river changed its course.   Over a period of 3,000 years this happened on more than 1,500 occasions.   The river changed some of its course on 26 occasions and a great part of its course on 9 occasions.   Since Liberation, the 1,800 km. of river dykes have been repaired and strengthened, flood-diversion sluices and thawing ice diversion sluices have been built, and flood-detention and flood-diversion basins have been opened to ensure that both the autumn flood season and the spring ice thawing season will pass safely.

In order to bring the Huanghe under permanent control and to develop its water resources, a long-term plan for multi-purpose utilization of the river was adopted at the National People's Congress in 1955.   Under this plan, a series of dams and power stations were to be built across the river in the section between the Longyang Gorge on the upper reaches at Guide in Qinghai Province, and Taohuayu opposite the mouth of the Qinhe River, in Henan Province.   Floods could thus be prevented and the river water could be used for irrigation and power generation.   At the same time, the plan required that large-scale work would be done to conserve the water and soil in the loess areas, so as to bring about a fundamental change to the physical features of the Huanghe basin.

Construction of permanent farm works, centring on water and soil conservation, has since been in full swing in the loess areas.   A big reservoir has been built at the Sanmen Gorge; a flood-detention basin was opened at Beijinti, in Henan Province; and flood-diversion basins were opened at Dongpinghu, Qihe and Kengli, in Shandong Province.   At the same time, the silted water from the Huanghe is being used to irrigate farmland, improve soil and develop agricultural production, thus providing favourable conditions for the complete transformation of the Huanghe and the development of its water resources.

The Huanghe has abundant water power resources, its mainstream alone having a potential capacity of more than 26 million kw. Big power stations and multi-purpose water conservancy projects have been built at the Liujia Gorge, Yanguo Gorge, Sanmen Gorge, Qingtong Gorge and Sanshenggong along the mainstream of the river. The biggest power station on the Huanghe, the Longyang Gorge Hydroelectric Power Station, with a designed generating capacity of 1,600,000 kw., is under construction. The operation of these stations and water conservancy projects has greatly improved the prospects of agricultural development in northwest China, and the irrigated area in the whole river basin has been extended to four million hectares. However, ways to solve the silt problem of the Huanghe are still under discussion.

The Zhujiang, in south China, has three main tributaries — the Xijiang, the Beijiang and the Dongjiang. These form a closely-knitted network of crisscrossing rivers and streams along its lower reaches. Seventy-seven per cent of the runoff in the Zhujiang comes from the Xijiang; 15.6 per cent from the Beijiang and 7.4 per cent from the Dongjiang.

Most of the Zhujiang basin is located in the rainy region of China's tropical monsoon area, and therefore it is supplied with abundant water. The runoff modulus of the whole basin is 24.5 l./sec. per sq. km., ranking it first among the major rivers in China. As the river is readily supplied by water vapours from the southern seas, its annual runoff variability is much smaller than that of the rivers in northern China, averaging less than 30 per cent. The annual runoff during a rainy year is two to three times that of a dry year.

The high water season in the Zhujiang lasts as long as six months a year, and its biggest flow occurs during the high water season. The Beijiang and Dongjiang rivers are characterized by mountain torrents with a rapid rising or lowering of river water. The Xijiang has more tributaries with a relatively big catchment area and therefore the change in the rising and lowering of water is somewhat slower. In the vast karst areas along the Xijiang, the surface water and the ground water supplement each other, and the water level and flow of the river are relatively stable, providing favourable conditions for irrigation and navigation.

The valleys of the Zhujiang are broad and deep and can therefore retain more flood water. However, the Zhujiang delta often suffers from floods when typhoons hit it or when the high waters from the three tributaries meet. The flood of 1915 destroyed most of the enclosure dykes in the delta, affecting 360,000 hectares of farmland and flooding part of Guangzhou. After Liberation, these dykes were repaired or strengthened, and a number of irrigation and drainage projects were built. This has ensured the safety of the river delta. The Zhujiang has abundant water power resources. The whole basin has an estimated potential capacity of 28 million kw., 88 per cent of which are concentrated in the Xijiang basin.

The Heilong, the boundary river between China and the Soviet Union, is located in the northern part of northeast China. The whole basin covers an area of 1,620,000 sq. km., about 890,000 sq. km. being on the Chinese side. The Songhua River, the biggest tributary of the Heilong, has a drainage area of about 550,000 sq. km.

The Heilong River basin lies in the monsoon regions of the cold-temperate and temperate zones. Its main supply of runoff comes from summer monsoon rains, but melting winter snow is also a source of water. Spring floods, caused by the melting snow, often occur in April or May. Torrential rains towards the end of summer often lead to the biggest flood peaks during the flood season, in August or September. Therefore, the seasonal variation in the runoff of the Heilong and its tributaries has a bimodel distribution. However, in the higher latitudes, the interval between the spring and summer flood seasons is shorter than it is in the section of the river that flows through the lower latitudes. The annual mean flow in the mainstream of the Heilong is 8,600 cu. m. per sec., but it rose to 12,400 cu. m. in 1897 and dropped to only 3,620 cu. m. in 1921. The difference between the two years was about 3.6 times. There are similarities in the flow of the Songhua River, although the difference in its runoff between high-water year and low-water year was 7 times.

The Heilong River basin has a freezing period in winter of about six months. On the upper reaches of the river the freezing period averages more than 160 days and the thickest ice is about 1.25 to 1.50 m. The freezing period on the middle reaches averages 140 to 160 days, and the thickest ice averages 1 to 1.25 m. The freezing period of the Songhua River averages less than 140 days and its thickest ice is around one metre. Both the Heilong and the Songhua begin to freeze in mid or late November and to thaw in mid or late April. There is an ice-flowing spell of 10 to 15 days before and after the freezing period.

Almost the whole mainstream of the Heilong is open to navigation; the Songhua is open to ships with a displacement of 1,000 tons or more from the city of Harbin downstream. Both rivers are so frozen in winter that the ice is thick enough to support horse-drawn carts.

The areas along both banks of the Heilong and its tributaries are covered with big forests and thick vegetation, and there is little soil erosion. Therefore, the rivers contain little sediment. For example, the Songhua has only 0.16 kg. of silt per cu. m. and an average fluvial erosion modulus of 22.3 tons per sq. km. In terms of fluvial erosion modulus, the difference between the Huanghe (at Shaanxian) and the Heilong and its tributaries is 100 to 200 times.

4. Lakes and Marshes

Lakes are widely distributed throughout China. There are more than 2,800 lakes with areas of more than one sq. km.

each, and 12 lakes with areas of more than 1,000 sq. km. The
total lake area in China is more than 80,000 sq. km.

The lakes can be divided into three types on the basis
of their locations:

1) Freshwater lakes in the east. Most of these are storage
and drainage lakes. Fluviatile lakes, or oxbow lakes, are found
along the Changjiang. The Qili Lake on the North China
Plain and the Taihu Lake in the Changjiang delta are of marine origin. The Baiyang and Wenan lakes on the North China
Plain, and the Chengdong, Chengxi and Wabu lakes along the
middle reaches of the Huaihe River are lakes of depression.
The big lakes, such as the Tongting and Poyang, as well as the
Dianchi and Erhai on the Yunnan Plateau, are related to the
subsidence of land or rifts caused by tectonic movements.

The bottoms of most of these lakes have become flat from
thick layers of sediment deposited over a long time. As a
whole, they are not deep. For example, the average depth of
the Taihu Lake is 1.29 m., the deepest section being no more
than 5 m.

The areas along the middle and lower reaches of the
Changjiang contain the most freshwater lakes. There are
more than 1,200 big or small lakes in this area, the largest being Poyang, Dongting, Chaohu and Taihu. These lakes help
to regulate and store high water from the rivers, thus preventing the occurrence of floods. For example, the Poyang Lake
can store one-third of the flood waters from the rivers in Jiangxi Province. The Dongting not only receives all the water
from the four major rivers in Hunan Province, it also stores
part of the water from Changjiang. The depressions and lakes
along the middle reaches of the Huaihe River and on the Haihe
River Plain are all good flood storage basins in summer. Many
reservoirs have also been built to divert floods, irrigate farmland, breed fish and generate electricity.

Moreover, there are also some volcanic lakes in the eastern part of China, among them the Tianchi in the Changbai

Mountains and the Huguangyan on the Leizhou Peninsula, with depths reaching dozens of metres.

2) Interior lakes in the arid regions of the northwest. Most of these are interior salt lakes formed where rivers end. Owing to intense evaporation from these lakes, the water is heavily mineralized. The Jartai in Inner Mongolia, and the Caka and Qarhan in the Qaidam Basin are all famous salt lakes. The Hulun Nur and Buir Nur in eastern Inner Mongolia are well-known big lakes, the waters from which flow into the Hailar River when it rises in summer.

Lakes in the desert basins, such as the Lop Nur and Manas in Xinjiang and the Juyan in western Inner Mongolia, have shallow water and often change their locations owing to sedimentation carried into them by summer torrents and sands deposited in them by heavy winds.

There are also lakes in the mountainous areas, formed by the action of tectonic faulting, such as the Ulungur (or Buluntokha) at the southwestern foot of the Altay Mountains, the Ebi Nur at the northern foot of the Tianshan Mountains, the Bosten at the southern foot of the Tianshan Mountains and the Aydingkol in the Turpan Depression.

3) Lakes on the Qinghai-Tibetan Plateau. Most of these, of which there is a large concentration, were formed by tectonic movements and glaciation. Others were formed after rivers became blocked by mud and rock flows. Most of them are interior salt lakes or mild salt lakes. The biggest is the Qinghai Lake, followed by the Nam Co, Qilin Co, Tangra Yumco, Banggong Co and Yamzho Yumco. The Qinghai Lake has an area of 4,456 sq. km. and a maximum depth of 29 m. With an average of 12.32 grammes of minerals per litre, it is the largest salt lake in China. Lying at 4,718 metres above sea level, the Nam Co, also called the Tenggri Lake, is one of the highest lakes in the world. The climate is cold on the plateau, and so all these lakes freeze in winter. The lakeside areas and the areas along both banks of the rivers that flow into them provide good pasture grassland.

China's marshes cover a total area of 110,000 sq. km. (an equivalent of about 11,000,000 hectares), and are a great natural resource. As a result of differences in topography and climate, the marshes are unevenly distributed. Most of them, however, are concentrated in the following regions:

1) Coastal marshes. Many marshes are located along the silted coastal beaches north of the Qiantang River or at the mouths of the rivers and sea bays. These are mainly covered by reeds. Due to the action of sea tides, they remain saline. The reed marshes in the Panshan area north of the Liaodong Bay have been brought under the plough. Apart from the paddy fields reclaimed from sections of these marshes, more than 100,000 tons of reeds are harvested every year. Most of the marshes in the Zhujiang delta have been turned into paddy fields and fish breeding ponds.

2) Northeast China marshes. Because of the cold and wet climate in this area, there is little evaporation in these marshes. Permafrost and seasonal frozen areas are widely distributed, and there are large marshes because of the poor drainage of the surface water. On the plain between the Heilong, Wusuli and Songhua rivers, where the terrain is low and flat with a thick cover of clay and silty clay, there is poor drainage and little water percolation. This is also an area with much rainfall in summer and autumn so that it has become the biggest marsh region, covering a total area of about 2,666,000 hectares. Marshes are also widely located in the valleys and gullies of the Greater Hinggan, Lesser Hinggan and Changbai mountains, and on lava platform areas 800 metres above sea level. Most of these marshes have peat layers that are a metre thick.

3) Saline marshes in arid regions. In the arid areas of northwest China, flood and groundwaters collect where interior rivers terminate, often forming interior saline marshes. The marshes in the eastern Qaidam Basin cover 1,100,000 hectares. Large marshes are also located at the northern foot

of the Tianshan Mountains, around the margins of the Yur-
dus Grasslands, the Bosten Lake and the Tarim River Plain.

4) Marshes on the Qinghai-Tibetan Plateau. The cold
and wet climate and the frozen soil in the eastern part of the
Qinghai-Tibetan Plateau provide favourable conditions for the
formation and development of the widely distributed marshes.
These include the marshes at Xingsuhai, where the Huanghe
rises, and at Xuanmatan, where the Changjiang rises. Marshes
with an area of 730,000 hectares are found in Nagqu Prefecture, 4,500 metres above sea level. These are mostly located
on flood plains, river terraces, lakesides and fan-fringing depressions, where drainage is poor. The marshes on the Zoige
Highland, in northern Sichuan Province, cover more than
266,000 hectares and contain large peat layers, 2 to 3 m. thick.

Moreover, the areas around the Dongting, Taihu, Hongze
and Qinghai lakes, soaked by water from these lakes, are saturated with groundwater. Rivers have carried sediments
with plants into the lakes, and because the plants cannot decompose entirely in the water, the lake areas have gradually
shrunk and become marshes.

Work has been started to transform and utilize the marshes. The vast areas of marshes have ample water and fertile
soil. They can be turned into good farmland, pastures or forests after water conservancy work, and after soil and crop
strains are improved. Peat is also a valuable natural resource
and can be widely used in agricultural and industrial production, as well as in the production of medicines.

5. Role of China's Rivers in the Formation of the Landscape

China's many rivers and its complicated hydrological
structure form an important part of the natural landscape. The
rivers were created under the influence of multiple physiographical elements, and they have played an important part in
the formation and development of the landscape.

First, the hydrological conditions in China reflect regional physiographical features. The arid highlands and basins in the west are interior drainage regions with little runoff and no drainage, except in a small part of northern Xinjiang and southern Tibet. The monsoon areas in the east are exterior drainage regions, with the distribution and variability of precipitation reflecting the advance or retreat of the summer monsoons and forming different hydrological zones. The rivers in the south have ample runoff. The Changjiang with its many tributaries is an especially long waterway that can provide surplus water to the northern parts of China where runoff is scarce.

Due to the percolation of rain water in the soil, soluble salts tend to shift and illuviate with runoff, forming different geochemical landscapes and mineralizing river water to different degrees. Studies on the mineralization and hardness of river water in China show that the geochemical features of the runoff are related to the humidity in the climate. As the river runoff in monsoon regions reaches the sea, its chemical properties, in most cases, contain heavy carbonates. The degree of mineralization rises as one examines the runoff from the coastal areas in the east and south to the areas of the north and west. For example, the river water contains 0 to 50 mg. of minerals per litre along the coast of Zhejiang and Fujian provinces, 200 to 300 mg. per litre in the areas north of the Huaihe River and 300 to 500 mg. per litre north of the Qinling Mountains. In the interior drainage regions, where precipitation is scarce and evaporation and concentration of natural waters are intense, the chemical properties of river water contain heavy carbonates in mountainous areas and gradually change to chlorides in arid basins, with the degree of mineralization rising to 500 to 1,000 mg. per litre.

Second, rivers form an important exogenetic force in the formation of China's landforms by changing the ground surface through erosion and deposition. Washed and cut by flowing water, the Loess Plateau has grown into a fragmented landform with a multitude of gullies and ravines. The sediments carried by river water have created vast alluvial plains. In arid areas, rivers carry matter from the high mountains into the basins, forming vast diluvial plains.

Third, water conservancy work is an important way to transform nature. The hydrological conditions in China are complicated and varied, and the seasonal variations and interannual variability of runoff are extremely clear. In most areas, the runoff concentrates in summer with high water flows and flood peaks that often cause floods. In dry seasons, water becomes far too scarce to meet the needs of irrigation and navigation. Therefore, it is important for China to prevent waterlogging in summer and drought in spring, regulate runoff and improve the hydrological conditions.

For thousands of years the Chinese working people have been aware of the importance of water conservation in farm production. The Grand Canal, the Dujiangyan irrigation project, the irrigation system at the Huanghe bends, the Huanghe dykes, the establishment of oases in Xinjiang and the Gansu Corridor and the *karez* wells to draw groundwater for irrigation in Xinjiang are all well-known water conservancy projects of ancient China. Due to long years of neglect, some of these projects fell into disrepair and brought much calamity and suffering before Liberation. Since then China has paid great attention to the development and construction of large water conservancy projects. Besides more than 2,000 medium-sized reservoirs and nearly 160,000 km. of river and coastal dykes, millions of small projects have also been repaired or built. And large numbers of pumping stations and wells have been put into operation. All these facilities have raised China's ability to resist floods and prevent waterlogging, and they have increased the irrigated area by several fold.

Chapter V

VEGETATION AND SOIL

Vegetation and soil are among the most active factors in the formation and development of the physical complex. Influenced by water, heat and other factors of physical geography, vegetation and soil are closely interrelated, and the patterns of their distribution are quite similar. The formation, constitution and distribution of vegetation and soils in China reflect the complexity and regularity of the conditions of physical geography in various regions of China.

1. Main Characteristics of Vegetation and Soil Formation

China is one of the countries that have the greatest variety of plant species and soil forms in the world. Botanically, China has 2,700 genera of seed plants with 30,000 species including almost all types of natural vegetation in the Northern Hemisphere. In this, it is second only to tropical Brazil. China's Yunnan Province, alone, boasts 12,000 plant species, or double the number found in all of Europe. As far as trees are concerned, China has 2,800 species. Ninety-five per cent of the ligneous angiosperms in the world can be found in China. Besides, we have quite a few endemic species, such as metasequoia, gingko, golden larch and eucommia. The metasequoia, known as a living fossil from the Cretaceous Period, has been grown widely in the Changjiang River basin since it was first discovered in Wanxian County, Sichuan Province, in the 1940s. The gingko, a palaeophytic plant of the Jurassic Period, was widely distributed over the Northern Hemisphere during the

Tertiary Period; now only one species and one genus remain in the world, growing in eastern China.

Vegetation in China is as varied as it is complex. There are coniferous forests, deciduous broad-leaf forests, evergreen broad-leaf forests, tropical monsoon rain forests and transition forests that include trees from more than one of these types of forests. The grassland vegetation includes temperate forest grasslands, temperate steppes and alpine meadow steppes. The desert vegetation includes arid deserts and alpine cold deserts. Intrazonal types such as halomorphic vegetation, meadow vegetation, bog vegetation, psammomorphic vegetation and coral reef vegetation can all be found in China.

Nearly all the major types of soil in the world are found in China, except polar tundra soil, tropical black earth and tropical desert soil. Moreover, these soils have their own features and are quite fertile. For example, the black earth and chernozem soils that develop under the meadow steppe vegetation in northern China are more fertile than the steppe chernozem soils in other parts of the Northern Hemisphere because of the meadowing process. The laterite soil in southern China still retains a certain fertility because allitic weathering there is not so profound as it is in other torrid zones of the world. And the purple soil in the Sichuan Basin, the dark loessial soil of the Loess Plateau, the *baijiang* soil (lessive) of the Sanjiang Plains and river valley in the northern part of the Changbai Mountains, and the alpine cold desert soil of the Tibetan Plateau are all formed under China's unique conditions.

(1) Current Processes in Plant Growth and Soil Formation

Of all the factors behind the formation of vegetation and soils in China, climatic conditions play the leading role, while topography causes variations in the availability of water and heat. Because of the influence of the monsoon climate, the processes in plant growth and soil formation differ from area to area.

In the eastern half of China, during the summer half-year, the concentrated precipitation, high temperature, long sunshine time and distinct diurnal range of temperatures favour the photosynthesis of plants. From north to south, plants grow rapidly, trees thrive with green leaves and stout branches, herbs flourish luxuriantly, and cultivated crops have good conditions for growth. During this time, the seeping of water into the soil gives rise to intensified leaching. Clay particles move downward, and most of the soluble salts and iron-manganese compounds that are active under anaerobic reduction conditions are carried deeper by the seeping water or leached away by lateral flow to concentrate at lower levels. Duff on the forest floor and herbage remains begin to decompose through bacterial reaction. This gives rise to all kinds of humus.

During the dry and low-temperature winter half-year, surface evaporation and plant transpiration consume a large amount of water in the soil. At this time, the soluble salts move towards the surface along with capillary water action, thus increasing the salt content in the top layer of soil. The salt and lack of water combine to inhibit the growth of plants, especially crop seedlings. Plants wither and even die under the onslaught of the spring drought and strong winds in the north. And seasonal frozen layers of soil stunt plant growth. In most areas, irrigation is required to replenish the water in the soil and to ensure the normal growth of winter crops.

Due to the alternation of a dry, cold season with a humid, hot season, caused by the advance and retreat of the winter and summer monsoons, deciduous forests and herb communities are widely distributed throughout China. Even the tropical monsoon rain forests of south China and southwestern Yunnan contain a considerable number of deciduous broadleaf trees, such as *Gossampinus malabarica*, *Albizzia Chinensis* and *Lannea coromardelica*. In the north, tree leaves fall mainly because of winter cold, while defoliation in the south is mainly caused by winter drought. Most of the forests in China are mixed forests, intermingling tree species of the south with those of the north. For example, certain species of Ulmusaceae, Tiliaceae and Betulaceae that normally grow in warm-temperate deciduous broadleaf forests are found in the subtropical evergreen broadleaf forests south of the Changjiang River; subtropical coniferous trees, including *Pinus armandii* and *Tsnga chinensis*, mingle with deciduous broadleaf holts on the southern slopes of the Qinling Mountains and Daba Mountain; and tropical trees of Proteaceae and Araliaceae species can be found in the evergreen broadleaf forests of the southern subtropical zone.

Owing to the various times of arrival for summer monsoons, the vegetation and soils from area to area experience different times in a year for cooling and heating, drying and wetting. The subtropical and tropical regions of the south enjoy a lengthy warm and wet period. Plants in this area grow tall and large, with a complex laminating structure to their foliage. Since they have a longer period of growth, they produce large quantities of organic matter. However, the swift decomposition of organic matter, the intensified leaching in the soil, and the serious degree of desilicification and allitic weathering combine to develop a thick red residuum. Ferric and manganic compounds in the soil accumulate to form nodules or a hardpan. Although the northern regions enjoy a shorter warm and wet period and plants grow there in less quantity, organic matter decomposes slower, and leaching occurs only in summer. Therefore, organic matter can accumulate in the soil, offering rich plant nutrients and increasing the natural fertility of the soil.

In the vast arid steppe and desert regions in northwest China, the insufficient supply of water inhibits the development of the vegetation and soils. Forests can be found only on the windward or shady slopes of the mountains. In nonmountainous areas, the vegetation changes from east to west in the following order: arid steppes dominated by grasses, desert steppes covered mainly with grasses and shrubs, and deserts with a scattering of perennial shrubs. Since plants cover only a small percentage of the land in these arid regions and grow in limited quantity, the organic matter they provide to the soil decreases as the extent of desert increases. Soils in these areas are inadequately developed and there is not much leaching so that they abound in salt accumulations. These are manifested in compact caliche or lime concretions in the soils of the arid steppe areas, and in gypsum accumulations and salt crusts in the soils of the desert basins.

Vegetation and soils in mountain and highland regions develop differently from those on the lower land, and the processes become increasingly complex with greater elevation, size of the mountain, and the gradient and location of slopes. Generally speaking, low temperature, much humidity and good natural drainage give rise to a variety of vegetations and soils with mountain features. These occur in an orderly vertical spectrum. Mountain vegetation mainly consists of coniferous forests, mountain meadows and mountain steppes. Perennial creeper or cushion-shaped semi-shrubs are found on the northern Tibetan Plateau and on high mountains 5,000 m. above sea level.

Mountain soils generally consist of a rather thin layer with a coarse composition. What is more, strong lixiviation soon rids the soil of soluble salts. The formative processes of mountain vegetation and soils are similar to those of non-mountainous areas, but the plants have different genetic characteristics. For instance, evergreen broadleaf forests at the top of Wuzhi Mountain on Hainan Island, in the subtropical vegetation and soil zone, are similar to those in the northern latitude subtropical lowland zone. They are predominantly trees of Lauraceae, Theaceae and Fagaceae families. But the evergreen broadleaf forests in the southern part of the subtropical plains are chiefly composed of *Crgptucarya chinensis* of *Lauraceae*, *Castanopsis* of *Fagaceae*, and *Schima Superba* of *Theaceae*, and the soil developed on the forest floor is mainly red earth. The evergreen broadleaf forests in the upper part of the tropical mountains contain a variety of tropical plants, such as Pentaphylacaceae, Myrtaceae and Anonaceae as well as *Dacrydium picrrei*, which are not found in the subtropical zone, and the soil formed under them is mountain yellow earth or mountain podzolized yellow earth. Coniferous forests of spruce and fir can be found on the temperate mountains and subtropical alpines. But hemlock trees, phyllostachys and alpine oaks are mixed in among the coniferous trees on the subtropical alpines, whereas none can be found on the temperate mountains. Conversely, dwarf shrubs, such as the cowberry and oriental blueberry, found on the floors of temperate mountain coniferous forests, are non-existent in subtropical alpine coniferous forests.

(2) Factors of Natural History

China's vegetation and soils formed and developed over a long period of time. When the global climate was warm during the Tertiary period, China had a subtropical or tropical climate in most regions. Subtropical plants grew all the way up to the northeast and plant forms of Mediterranean flora were distributed in Xinjiang's Ili area. When the Tibetan Plateau and the Himalayas upheaved and the Sea of Tethys disappeared during the Neocene period, northwestern China became dry and the monsoon circulation developed in East Asia, thus touching off the process of vegetative growth and soil formation under a monsoon climate. The global climate became cold during the Quaternary period. However, because no continental glacier cover ever formed in China during the successive ice ages, Quaternary glaciers did not exert much influence on China's climate. Thus many of the plant forms that were destroyed by glaciers in other parts of the world continued to grow in China, and China became a repository for plant forms from past geological times. That is why China not only has a rich variety of plant life but also preserves, in varying degree, some relic plants from the Cretaceous and Tertiary periods. Take the alpine oak forests in the Hengduan

Mountains, for example. They are similar in many respects to the hardleaf evergreen broadleaf forests widely distributed along the Mediterranean Sea in southern Europe. They evolved from remnant plants originating before the Oligocene Epoch. The subtropical regions in eastern China are also scattered with forests containing remnant plants from the Cretaceous and Tertiary periods, such as the mixed forest of metasequoia in Lichuan County of western Hubei and the small gingko woods in Zhejiang.

The characteristics of the processes of weathering and soil formation in China also reflect the influence of paleoclimates. For instance, paleosol has been discovered in the layers of loess accumulated at different periods in the earth's history, and modern dark loessial soil still contains some features of soil developed in the ancient steppe environment. In China's monsoon areas, the processes of leaching, residual clayization and aluminization, which are products of weathering and pedogenesis, all show evidence of having taken place over a long period of time. The mechanical and mineral properties of the clay particles in the soil show that they are heavier than most other clays of the world, reflecting greater mineral decomposition and deeper weathering. This effect tends to become more pronounced as one moves southward. Analysis shows that clay particles with a size below 5 microns (μ) account for 20 to 27 per cent of the content in the northern steppe soil, 24 to 38 per cent in various kinds of brown forest soil, 30 to 48 per cent in the subtropical yellow earth, and as much as 65 to 71 per cent in the red earth and the lateritic soil. Illite predominates in the soil of northern China with a siallitic ratio of 3.5 to 4.0 for grain sizes below 5 μ. Owing to stronger aluminization in the south, kaolinite gradually predominates among the clay minerals of the subtropical red earth and yellow earth, with a small percentage of montmorillonite and fullonite, the siallitic ratio being 2.0 to 2.2, whereas kaolinite, gibbsite, hematite and ilmenite are predominant in the tropical laterite and lateritic soil with a sial-litic ratio below 1.7 to 2.0.

The earth movements since the Tertiary period have greatly influenced the development of vegetation and soils in China. The cold desert vegetation and alpine cold desert soil on the Qinghai-Tibetan Plateau obviously resulted from the violent upheavals of the earth's crust since the Pliocene Epoch. Because of its high elevation, the plateau experienced a severe cold climate during the Quaternary glacial period, and some small mountain glaciers appeared. Today the vegetation and soils there are rather young and underdeveloped. Sandstones from the later Oligocene Epoch to the early Pleistocene Epoch, found at altitudes of 5,700 to 5,900 m. on the northern slope of Mount Xixiabangma, contain fossils of alpine oak and pollens of such forest plants as birch, hemlock and spruce. Such forests today are found at altitudes of only 2,500 to 3,500 m., which shows that Mount Xixiabangma must have risen 2,000 to 3,000 m. since the Neocene period.

The desert vegetation and soils in the vast inland basins of northwest China were also formed quite a long time ago, and reflect the extreme aridity caused by the depression of the basins and the heave of the surrounding mountains. The plateau in southwestern China had a tropical environment over a long time. Later, owing to the uplift of the earth's crust, the Tertiary lateritic residuum was preserved on the plateau surface, standing at 1,500 to 2,000 m. above sea level on the eastern Yunnan Plateau, and developed into plateau red earth. As the earth's crust rose and the climate cooled, plant colonies that originally grew at low elevations retained remnant plant species of paleotorrid flora, such as the *Dalbergia hupeana, Cephalotaxus sinensis, Cycas revoluta* and *Angiopteris sp.*

(3) Effects of Human Activities

Large-scale land reclamation and deforestation over a long period radically altered the natural development of China's vegetation and soils. Prolonged tree felling has disfigured China's natural vegetation beyond recognition. Virgin forests were preserved only in the Hinggan Mountains, the Changbai Mountains, the sub-alpine region in western Sichuan and some other higher mountains. Many woodlands have either been turned into farmland or have become secondary forests. Some wooded mountains and hills were so devastated by deforestation that they have become either barren or are now covered only with shrubs. There are also many useful forest areas where, thanks to human care, tree species useful to mankind have been preserved or cultivated, such as the China fir forests and bamboo groves in the subtropical low mountain and hilly regions.

The destruction of the natural vegetation on mountains and hills resulted in serious soil erosion. The fertility decreased and the soil layer became thin, making it difficult to regenerate or utilize the vegetation. Afforestation and soil conservation have been undertaken over large tracts of land since Liberation, and once barren mountains have gradually become verdant.

Livestock breeding has a long history in the northern grasslands and alpine steppes of the west. Most of these grasslands were overused or degenerated because of animal grazing and stampeding. Moreover the height, density and output of the grass in these areas dropped by varying degrees, which affected the ability of the grasslands to support the livestock. On the other hand, agriculture in China has a history of several thousand years. During this period people have turned many wild plants into cultivated ones and established all kinds of agricultural vegetation. While utilizing and improving soils, they have also nurtured a variety of soils suitable for growing crops.

Agricultural vegetation in China includes farm fields, orchards, cultivated pasturelands and forests that are harvested. Many well-known farm plants in the world originated in China, such as paddy rice and kaoliang among cereals, lichee and longan among fruit trees, and tea and tung-oil among industrial trees. China's agricultural vegetation is widely distributed, particularly in the densely populated eastern half of the country. There natural vegetation covers markedly less land than agricultural vegetation in the tropical and subtropical low-mountain and hilly regions of the south; and agricultural vegetation has entirely replaced natural vegetation on the Loess Plateau, on the North China Plain, in the Sichuan Basin and Changjiang River Delta, as well as in many other densely populated plains, basins and deltas, and on the oases of the arid regions in the northwest. Some of the cultivated plants in China were imported from other lands. Maize, tomatoes and potatoes were introduced long ago and have settled extensively in various places. The South China Botanical Garden is now growing several hundred adventive species of tropical plants; and the Borneo-camphor tree recently brought to Xishuangbanna has already grown into a semi-natural forest.

Agriculture alters the natural transfer of minerals in the soil, as well as the physical and chemical properties of the tilled layers of the soil. However farming techniques and many soil-improvement measures strengthen the cyclical transfer of substances in the soil, and thus give birth to various types of crop growing soils.

Paddy soil and yellow chao (light meadow) soil are the most important among China's crop growing soils. Paddy soil is created by the regular water-ploughing various zonal soils. Because the fields are irrigated from time to time and left dry for only short periods, the soil has strong oxidation-reduction properties and large amounts of residual crop roots and organic matter resulting from fertilization. Thus tillage, fertilizing, irrigation and other measures give rise to a unique form of paddy soil with its own physical, chemical and biological properties. This type of soil is distributed almost across the length and breadth of China, from Hainan Island in the south to Mohe at the northernmost tip of Heilongjiang Province in the north. Paddy soil in the north is slightly alkaline, while paddy soil in the south is acid and requires the application of a great deal of lime every year. Yellow chao soil is a dry type of soil that forms from ploughing just-settled loess alluvial deposits. Mainly located on the North China Plain, it is rather fertile and widely adaptable. This soil area has long been an important region for China's agricultural development.

2. Distribution of Vegetation and Soil

The distribution of vegetation and soils in China, basically influenced by the above-mentioned factors, is manifested in zonal characteristics. And the different zones have intrazonal features and vertical structures.

(1) Horizontal Distribution Pattern

The horizontal distribution of vegetation and soils reflects the prevailing monsoons and the topography. There are three major districts from the southeast to the northwest: forest, grassland and desert. Roughly speaking, the forest district lies to the east of a line that starts from the Greater Hinggan Mountains, passes through the southeastern edge of the Loess Plateau and the Hengduan Mountains and ends in southern Tibet. The desert district lies to the west of a line that starts from the central part of the Inner Mongolia Autonomous Region and moves southwestward to the western part of the Qinghai-Tibetan Plateau. Between these is the district of grassland, alpine shrubbery, meadows and steppes (Fig. 15).

The forest district in eastern China accounts for a little less than half of the country's total area. It has abundant rainfall. The variation of vegetation and soils in this district is mainly controlled by heat, showing obvious latitudinal marks from north to south. North of the Greater Hinggan Mountains are frigid-temperate deciduous coniferous forests, which are mainly composed of north larches. As heat increases southward, there appear in this order: mixed forests of temperate deciduous broadleaf trees and Korean pines (*Pinus koraiensis*), warm-temperate deciduous broadleaf forests dominated by oaks, subtropical evergreen broadleaf forests consisting chiefly of castanopsis, evergreen chinquapins and camphor trees, and tropical monsoon rain forests containing many tropical high plants (such as *Gossampinus malabarica*, Borneo-camphor, *Tarrietia parvifolia* and *Vatica astrotricha*). The deciduous or evergreen phenomenon of the broadleaf trees is closely related to the climatic environment. Leaves of the broadleaf forests in the frigid-temperate and temperate zones fall because of the severe cold in winter. The subtropical and tropical zones have warm winters, but owing to the monsoon climate of China, the leaves of some of the tropical high plants also fall in the dry seasons.

Soils are inseparable from vegetation and their distribution is also mainly related to the climate. Because of good drainage in the forest district in eastern China, the soluble salts (salt, lime and gypsum) in the soil are easily leached away to form various types of acid forest soil. Corresponding to the above-mentioned vegetation zones, the soils from north to south are brown coniferous forest soil, dark brown earth, brown earth, red earth, yellow earth and laterite.

The terrain in eastern China is rather level. Except for the west-east Qinling Mountains, which form a dividing belt between the warm-temperate deciduous broadleaf forest region and the subtropical evergreen broadleaf forest region, and the Nanling Mountains, which form a dividing line between the subtropical evergreen broadleaf forest region and the tropical monsoon rain forest region, the vegetation and soils on the plains change gradually, giving rise to many transition types. For example, the subtropical zone, which covers

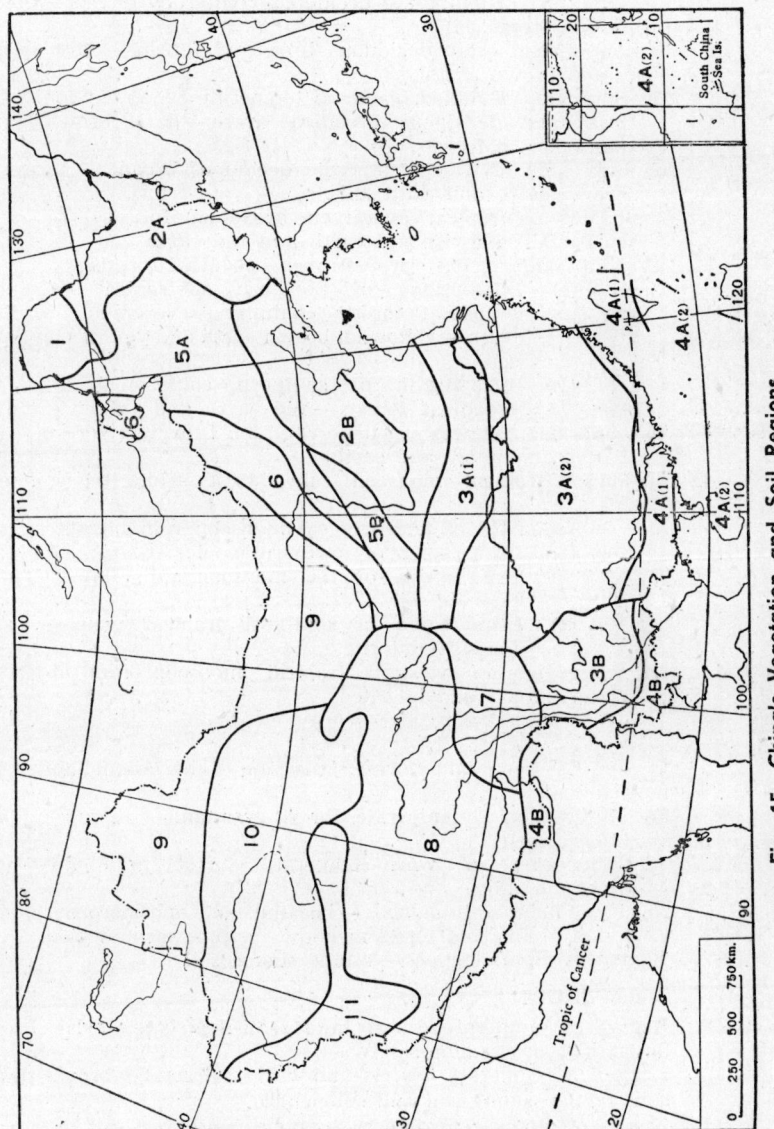

Fig. 15 China's Vegetation and Soil Regions

I. Forest district
1. Region of frigid-temperate deciduous coniferous forests — brown coniferous forest soil
2. Region of temperate deciduous broadleaf forests — dark brown earth and brown earth
  2A. Subregion of mixed forests of temperate evergreen coniferous trees and deciduous broadleaf trees — dark brown earth (dark brown forest soil)
  2B. Subregion of warm-temperate deciduous broadleaf forests — brown earth and drab soil
3. Region of subtropical evergreen broadleaf forests — yellowish brown earth, yellowish red earth and red earth
  3A. Subregion of eastern evergreen broadleaf forests
    3A (1) Infra-region of northern subtropical deciduous broadleaf forests containing evergreen broadleaf trees — yellowish brown earth and yellow cinnamon soil
    3A (2) Infra-region of southern subtropical evergreen broadleaf forests — red earth and yellow earth
  3B. Subregion of western dry evergreen broadleaf forests — red earth (mountain red earth)
4. Region of tropical monsoon rain forests — lateritic soil and laterite
  4A. Subregion of eastern tropical monsoon rain forests
    4A (1) Infra-region of northern tropical evergreen broadleaf forests of the monsoon rain forest type — lateritic soil
    4A (2) Infra-region of southern tropical monsoon rain forests — laterite
  4B. Subregion of western tropical monsoon rain forests — lateritic soil and laterite

II. Grassland district
5. Region of temperate forest grassland — chernozem and dark loessial soil
  5A. Subregion of temperate forest grassland — chernozem and black earth
  5B. Subregion of warm-temperate forest grassland — dark loessial soil
6. Region of temperate steppes — chestnut soil and sierozem
7. Region of alpine cold forest meadow — alpine meadow soil
8. Region of alpine steppes — alpine steppe soil

III. Desert district
9. Region of temperate deserts and semi-deserts — greyish brown desert soil and aeolian sandy soil
10. Region of temperate deserts and barren deserts — brown desert soil, aeolian sandy soil and solonchak
11. Region of alpine cold deserts — alpine cold desert soil

a large area in eastern China, is a transition type between the temperate zone and the tropical zone. The question of which zone a particular transition type of vegetation and soil belongs to is determined by the similarity in characteristics to the vegetation and soil of a given zone. Take the evergreen broadleaf forests of the monsoon rain-forest type in the northern tropical zone. The appearance and structure of the plant communities there have the characteristics of a tropical monsoon rain forest, and include buttressed plants, cauliflorous plants, ligneous vines, woody epiphytes and parasitic plants. The taller plants are scattered among some of the tropical tree species, and almost all the arborets and shrubs are from tropical genera and families. Also the herbs belong to typical species found on the floor of tropical monsoon rain forests, herbs such as *Akebia quinata, Alocasiapdora, Alpinia chinensis* and others with big or broad leaves. Therefore, we classify this as a tropical zone.

To the north of the Qinling Mountains and Huaihe River, precipitation gradually decreases from east to west and the vegetation and soils change correspondingly in a regular manner. The vegetation occurs longitudinally in this order: forest, forest grassland, steppe, semi-desert and desert. Owing to gradual decrease in precipitation, salt and gypsum in the soil are leached away, but lime remains in various layers to form different kinds of steppe soil: chernozem 1, dark loessial soil, and chestnut soil. In the westernmost desert district, lime and gypsum remain in the topsoil or close to it, giving birth to various kinds of desert soil, namely, greyish brown desert soil, brown desert soil and alpine cold desert soil. The wide area of deserts (approximately one-fifth of China's total area) is a salient feature of China's vegetation and soil distribution. These reflect the extremely dry environment of western China, which is in the centre of the Eurasian Continent. The sprawling alpine cold desert area in northwest Tibet results from the high elevation and extremely little precipitation. This area has its own unique vegetation and soil.

Though modified by the agricultural production of labouring people, the agricultural vegetation of China reflects the characteristics of local climate and soils. Thus, in eastern China, the vegetation shows the marks of latitudinal zonality to some extent. For instance, the cultivated trees are mainly apple orchard, vineyard and chestnut wood in the temperate zone; tea plantation and tea-oil wood in the subtropical zone; and lichee orchard, rubber plantation and anised wood in the tropical zone. This is also true of paddy soil and other crop growing soils. Paddy soil in the warm-temperate and temperate zones of the north has a pH value of 7.0 or more. Little lime is leached away, and hydromicas and montmorillonite predominate in its clay minerals. In the tropical and subtropical zones of the south, paddy soil has a pH value of 5.0 to 6.0, lime is all leached away and kaolinite is dominant in its clay minerals.

(2) Vertical Distribution Pattern

China has a rich variety of mountain vegetation and soil types, the distribution of which is subject to vertical zonality. However, the vegetation and soil types are also deeply influenced by the longitudes and latitudes, and so are closely related to the horizontal zones. Because of the specific water and heat conditions in the mountains, the mountain vegetation and soil types differ from the vegetation and soil types in the corresponding horizontal zones. Generally speaking, the vertical structure of the mountain vegetation and soil spectrum varies with the horizontal zones and with the height and exposure of the mountains. Therefore, the mountain vegetation and soil spectrum is very complex and may, according to the water and heat conditions of the basic zones, be divided into several types, such as a tropical humid region, semi-arid region, temperate humid region and arid region. As the mountains in northwestern China rise in elevation from foot to top, the temperature declines gradually, but the humidity increases, with some precipitation in limited areas. Thus, mainly owing to the influence of humidity, the vegetation and soil zones change from bottom to top in this order: desert, desert steppe, mountain shrub steppe or meadow steppe, forest, and subalpine meadow; while the soils change gradually from desert soil to mountain chestnut soil, mountain chernozem, mountain greyish brown forest soil, alpine meadow soil, etc.

No marked increase of humidity is registered from bottom to top for the mountains in eastern China, so that the vertical spectrum there largely reflects variations in heat and is basically dominated by forests of different types. For instance, the temperate mountains contain deciduous broadleaf forests in brown earth near the bottom; then mixed forests of needleleaf trees and deciduous broadleaf trees in mountain dark brown forest soil; spruces and firs in mountain brown coniferous forest soil; and subalpine meadow in alpine meadow soil near the mountain top. The southern subtropical mountain vegetation and soil zones have this in common: typical evergreen broadleaf forests in red earth, scattered with China firs and bamboo groves, on the lower part of mountains; mixed forests of evergreen broadleaf trees and deciduous broadleaf trees or deciduous broadleaf forests containing evergreen trees growing in mountain yellowish brown earth on the slopes of high mountains or on the upper part of mezzo-mountains; and south azalea shrubs and mezzo-mountain meadow in mountain shrubby-meadow soil at the mountain tops.

Rising 1,867 metres above sea level, the Wuzhi Mountains on Hainan Island in the tropical humid region contain tropical plants from bottom to top. No mixed forests of subtropical evergreen broadleaf trees and deciduous broadleaf trees ever appear at a height of more than 1,800 metres. Instead, there are tropical mountain pine woods and evergreen elfin forests peculiar to the tropical zone. The vertical spectrum of soils is as follows: laterite, mountain lateritic red earth, mountain yellow earth, mountain podzolized yellow earth, and mountain-top elfin-forest meadow soil.

The higher the mountain, the more complete its vertical spectrum and the more complex its composition. The vertical spectrum of Mount Qomolangma, for example, is most complete in comparison with other parts of the world. Conversely, the vertical spectrum of Dabie Mountain in the subtropical zone is far simpler. Exposure has a marked influence on the composition of the vertical spectrum. Especially when mountains lie between two horizontal zones, the soils of their different slopes will belong to different basic zones. For example, the basic zone of the northeastern slope of the Wuzhi Mountains is tropical monsoon rain forest and that of the southwestern slope is tropical savanna, so the vertical spectrum of the former changes from laterite through lateritic red earth to mountain red earth while that of the latter transits from savanna soil through mountain brown red earth and mountain red earth to mountain yellow earth.

Because the southern slopes of the Himalayas on the southern edge of the Qinghai-Tibetan Plateau and the Qilian Mountains on the northern edge lie in different basic zones and have different exposures, their soils have completely different structures, showing two types of vertical spectrums — maritime and interior. Influenced by the southwest monsoons and sheltered by the main body of the mountain range, the southern slopes of the Himalayas have a hot, humid climate, and contain tropical monsoon rain forests and rain forests. Their vertical spectrum structure is characterized by all kinds of developed forests and forest soils, with no grassland or steppe soil among them. The Qilian Mountains lying in an inland desert region, is influenced by a dry climate, and so mountain steppes and mountain deserts are widely distributed throughout its vertical spectrum structure, while relatively undeveloped forests and forest soils are only scattered on shady slopes in patches.

(3) Characteristics of the Intrazonal Vegetation and Soils

The most widely distributed types of intrazonal vegetation and soils in China are meadow vegetation in meadow soil, halophylic vegetation in saline soil, limestone vegetation in limestone soil, and sand-dune vegetation in sandy soil. Although their geographical distribution is controlled by subterranean water, lithology, mineral components and other nonzonal factors, they are still highly influenced by zonal factors in their formation and development.

Natural meadows can be found in every zone of China, mostly on delta plains and flood lands or in low-lying parts of basins, where the subsurface water table is shallow. There minerals converge with subterranean water flow and groundwater rises through capillary action to moisten the soil, thus providing sufficient water for meadow plants. Where the subterranean water is fresh, the meadows have been reclaimed and the meadow vegetation has been replaced by the cultivated vegetation, usually paddy rice. But the meadow soil still reflects the characteristics of different horizontal zones. For example, the dark meadow soil in Heilongjiang Province has a high content of organic substances (5 to 20 per cent) and a thick layer of humus (180 to 200 cm.) and is free of carbonates. The light meadow soil on the North China Plain generally contains carbonates and is more or less salinized. The meadow soil on the northern banks of the Changjiang contains carbonates but is not salinized except in the coastal areas, and that south of the Changjiang is neutral meadow soil free from carbonates. The meadow soil in the tropical zone is not salinized and sometimes is acid. Halophytic meadows are mostly distributed along the shores of lakes and rivers in the semi-arid and arid regions. They are also found in some low-lying places with a shallow subsurface water table. These meadows support the growth of *Aeluropus littoralis, Crypsis aculeata, Glaux maritin.a, Polygonum aviculare, Halerpestes ruthenica* and other typical halophytic meadow plants.   Generally, the drier the climate, the stronger the salinization.   The halophytes tend to be dwarf semi-shrubs that are fleshy and thorny, and saline scabs and thick salt crusts are often formed in the top soil of these saline soil meadows.

China has a long coastline where the coastal saline swamp vegetation shows the mark of latitudinal zones regulated by changes in heat.   In the marshland to the north of Fuzhou there are no ligneous plants but only cattails, weeds and other herbs. The area to the south of Fuzhou is in the tropical zone where mangroves are scattered throughout the tropical coastal salinized marsh soil. As the temperature rises from north to south, the variety of the mangroves becomes richer, their community becomes more complex in structure and their height increases. Mangroves along Fujian's coast in the northern part of the tropical zone are generally bushes 0.5 to 2.0 m. high. They grow sparsely and consist of only 3 to 5 species. On Hainan Island, in the southern part of the tropical zone, the mangroves form elfin forests, averaging 4 to 5 m. in height, with the tallest standing at 10 to 15 m., and comprising 16 to 18 species.

Unique karst landforms and hydrological features are found in the limestone areas where the soil layer is thin and dry and is composed of such calcareous earth as red limestone soil and rendzina.   The strong percolation through the limestone gives rise to a rather dry habitat, so that forests in the subtropical and tropical limestone areas mostly consist of calcipetes that lose their leaves in the dry season.   Some places are too dry for any forests to grow. The limestone areas also contain a number of primary limestone shrubwoods and coppices.

The South China Sea island groups are mostly coral reefs without soil or vegetation. On some of these there is phosphorous-rich calcareous earth — phosphorous calcareous soil on the parent material of reef limestone, guano and fine beach sand. The vegetation here is mostly composed of calcium-loving, salt-avoiding herbs, with some chylophyllous evergreen broadleaf elfin forests and coppices.

China's sandy land is mainly located in the arid and semi-arid regions. In places with a certain amount of atmospheric precipitation, such as the sandy areas of eastern Inner Mongolia, there are many deciduous broadleaf xero-mezzophilous shrubs and deciduous sparse forests, sometimes including sparse woods of scots pines or elms. These provide favourable conditions for soil development, and form a sandy soil of the chestnut soil type with no calcium carbonate reaction. The top layer of the sandy-ground soil in the semi-arid typical steppe areas has no calcium carbonate reaction and supports deciduous broadleaf xero-mezzophilous shrubs and perennial mezzo-xerophilous herbs. As for the sandy-ground soil in the arid deserts, this has a calcium carbonate reaction and sometimes shows signs of weak salinity. It mainly grows *Nitraria tangutorum, Lycium spp., Haloxylon ammodendron* and other xerophilous shrubs. It can be readily seen that varying water conditions create different environments for the growth and development of psammomorphic vegetation and sandy-ground soil.

3. Effect of China's Vegetation and Soil on the Formation of the Natural Landscape

China's vast territory and complex environment, coupled with human activities over thousands of years, have given rise to varied forms, combinations, distribution and evolution of the vegetation and soils. These markedly reflect the features of the physical landscape and also reflect to a certain degree the development of China's natural history. The felling of trees and tilling of land can make the vegetation and soils change in a relatively short period of time in relation to other factors of the physical environment. For instance, China's irrigated acreage has extended to about 46.7 million hectares since the founding of the People's Republic. This is more than twice the pre-Liberation figure, and has greatly altered the types and distribution of crop growing soils.

China abounds in both plant and soil resources. Of the taller plants, there are nearly 1,000 species whose timber is of great practical value. Chief among these are *Ormosia spp.*, *Dalbergia hupehana* and, rosewood of the tropical zone; Chinese fir, *Cupressus funebris*, *Crytomeria japonica*, *Pinus massoniana*, *Pseudolarix amabilis*, *Tsuga chinensis*, *Keteleeria fortunei*, *Cryptocarya konishii*, *Machilus spp.*, *Sassfaras tzumu*, *Castanopsis sclerophylla*, *Cyclobalanopsis glauca*, *Eucalyptus spp.* and bamboo of the subtropical zone; *Pinus tabulaeformis*, *P. densiflora*, *Thuja orientalos* and *Quercus acutissima* of the warm-temperate zone; *Pinus koraiensis*, *Picea ajanensis* and *Fraxinus mandshurica* of the temperate zone; *Larix dahurica*, *Pinus sylrestris var. mongolica* and *Betula platyphylla* of the cold-temperate coniferous forest region; various kinds of *Picea spp.* and *Abies spp.* of the subalpine coniferous forest region in the Hengduan Mountains; etc. The variety of special economic plants and medicinal plants is said to be countless. For example, there are tea-oil, tung-oil, oil palm, tallow, walnut and other oil-bearing plants; *Bupleurum Chinese* (the root of Chinese thoroughwax), *ephedra*, *Cordyceps sinesis* (Chinese caterpillar fungus), *Fritillaria roylei*, Chinese angelica, ginseng, cinnamon, *Ligusticum wallichi* (the rhizome of chuanziong), *Coptis chinensis* (the rhizome of Chinese goldthread), panax pseudo-ginseng and other medicinal plants; and lemongrass, lavender, camphor, aniseed, fennel and other aromatic plants. Besides, there are a great multitude of plants used for tanning, the production of fibre, the production of starch, forage, and plants whose fruit is used to make wines, etc.

In China there are large areas of land to be tilled, afforested or turned into pastures. These are the basis for land resources and for the development of agriculture, forestry, and livestock breeding in China. At present, China has 100 million hectares of cultivated land, about 11 per cent of the country's total area. They are mostly in the plains, deltas, intermontane basins and hilly regions. A preliminary estimate shows that about 33 to 47 million hectares of sizable and reclaimable wilderness can be opened in the immediate future. These are largely distributed in the northeast region and in Xinjiang. In Xinjiang alone there are 10 million hectares of reclaimable wasteland. The acreage of red earth (including laterite) exceeds 100 million hectares in the 11 provinces and autonomous regions of southern China (exclusive of Taiwan Province). Large tracts of barren fields in these provinces and autonomous regions can be used for farming, forestry and livestock breeding.

China's woodland is limited. In the early post-Liberation days it came to only 50 million hectares, 5.2 per cent of the total land area. The acreage has now more than doubled to some 12.7 per cent of the total area. But there are still vast areas suitable for planting trees, providing a great potential for artificial afforestation. The state has set up 15 nature preserves to protect and revive precious wildlife.

China has great expanses of grassland and steppes. Some 220 million hectares of grasslands and steppes can be utilized throughout the country, more than twice as much as the cultivated acreage. Animal husbandry is an important component of the national economy, and the development of agriculture needs to be combined with the growth of animal husbandry. It is necessary to protect the grasslands, ban indiscriminate reclamation or grazing, prevent the grasslands from aging, and make great efforts to build up the grasslands and steppes so as to speed the development of animal husbandry.

Chapter VI

COMPREHENSIVE PHYSICAL REGIONALIZATION

1. Content and Importance of Physical Regionalization

All elements of physical geography, such as climate, terrestrial water, vegetation, soil, animals and landforms, are interconnected and conditioned by each other. They constitute an integral whole, that is, the physical complex. On the basis of similarities and differences in the physical complex, we can divide the surface of the earth into units, and then on the basis of the divided units discuss and study the formation, development and distribution features of the physical complex. This is the content of comprehensive physical regionalization. Comprehensive physical regionalization is called physical regionalization for short, the object of its study being the physical complex and the divided areas being the physical regions, or natural regions.

The elements of physical geography that constitute a physical region are mainly divided into two groups. One is a group of biological and climatic elements, including climate, soil, vegetation and animals. Their formation and development are governed mainly by water and heat conditions. Distributed with zonal regularity, they are therefore called zonal elements. The other is a group of geological and geomorphological elements. Their formation and development are governed mainly by internal forces. As they are not distributed in zones, they are called non-zonal elements. Each physical region includes both zonal features and non-zonal features. It is therefore obviously incorrect to separate them entirely.

Physical regionalization is a basic task that needs to be performed in the process of knowing and transforming the nature. Its importance to production is mainly: (1) to point out the possibility of transforming and utilizing nature in different regions, and to propose different means of utilization and transformation; (2) to explain the advantages and disadvantages of the physical conditions in different regions to production and construction; and (3) to provide an understanding of the physical conditions as the basis for agricultural regionalization.

2.   Basic Principles of Physical Regionalization

In view of the importance of physical regionalization, we believe that the following two basic principles should be followed in the study of physical regionalization:

1)   The comprehensive principle. The purpose of physical regionalization is to examine regional differences in the physical complex. The divided units are physical complexes of different grades. They are not heat region units, moisture region units, or soil region units, isolated from the object of the study, although these elements form an important basis for the division into physical regions. In the course of physical regionalization, emphasis is placed on the leading elements, discovered on the basis of synthesis and analysis, rather than paying equal attention to all elements.

The leading elements for the differentiation of physical regions are not absolutely constant; they can vary from time to time or from place to place. For example, the Qinghai-Tibetan Plateau did not rise very much before the Neocene period, and so the topography was not the principal element in the regional differentiation of the plateau at that time. But today, the plateau has a high terrain and so this non-zonal element (the landform) has become the principal element in its regional differentiation.   In the plains and low hill areas zonal elements become the principal elements. Here the distribution of water and heat, among climatic elements, and their effectiveness in the process of physical geography also varies from area to area. In areas with ample water, differences in heat conditions have a marked effect on agriculture. In areas short of water, although there may be ample heat, the physical geography and potential for the development of agricultural production are greatly affected by the availability of water. In the former case, heat is the principal element; while in the latter, water is the principal element and heat becomes a secondary factor in determining regional differentiation and agriculture. The former case applies to the eastern part of our country and the latter to the northwestern part (Inner Mongolia and Xinjiang). Therefore, the leading elements of physical regionalization generally correspond to heat zones in the eastern part of China. But this is not true elsewhere.

The indices for regionalization are used to denote the boundaries among different regions. These can be based on accumulated temperature, aridity and elevation, or on soil and vegetation. They are the most typical features, or numerical values, that best illustrate the leading elements for regional differentiation. Because the leading elements that determine regional differentiation vary from region to region, we cannot use the same principal index to divide all the regional units of a country. Instead, after an overall analysis based on the objective conditions that exist in the different parts of the country, we use different indices to divide the physical regions. This is what we call the "multi-index method". For example, the three large physical districts (physical sectors) — the eastern monsoon district, the Mongolia-Xinjiang district and the Qinghai-Tibetan Plateau district — have been divided by the Physical Regionalization Committee of the Chinese Academy of Sciences on the basis of the three major indices of heat, water and topographical conditions.

Owing to the peculiarities of the physical conditions in the different regions of China, one cannot just use a single value, such as heat, in regionalization. The Tibetan Plateau, because of its peculiar conditions, has a long period of sunshine, strong solar radiation, big daily temperature range and small annual temperature range. Therefore its accumulated temperature value has a different effect on the growth of plants in comparison with the same value for the low-lying areas of the frigid temperate zone. Also, because of different seasonal distributions and varying degrees of dryness and humidity, the same accumulated temperature value in different regions may have a different effect on cultivated trees and crops. For example, the southern part of Yunnan Province is not affected by cold waves and has more foggy days and humid air in the winter than do Guangdong and Guangxi. Therefore, the accumulated temperature value for the northern tropical or quasi-tropical zone in Yunnan is slightly lower (see Chapter XI).

In short, the purpose of physical regionalization is to analyse all the physical elements of a region and then to define the leading ones so as to determine the regional differentiation. The physical regions thus delimited have similar geographical features and common ways of utilizing and transforming nature. We refer to this as a comprehensive principle, and different grades of the physical regions are delimited on the basis of this principle. The lower the grade of a physical region, the greater its internal similarity.

2) The genetic principle. The differentiation of physical regions and the particularities of physical complexes came into existence through a historical process. Therefore it is necessary to consider this historical process in the course of physical regionalization. This is the genetic principle that has been widely recognized by physical geographers throughout the world. The genetic principle includes not only the historical process in the formation and development of physical complexes as a whole, but also the historical process embodied in the differentiation of a region into different lower units. The geographic process is one of synthesis, not one of the formation and development of some particular element. From the genetic viewpoint, the origin and formative history of a physical region is relatively identical to that of its subregions.

For example, on the basis of the genetic principle we have classified Yunnan and the southwestern part of Sichuan into the same region, namely the Southwest China Region, a "tropical mountainous plateau region". To the west of the quasi-stationary weather front of Kunming, Yunnan is influenced by a tropical air mass almost all year round. The complicated relief of this mountainous plateau gives rise to tropical, quasi-tropical, subtropical and temperate zones. Yunnan and south-western Sichuan have similarities in geographical development. Extensive differential uplift in the late Cenozoic Epoch caused a gradual change and differentiation of landscapes in this region.

Genetically, the Southwest China Region has obvious unity. (a) The origin of the various landscape characteristics is relatively identical. Because this is a tropical mountainous plateau, its geographical process has been quite different both in quality and quantity from that of the eastern coastal regions. (b) The formative history of the landscapes is relatively identical. They have taken shape gradually as a result of the extensive uplift since the Neogene Period. (c) The differential processes of the subregional units are relatively identical. They were mainly effected by topographic conditions made possible by differentiation on a tropical basis, with the law of vertical zonality playing a leading role.

The eastern boundary of this region is clearly divided by a boundary, approximately the Beipan River between Guizhou and Yunnan provinces. To the west of the boundary is an area of red earth over which sunny days in winter enable Yunnan pines (*Pinus Yunnanensis*) to grow. To the east is an area of yellow earth with masson pines (*Pinus massoniana*), where there is "hardly a fine day". It is obvious that the tropical mountainous plateau is a unity of zonal elements (the tropics) and non-zonal elements (mountainous plateau). If only biological and climatic elements, or geological and topographical elements, were taken into consideration, it would be impossible to work out a regionalization programme that conformed with objective reality.

Take the Qaidam Basin as another example. We have placed it in the Northwest China Region. From the viewpoint of its geological history and elevation, it is part of the Qinghai-Tibetan Plateau. But, over a long period of little or no water reaching the area, the Qaidam Basin has developed into a desert area, similar to that of the Tarim Basin, Junggar Basin and Gansu Corridor. The formation of this interior desert landscape, its subsequent history and development and the present physical processes that operate there are similar to those in the arid regions of northwest China and quite different from those of the Qinghai-Tibetan Plateau. (a) The Qaidam Basin is extremely arid due to the limited amount of precipitation that reaches the area. Its west has an annual precipitation of less than 20 mm. and an aridity index above 10. This is fundamentally different from the situation on the Qinghai Plateau, where the annual precipitation is about 200 to 300 mm. and the aridity index is less than 1.0 to 1.5. (b) The whole Qaidam Basin is an inland drainage system with a stable supply of water in the mountainous areas and a fair amount of heat in summer, all good for the development of irrigated farming, while the Qinghai Plateau or the northern Tibetan Plateau has no such water and heat conditions. (c) The desert landscape of the Qaidam Basin also manifests itself in the composition of the desert soil, plants and animals that have developed there. As in Xinjiang, the soils and vegetation of the desert type are widely distributed throughout the basin. Many features in the soil formation (such as the shortage of organic matter, gypseous accumulations and even crusts and layers of soluable salt) are similar to that of southern Xinjiang. However the Qinghai-Tibetan Plateau is covered mainly by alpine desert soil, alpine and subalpine meadow soil and steppe soil, and the formative processes of these soils are quite different in quality from those of the Qaidam Basin. The desert vegetation in the Qaidam Basin, which is characterized by its sparse distribution, deep roots and small leaves on perennial bushes, is not the high-altitude cold desert type but is similar to the temperate desert type of the Gansu Corridor. Therefore the Qaidam Basin can be regarded as part of the desert region linking Xinjiang with the Gansu Corridor.

It is obvious that, although the Qaidam Basin is connected with the Qinghai-Tibetan Plateau in topography and elevation, it has a relationship to the arid Northwest China Region in genesis. It not only has a smiliar desert landscape to Xinjiang and the Gansu Corridor, but it is also closely connected with the latter by the Altun Mountains, which have a desert landscape from foot to top. Therefore, if we merely took geological history and geomorphology into consideration, the Qaidam Basin would be included in the Qinghai-Tibetan Plateau Region, but when we take the whole historical process of genesis and evolution of the landscape into consideration, we undoubtedly must classify it as part of the Northwest China Region.

3. Plan for Physical Regionalization Used in This Book

In line with the above-mentioned principles, the physical regionalization of China is developed at three levels in this book: regions, subregions and areas. The whole country is divided into 8 regions, 26 subregions and 58 areas. They are all given common place names. No special terms for heat, humidity, vegetation and soil are used and so the names of the physical regions and subregions are not long (Fig. 16).

1) Physical regions. The whole country is divided into eight physical regions: Northeast China, North China, Central China, South China, Southwest China, Inner Mongolia, Northwest China and Qinghai-Tibet. Four of them (Northeast China, North China, Central China and South China) are located in the eastern part of the country. They have relatively ample water, and their topography is characterized mainly by plains

and low mountains. The differentiation of the physical land-scapes in these regions and the consequent differences in vegetation and soil are mainly caused by differences in the quantity of heat. We have therefore roughly classified these four regions on the basis of the different quantities of heat they receive.

The primary index for dividing the heat zones is the annual total daily average temperature over a period of time when the daily average temperature is higher than 10°C. This is the simplest and most direct indicator of the heat resource. The specific norms for dividing the heat zones are roughly indicated as follows:

Heat zones	Total active temperature (C.)
Tropical zone	7,000° to 9,000° or above
Northern part	7,000° (or 6,500°) to 8,000°
Southern part	8,000° to 9,000° or above
Subtropical zone	4,500° to 7,000° (or 6,500°)
Northern part	4,500° to 5,000°
Southern part	5,000° to 7,000°
Warm temperate zone	3,000° to 4,500°
Temperate zone	1,700° to 3,000°
Frigid temperate zone	smaller than 1,700°

Heat exerts an impact on all processes of the physical complex, and, of course, greatly affects agriculture. However, it would be wrong to rely on heat alone to divide the temperate, subtropical and tropical zones, since there are multiple indices, including vegetation, soil and animals. Yet it is necessary to give due consideration to heat and its reflection on the vegetation, soil, animals and agricultural vegetation in order to define the boundaries of the physical zones. At the same time it should be noted that there is some subjectivity involved in the decision if a certain value of accumulated temperature is used as the boundary for a certain heat zone. Whether the choice is correct or not should be tested by other factors in the objective natural environment and agricultural vegetation.

Each of the four physical regions in the eastern part of China is equivalent to a heat zone. The Northeast China Region is mainly a temperate zone. Only a small part of the Northeast China Region is in a frigid temperate zone and so this is not viewed as a separate region. Most of the North China Region occupies a warm temperate zone; the Central China Region occupies a subtropical zone, and the South China Region occupies an area approximately equivalent to a tropical zone.

The annual accumulated temperature in the frigid temperate zone is 1,100° to 1,700°C., but the average temperature in the hottest month can still rise to 20°C. and the frost-free period extends from 70 to 100 days. The annual accumulated temperature in the temperate zone is 1,700° to 3,200°C. with a frost-free period of 100 to 180 days. Thus the Northeast China Region has a long winter and low temperature, making it difficult to do farming. A one-crop system of farming exists in most parts of this region.

The warm temperature zone has an annual accumulated temperature of 3,200° to 4,500°C. and its frost-free period lasts from 180 to 240 days. Three crops are grown there every two years, but double-cropping is also practised on the plain between the Huanghe and Huaihe rivers (the southern part of the warm temperate zone). The southern boundary areas of this North China Region are roughly the Bailong River, the Qinling Mountains and the Huaihe River. South of this region is the subtropical zone, or an area where the farming system produces two crops a year.

The Central China Region, a subtropical zone, is located between the Qinling Mountains and the Huaihe River on the one side and the Nanling Mountains on the other. It has an annual accumulated temperature of 4,500° to 6,500° or 7,000°C. and a frost-free period of 240 to 300 days. The four seasons here are distinctly divided. In the northern part of this region two crops are harvested each year. And in the southern part, five crops are harvested every two years, that is, three crops are harvested one year and double-crop rices are grown the other year.

To the south of the Nanling Mountains is the South China Region, a tropical zone. Both the tropical and subtropical zones in the eastern part of China are considerably affected by cold waves in winter and can experience quite low temperatures. Even the northern part of Hainan Island can have temperatures below 0°C. occasionally. This makes these zones unique in comparison to other tropical and subtropical areas of the world, such as the Mediterranean area. Guilin and Shaoguan, because of the cold waves that extend southward, have relatively low temperatures in winter and a natural vegetation comparable to that of the subtropical zone.

On the basis of climate and composition of the whole physical landscape, we have set the following indices for the northern boundary of the tropical zone in China: accumulated temperature of 6,500° or above 7,000°C.; average temperature in the coldest month above 13°C.; most areas frost free all year round, and only one or two light frosts every year in the areas hit by cold waves. The warm winter makes it suitable for growing winter corn, winter sweet potatoes and sugar cane. This is distinctly different from the subtropical zone. Tropical fruit trees and plants such as mangos and papayas are grown and harvested widely in this tropical zone, but, generally speaking, they do not grow in the subtropical zone.

The tropical zone in China includes Taiwan, the coastal areas of Fujian, the southern parts of Guangdong, Guangxi and Yunnan, the southeastern part of Tibet and the islands in the South China Sea. The zone can be divided into two parts, east and west, owing to differences in atmospheric circulation and topography. Dominated by a tropical air mass all year round, Yunnan is almost never hit by cold waves. It has a relatively high minimum temperature, aboundant sunshine, a more effective heat response and better conditions of hibernation for plants. Therefore, judging from the actual growth of tropical plants in this region, the index of accumulated temperature at the northern boundary of the tropical zone can be a little lower than elsewhere in the zone, that is, about 6,500°C. Furthermore, points as high as 1,000 to 1,200 m. above sea level can still be a part of the tropical zone. Its northern boundary in western Yunnan extends to Latitude 25° N. and in the southeastern part of Tibet to Latitude 28° N.

On the other side of the tropical zone, Guangxi and Guangdong are affected by cold waves in winter,and have less favourable conditions of hibernation for crops. Judging from the physical landscape and the growth of crops in this eastern half of the tropical zone, the accumulated temperature at the northern boundary should be around 7,000°C. Therefore the northern boundary here is roughly confined to areas south of the southern foot of the Nanling Mountains, and points only as high as 500 m. above sea level can be considered to be part of the tropical zone. The northern boundary of the tropical zone in the coastal areas of Fujian and Taiwan also extends to Latitude 25° N. because the temperature here is regulated by the sea.

The landscapes in the four physical regions in eastern China gradually change from one type to another, and the boundaries of these regions are therefore indistinct. The division lines drawn on the map are, in fact, quite broad transition belts. For example, the southern margins of the subtropical zone (the Nanling Mountains and southeastern Fujian) are covered with the natural vegetation of subtropical evergreen broadleaved forests mixed with tropical tree species, and tropical fruit trees such as the lichee and *bajiao* banana can be grown in localities that have a suitable micro-climate. The natural vegetation in the broad areas between the Huanghe and Huaihe rivers in the southern part of the warm temperate zone consists of deciduous broadleaf forests mixed with subtropical deciduous tree species. Biannual crops are harvested in these areas wherever the soil has a better water and fertilizer supply. These areas obviously constitute a subzone of transition from the warm temperate zone to the subtropical zone.

To the northwest of the line from Greater Hinggan Mountains to the Great Wall, areas less affected by southeastern monsoons, water replaces heat as the leading element in regional differentiation. This area is divided into the Inner Mongolia Region, with mainly a grassland landscape, and the Northwest China Region, with mainly a desert landscape. The boundary lines roughly run from north to south (longitudinal), rather than from west to east (latitudinal) as they do in dividing the four physical regions of the eastern part of China. The landscape variations from west to east result from differences in aridity (Table 8).

Table 8. Changes in China's Physical Features as Determined by Humidity

Regions	Percentage of total area	Aridity	Landscape features
Humid	32.2	<1.0	Forest vegetation, soil free of lime accumulation, acid reaction
Semi-humid	15.3	1-1.5	Forest grassland and fairly arid forest, part of the soil with lime accumulation, neutral-slightly alkaline reaction
Semi-arid	21.7	1.5-2.0	Arid steppe; soil containing considerable lime accumulation and salinized
Arid	30.8	>2.0	Desert steppe and desert; soil salinized in most areas

The Qinghai-Tibetan Plateau, which stands 3,000 to 4,000 metres above sea level, has a landscape consisting mainly of cold deserts, alpine meadows and steppes. These are the product of both the zonal element of a westerly belt at the middle latitude and the non-zonal element of great elevation. But the topography is the primary one in determining the physical features of the Qinghai-Tibetan Plateau. If the Qinghai-Tibetan Plateau were not as high and if the Himalayas and other high mountains did not act as a natural barrier, the monsoons from the Indian Ocean would drive straight across the plateau, and it would obviously be a warm and humid region with a physical landscape totally different from what it now is. The Kunlun Mountains, north of the plateau, form a boundary between it and the northwest desert region.

The Southwest China Region includes Yunnan and the southwestern part of Sichuan, an area roughly west to the Greater and Lesser Xiangling Mountains and the Beipan River. This region is mainly a mountainous plateau 1,500 to 2,000 m. above sea level. So far as heat is concerned, the climate in this region can be considered as subtropical, but it is unlike the subtropical zone in eastern China because elevations of 1,500 to 2,000 m. there (the western Hubei Highland and the western Guizhou Highland) do not have a subtropical climate. The most salient characteristic of the Southwest China Region is that this is a tropical mountainous plateau, meaning that its horizontal belt belongs to a tropical zone as its landform to a mountainous plateau. It has a climate of "spring in all seasons", which is peculiar to such a tropical mountainous plateau, and its vegetation and soil result from that climate. Therefore, it can be separated from the Central China Region as an independent physical region of its own.

The formation of the tropical mountainous plateau landscape in the Southwest China Region mainly results from its atmospheric circulation system, that is, the influence of southwest monsoons in the summer half of the year and the influence of the tropical continental air mass in the winter half.

Therefore, the scope of influence of the tropical continental air mass can be used as the major indicator in determining the eastern and northern boundaries of the Southwest China Region.

Since China is a country with many mountains, the boundaries of physical regions often pass through mountainous areas. Determining which physical region a mountain fits into can be a complicated matter. The principles followed in this respect are: (a) If the foot of a mountain on both sides belongs to the same landscape, the whole mountain is included in the region characterized mainly by that landscape. For example, both sides of the Tianshan and Altun mountains belong to a desert landscape, and so they are included in the Northwest China Region, which is covered mainly by desert. (b) If the two sides of a mountain belong to two different types of landscape, then the principal one is taken as the basis for deciding which region the mountain should be in. For example, the northern side of the Kunlun Mountains is a desert and its southern side is a cold desert, and the Kunlun Mountains themselves are covered mostly by a cold desert. Therefore the Kunlun Mountains are included in the Qinghai-Tibetan Region instead of the Northwest China Region.

2) Subregions. The eight physical regions all cover large areas that have differences in their interior landscapes and in land utilization. We can therefore divide the regions into many subregions. For example, the Central China Region covers an area of 12° latitude, and the heat accumulation differs from north to south so that the physical landscapes in the region are also distinctly different from each other and can be divided into two subregions (south and north) (Table 9).

The Inner Mongolian Region covers an area of 20° longitude from west to east. As a result of the different water conditions, the region can be divided into three subregions: eastern meadow grassland, central typical steppe and western desert steppe.

The division into subregions in the other physical regions

Table 9. Comparison of the Physical Characteristics for
the Two Parts of the Central China Region

Subregion	Climate	Vegetation	Soil	Crops	Cultivated trees
Northern subtropical zone, Jianghan-Qinling Subregion	Accumulated temperature 4,500° to 5,000°C.	Deciduous broadleaf forest mixed with ever-green trees	Yellow-brown earth	Rice, one crop a year	No camphor trees or oranges
Southern Subtropical zone, South Changjiang-Nanling Subregion	Accumulated temperature 5,000° to 7,000°C.	Subtropical evergreen broadleaf forests	Red earth and yellow earth	Rice, two crops a year	Camphor trees, tea-oil trees and oranges

is also based on the principle of making an overall analysis of all physical elements and thus determining the principal one. The relief of the high mountains and big basins in the Northwest China Region makes for great differences in the water and heat conditions. For example, the Tianshan Mountains partition the southern and northern parts of Xinjiang, and southern Xinjiang, with more heat, belongs to the warm temperate zone, while northern Xinjiang belongs to the temperate zone. The high elevation of the Qaidam Basin also leads to a differentiation in its desert landscape. Therefore, on the basis of the geomorphic boundaries, the Northwest China Region can be divided into six subregions: Northern Xinjiang, Southern Xinjiang, Tianshan Mountains, Alxa-Gansu Corridor, Qilian Mountains and Qaidam Basin.

Generally speaking, a subregion, as defined in this book, covers only one physical zone, but it can also include two physical zones in cases where to do otherwise would distort a logical geographical unit. For example, Taiwan should be one physical geographical unit, but if it is mechanically divided into subregions on the basis of physical zones, it will be separated into two parts, a tropical north and a tropical south. But the tropical south covers only a small area, limited to the southern cape of Taiwan Island. If it is divided this way, the southern edge of Taiwan would have to be linked as a subregion to Hainan Island across the vast South China Sea, and this would be obviously inappropriate

3) Areas. The third level of physical regions are called areas. They are divisions of the subregions based on the same principles used in dividing the subregions. For example, the Qaidam Basin is an interior basin that originated as a single unit and has a common landscape throughout. It is therefore regarded as one subregion. But in view of differences in humidity, the basin itself can be separated into two areas — east and west — the former being a semi-desert area and the latter a desert area.

Another example is the South Changjiang-Nanling Subregion in the Central China Region. This covers a large area and has complicated landforms. On the basis of the distinct geographical characteristics, this subregion is separated into five areas: South Changjiang Low Mountains, Hills and Basins; Sichuan Basin; Guizhou Plateau; Nanling Mountains, and Northern Guangxi.

Chapter VII

THE NORTHEAST CHINA REGION

The Northeast China Region is located in China's highest latitudes. Its north, east and southeast extend to the nation's boundaries. Its west links up to the Hulunbuir Plateau in the Inner Mongolian Region across the Greater Hinggan Mountains. The northern section of the Greater Hinggan Mountains is a distinct natural boundary which coincides roughly with the aridity 1.2 isopleth. It stretches from the mouth of the Genhe River southeastward through the area between Hailar and the Xuguit Banner (Yakeshi) until it reaches the Aher Mountains in the south. The southern boundary of the Northeast Region is less obvious. Starting from the Aher Mountains, it runs eastward along the Taoer River valley and Ulanhot, turns southward through Shuangliao to connect with the isopleth of the accumulated temperature of 3,000°C., and then moves southeastward to reach the bank of the Yalu River.

Administratively, the Northeast China Region includes the whole of Heilongjiang Province, most parts of Jilin Province, the northern part of Liaoning Province and the eastern part of the Inner Mongolian Autonomous Region. West of Jilin Province, the aridity is above 1.2, and there are large expanses of sandy land, including the Kerqin Sandy Land in the Inner Mongolian Region.

Topographically the Northeast Region contains three semi-circular zones. The outermost zone is formed by the valleys of the Heilong and Wusuli rivers, which is adjoined by mountains, including the Greater Hinggan Mountains in the western part of the region, the Yilehuli and the Lesser Hinggan Mountains in the north, and the Zhangguangcai Ridge and Changbai Mountains in the eastern part of the region. Surrounded by these mountains and hills is the Songnen Plain, while in the east, there is the low-lying and humid Sanjiang plain in the lower reaches of the Songhua River and on the left bank of the Wusuli River.

The Greater Hinggan Mountains are a north-north-east range, stretching for 1,400 km. from Mohe on the right bank of the Heilong River to the left bank of the Xilamulun River. The mountain range is divided by the Taoer River into northern and southern sections. The northern section is a wide range extending for 670 km. and standing 1,000 metres above sea level. Its peaks exceed 1,700 m. in height, and its eastern slopes are steep, having a dense drainage network. Its western slopes are gentle, with weak dissections. The southern section of the Greater Hinggan Mountains is formed of low mountains, but some peaks do rise to 1,050 m. This section is composed of a forest grassland landscape, although forests exist only on some parts of the eastern slopes. The physical geography of the western part of this section is similar to that of the Inner Mongolian Plateau while the eastern part is similar to the Xiliao River Plain. Thus the southern section of the Greater Hinggan Mountains is included in the Inner Mongolian Region.

Usually the name Lesser Hinggan Mountains refers only to the north-west mountains with round tops and gentle undulations in the northern part of Heilongjiang Province. The eastern extension, known as the Changbai Mountains, is composed of many parallel folded-block mountains running in a north-east direction. The Changbai Mountains include Wanda Mountain, Zhangguangcai Ridge, Laoye Ridge, Taiping Ridge, Changbai Mountain, and other peaks. Generally speaking, these ridges are 500 to 1,000 m. high. The mountain range is intersected by rivers that form wide flat valleys, among which are a scattering of wet lands.

Geotectonically, both the Songnen and Sanjiang plains are subsidence areas where accumulation is much in evidence and subsidence is still in progress. This is why the terrain is flat and there are huge expanses of marsh land in the low-lying areas.

The macromorphologic contour of the region tends to increase the coldness and humidity of the climate and constitutes an important factor in the shaping of different landscapes in the Northeast China Region. The mountainous areas have a forest landscape with vertical zonal structure, while the plains are composed of forest grasslands and meadows interspersed with wet lands.

1. Humid Forest Landscape and Forest Grassland Landscape

Forests are widely distributed throughout the Northeast Region. The Greater and Lesser Hinggan Mountains and the other northeast mountains are China's foremost natural forest zones. They cover 47 million hectares with a total timber reserve of 3,000 million cu. m., accounting for 60 per cent of the country's total forest resources. Moreover, the timber is of high quality. Thus the area has been described as China's "treasure house of green gold". The Songnen Plain is one of the most fertile large plains in China, providing a rich potential for agriculture and livestock breeding. The wide distribution of temperate forests and forest grassland vegetation, interspersed with meadows and marshes, constitutes the main feature of the natural resources and physical landscape of the northeast.

Among the factors contributing to the creation of the humid forest and forest grassland landscape in the Northeast Region, the temperate monsoonal climate plays the leading role. Its influence is also reflected in various aspects of the physical geography.

(1) Main Characteristics of the Temperate Zone Monsoonal Climate

The Northeast Region is located in the path of the prevailing westerlies of the central latitudes, resulting in a temperate monsoon-type continental climate. Most of the weather systems move from west to east, and reinforce the northwest monsoons in winter and weaken the southeast monsoons in summer.

Located between Latitude 42° and 53°34' N., the Northeast Region is the coldest physical region in China. The predominance of the powerful Mongolian high, with strong winds and recurring cold waves, makes the region particularly cold in winter. The January isotherm is roughly parallel to the latitudes, and there are vast differences in temperature between north and south. For every 1° rise in latitude, from the -10°C. in the south to -30°C. in the north, the temperature drops by 1.5°C. The northern part of the Greater Hinggan Mountains is the coldest area in the country, with the extreme minimum temperature dropping to below -45°C.

Winter is long and the low temperatures last for a long period. Generally speaking, the average daily temperature in the Greater Hinggan Mountains stays below 0°C. from early October to April, a period of six and a half months. The period when average daily temperatures stay below 0°C. in the Songnen Plain and the Changbai Mountains lasts for five to six months. During this period, the soil is frozen, snow doesn't thaw, rivers are iced over and agricultural activities come to a standstill. But it is a busy period for forestry, because the frozen land facilitates timber felling and transportation.

In the spring, due to continental heating, the Mongolian high is weakened and a low pressure begins to appear along the banks of the Heilong River. This leads to a converging of air currents from the north and south, resulting in frequent cyclones. And the strong wind currents created by the low pressure often lead to the southward movement of cold air and a late frost. In spring there is often a strong southeast or southwest wind, with a wind force of 10 to 20 m. per sec. Such winds frequently occur in the Songnen Plain and in the watershed of the Songhua and Liaohe rivers, with wind speeds reaching 30 m. per sec. Gongzhuling, for instance, registered a gale of 46.3 m. per sec. on March 23, 1919. In the western part of the Songnen Plain, the snow cover is thin and the earth surface sandy. Dry wind and sandstorms, therefore, often play havoc with agricultural production in the spring.

North of Aihui, there is usually no summer, but in rare cases when there is, it lasts only one or two pentads. July is the hottest month in this region, with the temperature in most areas rising to 20°C. and above. The isotherm in the central plains then shows a general trend of turning to the north. Here the isotherm is sparse with each degree of latitude differing by an average of only 0.4°C. Although the July mean temperature is rather low in comparison to other parts of the country, when the Pacific high finds its way into this region, there may be short periods of hot weather with temperatures rising above 35°C.

Autumn comes rapidly in this region. As the Mongolian high enters the region, the temperature generally drops about 8°C. from August to September and about 10°C. from September to October. The October mean temperature is below 10°C., with the northernmost part, where winter has already set in, below 0°C.

The region's agricultural season for the whole year (average daily temperature > 0°C.) is only about 190 to 220 days, and the growing season is 140 to 190 days. The growing season increases from north to south and from high land to low land. Although the active accumulated temperature is less than 3,000°C., both the days and sunshine time are long in the summer, the effective temperature is high and the stable duration of active temperature lasts about four to five months. This meets the requirements for ripening of crops in general. For instance, the survival rate of spring wheat grown on the plains of this region exceeds 95 per cent, and even in the Heilong valley it is about 90 per cent. Soybeans, sugar beets and potatoes have a survival rate in this region of over 95 per cent. Moreover, the Yanbian Korean Autonomous Prefecture of Jilin Province is an area where rice is grown over large areas at high latitudes.

The southeast monsoons are the main source of precipitation in this region. The Suifen River area, at the eastern tip of this region, is only 100 kilometres from the Sea of Japan, and so the southeast monsoons can enter the region directly. In most parts of the region, 60 per cent of the rainfall for the whole year occurs in summer, and in some places more than 70 per cent. The distribution of precipitation is affected by the terrain. The windward slopes of the mountains have much more rainfall than the western leeward slopes. For example, the southeastern slopes of the Changbai Mountains have as much as 1,000 mm. of rainfall and the eastern slopes of the Lesser Hinggan Mountains over 600 mm. But the amount reduces to 400 to 500 mm. on the Nenjiang Plain, is only slightly more on the eastern slopes of the Greater Hinggan Mountains, falls to below 400 mm. across these mountains and decreases gradually on entering the Inner Mongolian grassland area.

The total annual precipitation in the Northeast Region is not abundant. Yet, owing to the low temperature and small evaporation, there is a relatively large amount of effective precipitation. The aridity of the region is generally below 1.2, and that in the eastern mountains and the Greater and Lesser Hinggan Mountains less than 1.0. Snowfall in winter and the long accumulation of snow make the conservation of winter precipitation possible. After the spring thaw, there is adequate humidity for the soil and river runoff forms spring floods. Due to the concentrated rainfall and high temperatures in summer, plus fertile soil in most places, the physical conditions in this region are suitable for the growing of high-yield single crops.

(2) Frozen Earth and Permafrost

The high latitudes and mountains result in a wide distribution of frozen earth in the Northeast Region. This frozen earth can be divided into perennial frozen earth (permafrost) and seasonal frozen earth.

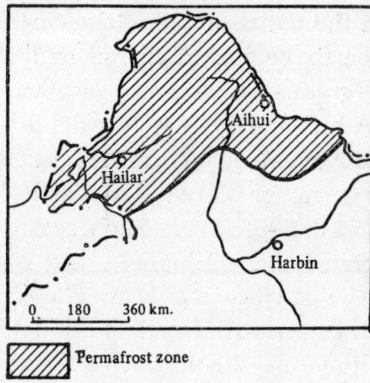

Permafrost zone

Fig. 17 Distribution of Permafrost in North China

The permafrost is distributed in mountainous areas north of Latitude 47° N. (Fig. 17). Its southern boundary roughly coincides with the January -26°C. isotherm (annual mean temperature of 0°C. isotherm). The distribution of permafrost is mainly dominated by latitudinal zones, gradually shrinking in area and thickness from the northwest to southeast. The northwestern part is the coldest, with an annual average temperature of less than -5°C., where the permafrost extends over large expanses, and with a thickness of 50 to 100 m. The southeastern part has an annual average temperature of -3° to 0°C. Consequently the permafrost here is distributed in the shape of islands and the thickness of the frozen earth is only 5 to 20 m. The top soil of these permafrost islands thaws in summer, resulting in the phenomenon called a "seasonal thawing layer". In some of the mountains, the maximum thawing depth is about 0.5 to 3.5 m., with the permafrost remaining below this. Wherever there is permafrost, it constitutes an impermeable layer that obstructs the seepage of surface water and soil water, and keeps the ground in a humid condition.

The seasonal frozen earth freezes and thaws with changes in temperature, i.e., it freezes in winter and thaws completely in summer. When the temperature of the earth's surface drops below 0°C., the earth begins to freeze and the thickness of the frozen earth gradually becomes greater. In the Heilong valley between Aihui and Huma, the depth of frozen earth reaches 50 cm. in November, one m. in December, two m. in February and three m. in March. The earth then completely thaws in August and September. Such seasonal frozen earth is distributed extensively throughout the region. When the snow on the earth's surface thaws in late spring, the upper layer of frozen soil begins to defrost, and this thawing gradually deepens. At this juncture the unthawed frozen earth forms an impermeable layer while the water formed by the thawing of the upper layer begins to move laterally to converge in streams or rivers. In summer the frozen earth thaws completely, which facilitates the permeation of large quantities of rainfall, and the soil is excellently aerated. Thus seasonal frozen earth not only moistens the soil and facilitates spring sowing, but it also affects the evolution of the soil.

An important characteristic of the natural landscape in this region is the wide distribution of marshes which make up a large proportion of the total land. They are scattered not only on the plains and low-lying land, but also on flat highlands and terraces. The cold and damp weather, weak evaporation, shrinking forests, clay layer on the underlying surface that prevents smooth drainage, and the wide distribution of permafrost and seasonal frozen earth are important factors contributing to the formation of these marshes. Geomorphically, the existence of perennial and seasonal frozen earth restricts the down-cutting role of surface water. Thus wide valleys and flat terraces are geomorphic characteristics of the frozen earth zone.

The frozen earth and freezing of rivers have increased the humidity of the earth surface in the Northeast Region. By late October every year, ice floes appear in the Heilong River, and two weeks later the river is completely frozen to a maximum thickness of two metres. The thaw starts in mid-April and the ice floes disappear by early May. The river is thus frozen for six months every year. The freezing period of the Nenjiang and Songhua rivers is about five months. The melting of snow on the ground in spring and the thawing of rivers often bring about big spring floods. This is particularly true of those rivers flowing from south to north, such as the Wusuli and the tributaries of the Songhua. In these rivers the thaw starts in the upper reaches, resulting in difficulties in the lower reaches where the water cannot discharge because the river is still frozen. Thus the water from the upper reaches flows over the land surface.

(3) Forests and Forest Grasslands

The Northeast Region has an excellent environment for the formation and development of temperate forest and forest grassland vegetation, and their corresponding soils. The northern section of the Greater Hinggan Mountains is an area where deciduous-coniferous forests are concentrated. Coniferous-deciduous broadleaf forests and deciduous broadleaf forests are widely distributed in the Lesser Hinggan Mountains and the adjoining Eastern mountains. Owing to the relatively high temperature and less precipitation on the Songnen Plain, herbaceous plants predominate there, forming meadow grasslands.

As the entire region has plentiful rain in summer, soil leaching and grass growing processes are conspicuous, resulting in the limited but deep illuviation of calcium, universal eluviation of clay particles and the acid reaction in the soil. The freezing in winter causes the suspension of organic activity in the soil and the inhibition of the decomposition of organic matter. Consequently soil evolution takes place only in certain seasons of the year and rich organic matter accumulates in the soil, making it highly fertile. This is particularly true on the Songnen Plain, where fertile black soil and chernozem have developed as a result of the thriving grass growing process.

Under such water, heat, biological and climatic conditions, the distribution of vegetation and soils is characterized by clearcut zonality. In the mountainous areas of the north, there is a zone composed mainly of frigid-temperate coniferous forests with brown coniferous soil. In the mountainous areas to the east and south, there is a zone composed mainly of temperate mixed coniferous and broadleaf forests with dark brown forest soil. The Sanjiang Plain in the east is composed mainly of marshes and meadows; the low mountains and hills contain deciduous broadleaf forests with thin layers of dark brown forest soil; and the Songnen Plain is a zone of meadow grassland with black soil.

1) Frigid-temperate coniferous forest with brown coniferous soil zone. This is chiefly located in the northern part of the Greater Hinggan Mountains that rise 800 m. above sea level. The zone in the country is a vertical zone except for a small horizontal area, and it is somewhat shaped like a wedge along the Greater Hinggan Mountains. The plants that grow here are an extension of the famous Siberian taiga. They are mainly heliophilous larches, which can stand up to the most severe cold, but their leaves fall off in winter. The constructive species are chiefly Dahurian larch (*Larix dahurica*) and Mongolian pine (*Pinus sylvestris var. Mongolica*). The distributional elevation of the frigid-temperate coniferous forests varies in the Greater Hinggan Mountains with different latitudes. For example, in Latitude 47° to 48° N., on the eastern foot of the mountains (400 to

900 m. above sea level) there are temperate forest grasslands. On the slopes up to 1,200 m. there are temperate deciduous broadleaf forests and the mixed coniferous and broadleaf forests, and only above 1,200 m. are there frigid-temperate coniferous forests. But in the section of the Greater Hinggan Mountains at Latitude 51° to 52° N., the frigid-temperate coniferous forests begin to spread extensively at 700-800 m. above sea level. Such vertical distribution, of course, shows that various sections of the Greater Hinggan Mountains receive different amounts of heat because of their different latitudes.

The soil that has developed under the frigid-temperate coniferous forest is brown coniferous soil. Because the climate here is humid and severely cold for long periods in a year, acid leaching has become the main soil forming process and the soil profile shows much acidity (pH 5.0 to 5.5). Because this zone belongs to permafrost area, the earth is generally frozen for seven months, thawing only in summer. During the thawing period, the leached matter in the soil rises into the upper layer of earth along with the rising water, and so there is little or no differentiation of minerals and leached horizon in the layers of soil.

2) Temperate coniferous and broadleaf forest with brown forest soil zone. This is mainly distributed in the Lesser Hinggan Mountains and Eastern mountains, as well as on the eastern slopes of the Greater Minggan Mountains below the coniferous forest zone. The forests on the low mountains and hills of 500 to 700 m. above sea level are composed mainly of deciduous broadleaf trees, chiefly ulmus, acer, tilia, and Mongolian oak, with a small number of Korean pines (*Pinus koraiensis*). As the area is close to the sea and there is much humidity in the atmosphere, an abundant number of vines grow in the forests. On the forest ground also grows ginseng (*Panax ginseng*), a residual herbaceous plant of the Tertiary period. Wherever these forests have suffered human destruction, the trees that now grow are the pure deciduous broadleaf trees,

such as acer, tilia, ulmus and birch. And because these forests
have a great variety of broadleaf trees, they are called locally "forests of miscellaneous trees". Three kinds of famous hard-
woods grown in northeast China — Manchurian walnut (*Jug-
lans mandshurica*), Manchurian ash (*Fraxinus mandshurica*) and
Amur corktree (*Phellodendron amurense*) — are found here.

On the mountains between 800 and 1,300 m. above sea
level there are temperate coniferous forests, the Korean pine
forests being the best known. Korean pines often mix with
deciduous broadleaf trees, but in some places the forests are
composed solely of Korean pines. At places of higher altitude in
this zone there are spruces and firs, mainly Yeddo spruce (*Picea
jezoensis*) and Khingan fir (*Abies nephrolepsis*). In this zone
the lower limit for the growth of the Korean larch (*Larix olgen-
sis*) reaches the foot of the mountains, and the forests composed solely of this kind of tree can be found in the low-lying
wet marshland of the mountains, which is called "Korean
larch bog". The herbaceous plant on the forest ground is carex.

The climate of the Eastern mountains is extremely humid,
and the aridity at such places as Yichun is only 0.8. The mountains are foggy in summer, with the annual average relative
humidity reaching 70 to 80 per cent. There is much leaching
in the soil, so it has little acidity, good water permeability and
marked oxidation. The top soil is brown in colour and the
humus content reaches 8 to 15 per cent, but the soil is thin.
In general, the zone is fit for afforestation, not for agriculture.

3) Temperate forest grassland and grasslands with black
soil and chernozem zone. This is centred in the Songnen Plain,
which is located between the Greater Hinggan, Lesser Hinggan
and Eastern mountains. The plain is in a rain-shadow area
where there is less precipitation and an aridity of about 1. The
natural vegetation on the lower slopes of the Lesser Hinggan
Mountains, the western foot of the Eastern Mountains and the
eastern foothills and mounds of the Greater Hinggan Mountains
is forest grassland. On the plain between these mountains the
precipitation decreases and the natural vegetation changes

gradually into temperate grassland and meadows. The aridity at the centre of the plain (Anda city area) reaches 1.3, which is that of a dry steppe area.

The forest grasslands grow perennial grass and miscellaneous grass. The vegetation is mainly of the gramineae, asteraceae and leguminosae families, mixed with such shrubs as Mongolian oak, Ansu apricot (*Prunus armeniaca Var. ansu*) and shrub lespedeza (*Lespedeza bicolor*). The corresponding soil is black soil with a deep humus layer, generally 30 to 70 cm. thick, and in individual cases more than 100 cm. The soil profile has no calcification layer or lime reaction, and the soil formation includes not only the process of humus accumulation that takes place in the shaping of meadows but also the process of forest soil formation, such as base leaching. The soil has little acidity, its pH value being 5.5 to 6.5. The surface layer has a high humus content, often 3 to 6 per cent, and in some cases more than 15 per cent. There is also a rich content of nitrogen and phosphorus. This and its fine granular structure make the black soil highly fertile. Most of the black soil areas have been turned into farmland.

On the grassland there are mainly *Aeurolepidium chinense* and miscellaneous grasses. The former, a broadleaf perennial grass of 50 to 100 cm. in height, grows luxuriantly together with *Filifolium sibiricum, Stipa baicalensis,* etc. During the growth period, the grassland has such a gorgeous look, owing to the various kinds of grasses that blossom forth at different times and the beautiful flowers that present a riot of colour in different seasons, and the area is called locally "grassland of sundry flowers". The corresponding soil is chernozem. Because there is so little precipitation, the base lixiviation in the soil is incomplete, illuvium is formed in the soil profile (B horizon) and the accumulation of calcium carbonate is distinct. Chernozem is neutral to slightly alkaline, has a pH of 6.5 to 8.5, and has a deep humus layer. It is also a soil with high natural fertility, being rich in nitrogen, phosphorus, potassium and other nutritious elements. It is thus suitable for the cultivation of crops. Wide reclamation of such soils has been completed, but large tracts of land remain to be opened for cultivation.

The centre of the Songnen Plain is a semi-arid steppe, the grass generally growing 30 to 50 cm. in height, but sparsely. The soil is dark chestnut in colour. Because marshes, lakes and sandy land are scattered widely throughout this area, the ground is covered with sandy soil and meadow soil, which is saline to alkaline.

(4) Marshes and Meadows

The extensive distribution of marshes and meadows is another major characteristic of the physical geography in the Northeast Region. According to preliminary estimates, the region has 82,000 sq. km. of marshes, accounting for 6.2 per cent of the total area. In the mountains, the marshes are mostly distributed in valleys or on lava tableland. The peat layer on these marshes is generally 0.5 m. thick, with that in the Changbai Mountains reaching a thickness of one metre. On the plain, the marshes are mainly distributed in old river channels, shallow depressions and by lakesides. They are most extensively distributed over the Sanjiang Plain, and less extensively along the Wuyur and Shuangyang rivers and along the lower reaches of the Alun River on the Nenjiang Plain. The remainder, scattered in isolated spots, have thin layers of peat and salination in the top layers of their soil.

The formation of marshes in the Northeast Region is the result of a number of physical conditions working together. These are:

1) The concentration of summer rain. Because the permeability of the soil in the region is weak and evaporation in summer cannot keep pace with the precipitation, there is excessive humidity in the soil.

2) The impermeability of the frozen earth. Large amounts of water are held as ice in the upper layer of the soil during

the winter. This melts in the summer, but the water remains in the upper layer because it can't permeate the frozen lower layers. Marshes thus form even on high terraces, watersheds and slopes.

3) The extensive clay deposits. On the valley terraces of the Heilong River and on the Songnen Plain, fluvio-lacustrine clay deposits, with very poor permeability, cover big areas. Drilling proves that these clay deposits have a thickness of more than 30 to 50 cm., forming an impervious layer.

4) The existence of wide and flat alluvial terraces. The old alluvial terraces along river banks are not much higher than the river levels themselves. In summer, when the rivers are inundated, the water flows over their banks to form marshes.

5) Abandoned channels and oxbow lakes develop into marshes as they gradually dry up and are overgrown with plants.

6) The destruction of forests. In places where tree felling or forest fires have occurred, the surface soil becomes compact, and because soil evaporation and plant transpiration decreases, the land surface becomes excessively humid and marshy. The "Korean larch bog" in the Changbai Mountains is an example of this process.

The marshes in the Northeast Region have a marsh vegetation of humid perennial herbaceous plants, chiefly of the Cyperaceae and Gramineae families. The marshes often form grass mounds because of the constant accumulation of withered grass. Between these grass mounds are all kinds of mosses and garden burnet. On marshes formed recently short shrubs grow. Wula sedge (*Carex fosicula*), which grows extensively in these northeast marshes, is one of the "three treasures of Northeast China". It can be used inside boots to keep the feet warm.

The soil in the marsh areas is constantly in a state of water saturation and it is poorly aerated. Thus the activity of microorganisms in the soil is inhibited and large quantities of organic matter cannot fully decompose. As a result, a thick layer of peat or humus is formed in the upper part of the soil, with the peat layer having an organic content of 60 to 70 per cent. Affected by waterlogging and reducing materials produced by the decomposition of organic matter, the lower part of the soil is constantly in a state of reduction, resulting in the development of a greyish blue or light grey gley horizon having a heavy texture. Such soil is called marsh soil. It exhibits a neutral or slightly acid reaction. After adopting appropriate drainage and other improvement measures, marsh soil can be reclaimed for the planting of crops.

Meadows in this region are often found in river valleys and on low terraces where the underground water level is usually at one to two metres in depth. During the season of plant growth, ground water continuously rises to the surface keeping the soil in a humid state. The meadows are covered by dense vegetation, composed of meadow plants and marsh meadow plants, usually *Calamagrostis hirsuta*, Carex, Garden burnet and Chinese globeflower *(Trollius sinensis)*.

Under such hygrophilous vegetation, *baijiang* soil (lessive) develops. The characteristic of such soil is the great disparity between its upper and lower layers. The upper layer is a humus horizon, generally 10 to 20 cm. thick, which is loose and has few clay particles. The lower layer, usually clay, is greyish white, compact, and contains many iron particles and rust mottles. This "two-layer character" of *baijiang* soil is derived from the fact that the upper layer experiences intermittent waterlogging, which reduces and activates the iron, manganese and other elements in the soil to make them wash away through lateral leaching. This results in the lower layer losing colour and becoming a special greyish-white lessive layer. Meanwhile, owing to abundant rainfall, the clay particles in the upper soil layer leach out in large quantities, moving downward to illuviate the lower layer and make it very heavy. *Baijiang* soil has a slightly acid reaction, its pH value being 5 to 6. As the humus horizon is very thin, the total storage of humus in the entire soil profile is not high. At present most *baijiang* soil has been turned into farmland. But because the soil is clayish and poorly aerated, it is necessary to adopt drainage, turning over and other measures to improve it.

2. Regional Differentiation of the Natural Landscape

From the above description, it can readily be seen that climate plays the predominant role in shaping the natural landscape of the Northeast Region. The main feature of this landscape is forest vegetation, and the topography only deepens the coldness and humidity of the climate to varying degrees. Lush vegetation and the distribution of meadows and marshes over large areas reflect an abundance of water on the ground and excessive humidity in the soil.

Due to the geomorphic factor, the physical zones in this region are roughly in the shape of a horseshoe, with obvious distinctions between various zones. These can be divided into three subregions and four smaller areas. In each subregion, along with the difference in the local terrain and exposure, there are marked differences in the natural landscape. Hence each subregion includes two or more types of natural landscape.

IA The Northern Greater Hinggan Mountains Subregion
IB The Lesser Hinggan and Eastern Mountains Subregion
    IB_1 The Sanjiang Plain Area
    IB_2 The Lesser Hinggan Mountains and Eastern Mountains Area
IC The Songnen Plain Subregion
    IC_1 The Low Mountains, Hills and Mounds Area
    IC_2 The Songnen Plain Area

(1) Northern Greater Hinggan Mountains Subregion

The Greater Hinggan Mountains run in a north-north-east direction in keeping with the tectonic strike. The eastern slopes are steep, falling in steps towards the Songnen Plain, while the western slopes are gentle and slant towards the Inner Mongolian Plateau. Since the Neogene Period, tilting movement has repeatedly occurred in the strike fault area on the eastern flank of the Greater Hinggan Mountains, bringing about the asymmetric inclines on the eastern and western slopes. Most peaks of the Greater Hinggan Mountains in the Northeast Region rise 1,000 to 1,400 m. above sea level. They have round tops and indistinct ridge lines, as well as many mountain passes and transversal valleys between the peaks.

This subregion is one of the coldest in China. It is also the only large frigid-temperate area. The permafrost is extensively distributed and the snow on shady slopes does not thaw even in summer months. The rivers are frozen for six months a year. According to seasons divided by pentad temperatures, this subregion has no summer and its winter extends for more than eight months. For instance, the Ergun Left Banner along the Genhe River (50°41′ N., 720 m. above sea level) has a January average temperature of -31.1°C., being the lowest temperature in the Northeast Region. The extreme lowest temperature at Mohe, in Huma County, reached -52.3°C in 1969, being the record of extreme minimum for all of China. The frostless season at the Ergun Left Banner is only 81 days in a year, and annual precipitation there is generally 400 to 500 mm. Owing to the low temperature, the aridity is only 0.7. Xingan on the watershed is even more humid, as it has a precipitation of 600 mm. due to its higher altitude (980 m. above the sea).

The subregion's natural landscape is composed mainly of frigid-temperate Dahurian larch forests in which, due to ample sunshine, shrubs and herbaceous plants grow luxuriantly. In places where the drainage is poor and in the neighbourhood of streams, the larches form an almost unmixed forest. On the gentle northern slopes where drainage is good, limited numbers of white birch (*Betula platyphylla*) and Mongolian pine grow in the forests. North of the Genhe River, coniferous forests spread from the foot to the top of mountains. In the southern part of this subregion, owing to greater heat, temperate mixed coniferous and broadleaf forests and deciduous broadleaf forests appear on slopes below 1,000 m. above sea level, but these take up only a narrow area on the eastern slopes of the Greater Hinggan Mountains. Therefore this area is still included in this subregion.

As forests provide a favourable animal habitat, the subregion boasts a great variety of animals and is an important fur-producing area. Because of the coldness of the climate, the fur that the animals grow here is soft and glossy, making this the leading area in China for acquiring furs both in quantity and quality. The most precious fur-bearing animals that are found here are the sable, otter and lynx. The most prolific ones, however, are the squirrel, northeast rabbit, alpine weasel, fox and roe deer. The antlers of the red deer and the sika deer and the musk of the musk deer are also of high economic value. Furthermore, in this subregion there are moose, the largest deer in the world. The Oroqens, the national minority that lives in this area, mainly engage in hunting, though they also raise reindeer.

The short growing period and the excessively humid and thin soil in this subregion make it unfavourable for agriculture, but good for tree growth. Therefore forestry takes the foremost place in its economy. Railway lines have been extended to the forest areas in the northern part of the Greater Hinggan Mountains since it has become one of the major timber producing areas in the country.

This subregion also includes the Sanhe-Yakeshi area at the western foot of the Greater Hinggan Mountains. Because the water condition on the western slopes of the Greater Hinggan Mountains is poorer than it is on the eastern slopes, there is a forest grassland-chernozem zone just below the Dahurian larch zone in low mountains and hills. Aridity here is roughly around 1 at Yakeshi. From east to west along the entire western foot of the mountains, the aridity gradually increases and the natural landscape varies correspondingly. On the eastern part is forest meadow, the middle and upper parts of the shady slopes are composed of white birch and aspen (*Populus davidiana*) forests with grey forest soil. On the lower part of the shady and extensive sunny slopes and valleys is a "grassland of sundry flowers" with luvic chernozem. The middle part is composed of meadow grassland, with a little forest area on the middle and upper sections of the shady slopes. Most of the ground is covered by a grassland of sundry flowers with ortho chernozem. The western part is a transitional area between the meadow grassland and the steppe of Inner Mongolia. On the shady slopes is mainly meadow grassland and on the sunny slopes steppe, the soil being chernozem with a little humus. It is thus clear that the western foot of the Greater Hinggan Mountains is an area suitable for agriculture and animal husbandry. As this area is located in the west, where there is little population and little cultivated land, large tracts of land are available to be reclaimed and the area is one of the hopeful reclamation areas of the Northeast Region.

(2) Lesser Hinggan and Eastern Mountains Subregion

The Lesser Hinggan Mountains extend from the banks of the Heilong River to the area north of the Songhua River. They stretch for 360 km. from north to south, with a width of 80 to 320 km. The terrain is rather low and the average elevation is only 400 to 600 m., with the peaks generally below 1,000 m. The highest peak, Mount Duimian, is less than 1,200 m. The mountains are gentle and the valleys are wide. The slopes on the two sides of the Lesser Hinggan Mountains are also asymmetric, the northeastern slope being short and steep and the southwestern slope long and gentle.

The mountains to the south of the Songhua River are generally called the Eastern Mountains, or Changbai Mountains. Most of the peaks are above 1,000 m. The northern section is composed of many parallel northeast-southwest mountain ridges, such as Zhangguangcai and Laoye. Between the mountains are wide river valleys, such as the Mudan and the Muling. The highest section of the Changbai Mountains towers over the China-Korea border, with one peak, Mount Baitou, rising 2,744 m. above sea level. Tianchi, the top of this peak, is a typical volcanic lake with an area of 9.2 sq. km., the lake surface rising 2,155 m. above sea level and the lake water being 312.7 m. deep. The water from Tianchi flows out of a breach in the north wall of the peak and falls precipitately for 250 m. to form a huge waterfall that becomes the Erdaobai River, one of the two sources for the Songhua. Mount Baitou is a dormant volcano which, according to historical records, erupted in 1597, 1668 and 1702. Hot springs (about 30°C.) still spurt in the vicinity of this mount.

Another important geomorphic feature of the Changbai Mountains is the widespread distribution of basalt, forming a huge basalt platform in the Dunhua-Jingbo Lake-Muling-Dongning area. In prehistoric times, the basalt flow in the Mudan River valley blocked the main stream of the river and formed Jingbo Lake. The lake water flows out from two outlets in the north to form a waterfall of 20 to 30 m. in height that is now used for power generation.

The Lesser Hinggan Mountains with their lower average altitude have an underdeveloped vertical zonation. The middle and southern sections are generally 800 m. above sea level. Their main vegetation is mixed coniferous and broadleaf forests, including large tracts of Korean pine forests. Korean pine, a rare species, has huge and straight trunks and its timber is corrosion-resistant softwood. It is good building and furniture timber and can be used for many industrial purposes. This area is one of China's major natural forests and Yichun, in the southern section of the Lesser Hinggan Mountains, is known as China's "forest capital". The northern section of the Lesser Hinggan Mountains generally stands 500 to 700 m. above sea level. It chiefly has deciduous broadleaf forests, the main species being Mongolian oak, Dahurian birch (*Betula dahurica*) and aspen.

The Changbai Mountains are high and have clear vertical zonation. At 500 m. above sea level there are mainly forests of miscellaneous trees. Above 500 m., mixed coniferous and broadleaf forests gradually appear, with the main coniferous trees being Korean pine, Manchurian fir, (*Abies holophylla*), Khingan fir and Yeddo spruce. At 1,000 m. begin evergreen coniferous forests, and farther up the proportion of Korean larch gradually increases. At 1,800 to 2,200 m. there are mixed Korean larch and Ermans birch (*Betula ermani*) forests, and above 2,200 m. there is alpine vegetation. Here the wind is strong, the temperature is low, and only shrubs, herbs, bryophytes and lichens grow. The shrubs are mostly crawling or dwarf ones, such as *Ledum palustre, Dryas octopetala* and *Pedicularis verticillata*. On the peaks above 2,500 m. there are isolated *Sedum elongatum*, showing the grim physical conditions at the tops of these mountains.

The Changbai Mountains are also one of China's major timber felling areas. Among the broadleaf forests grow Chinese magnoliarine, ginseng, wild ginger and other precious medicinal plants. Furthermore, other products are cultivated here, such as tussak silk, mushrooms, Jew's-ear, ginseng (artificially grown), and herds of deer.

Another characteristic of this subregion is that the wide valleys in the mountains, the wide areas of fertile black soil in the lower part of the sunny slopes and terraces, and the meadows and marshes of the lower valleys are all fit for agriculture. In particular, most of the Heilong valley plain in the Aihui area at the eastern foot of the Lesser Hinggan Mountains has been reclaimed. This area is 50 to 100 m. above sea level and has black soil and *baijiang* soil. The latitudes of this subregion are rather far to the north. Huma (51°43′ N.) has a short summer of only 10 days, but the July average temperature is above 20°C. and the highest temperature exceeds 30°C. Moreover, the length of daylight is long (in July it is 292.7 hours at Huma compared with 212.3 hours at Shanghai), which can compensate for the insufficient temperature in facilitating crop growth. Therefore rice can be grown in Huma, and the Yanbian Korean Autonomous Prefecture in this subregion is one of the important rice producing areas of northern China.

The eastern part of this subregion is a vast marsh area known as the Sanjiang Plain. It has an area of 50,000 sq. km. and is the location for the confluence of the Heilong, Songhua and Wusuli rivers. Geologically this is a rift area. At the end of the Tertiary period a large-scale subsidence and accumulation process began here. The accumulated material is now more than 1,000 m. thick, forming the flat plain. Under the Sanjiang Plain are thick layers of clay. Poor drainage on the surface has resulted in the wide distribution of marshes. Many marshy rivers meander across the wide plain without any obvious river course. The Wanda Mountains stretching across the Sanjiang Plain run in a northeast-southwest direction. They are gentle low hills about 500 m. above sea level. There are also a small number of isolated low mountains and broken hills, with a relative height of 20 m., on the marshy plain.

The Sanjiang Plain forms a distinct area in this subregion. It has a frostless season of 130 days, much like the central part of the Songnen Plain. After Liberation a number of large mechanized farms were set up here. Through drainage, regulation of the soil and water and other measures, the area has become a major marketable grain base for wheat, soybean, maize and rice.

(3) Songnen Plain Subregion

The Songnen Plain is surrounded by mountains on the west, north and east sides. The southern side is bordered by the Lower Liaohe River Plain, and so the area is also often called Songliao Plain. The watershed between the Songhua

and Liaohe rivers is relatively low. The Changling-Gongzhu-
ling area is a north-west-west low highland rising only 200
to 250 m. above sea level. It was formed of alluvial and diluvial materials covered with loess. During the Quaternary
period, the watershed between the Songhua and Liaohe rivers
was in the Faku-Tieling area, about 150 km. south of the present watershed. In the past, the West Liaohe River flowed
northward into the Songhua River, so that on top of the Chang-
ling-Gongzhuling watershed are also distributed earlier alluvial
materials of gravel and sand.

Since the Mesozoic Era the Songnen Plain has experienced
a great deal of subsidence that has resulted in very thick deposits. The western part has experienced more subsidence,
and so the present position of the main stream of the Nenjiang
River is on the western side of the plain. The geomorphical
structure of the Songnen Plain is basically shaped in three
concentric circles. (a) The peripheral circle is piedmont diluvial and alluvial aprons, which have been turned into hills,
mounds and terraces by recent uplift. With an undulating
land surface covered by thick loess-like sediments this area is
a forest grassland rising 250 to 300 m. above sea level. There
are a number of small volcanoes in the Dedu area at the
western foot of the Lesser Hinggan Mountains in the northeastern part of this subregion. As recently as 1720, the spurting
of the basalt lava blocked up the Baihe River, a tributary of
the Namor River, forming a string of five blocked lakes, called
the Five Joined Lakes. (b) The middle circle is the flat alluvial
plains of the Songhua and Nenjiang rivers, an area of meadows
and grassland rising 200 m. above sea level. (c) The inner circle
rises 150 m. above sea level, with a low-lying land surface that
is dotted with marshes and small lakes. The Daqing oilfield
in this area includes a number of closed, semi-salt water lakes.
Owing to the distance from the sea, the low-lying terrain and
poor water conditions, this area has become a semi-arid grassland.

There is not as much precipitation in the Songnen Plain

as there is in the Eastern Mountains.   Here the rainfall is between 400 to 600 mm., and it is concentrated in summer.   Inundation at this time expands the Nenjiang River to a width of a dozen kilometres or so near Qiqihar.   In winter, owing to dry and bitterly cold climate, the rivers freeze over, the ground also freezes and there is little evaporation.   The east bank of the lower reaches of the Nenjiang River is extremely low-lying and many marshes are formed after rainfall.   This area is called the Anda closed drainage area.

There is no clear geomorphical boundary between the southern part of the Songnen Plain and the North China Region or between the western part of the plain and the Inner Mongolian Region, and so the boundary in both cases is formed by climate.   The boundary between the southern part of the Songnen Plain and the North China Region is one of an accumulated temperature of 3,000°C.   This is of great significance in physical geography since it is the boundary between the area that produces one crop a year and the one that produces three crops in two years.   Both Changchun in the southern part of the Songnen Plain and Siping in the northern part of the Liaohe Plain (south of the watershed of the Songhua and Liaohe rivers) have accumulated temperatures of 2,700°C., which is similar to that of Harbin.   But in the Shenyang area the accumulated temperature exceeds 3,200°C.   This is why we take the now abandoned Faku-Tieling watershed of the Songhua and Liaohe rivers, north of Shenyang, as the boundary line between the Northeast Region and the North China Region. Here the Songnen Plain subregion also includes the northern part of the Laohe Plain.

The demarcation line between the western part of the Songnen Plain and the Inner Mongolian Region is the area of aridity 1.2.   This line is roughly parallel to the railway line from Baicheng to Shuangliao.   To the west of this railway line there are large tracts of sandy land and a great number of crescent dunes.   There is also dark chestnut-sandy soil, and the vegetation has the characteristics of xerophytes. East of the railway are scattered sandy lands and sandy soil of the black soil type. The vegetation here does not have the characteristics of xerophytes. Although climatically the Anda-Daan area in the centre of the Songnen Plain also belongs to the semi-arid zone, it receives an ample supply of water and so most parts of the land are covered with marshes. In recent years wheat has been grown around Anda with good yields. For this reason the area is still included in the Northeast Region. The climate to the south and west of the Songnen Plain changes gradually. Thus the boundaries between the Northeast, North China and Inner Mongolian regions are actually wide transitional zones.

Most parts of the Songnen Plain have appropriate climate and fertile soil. They have, therefore, been opened up to farmland. This is an important commercial grain producing area in China. The foodgrain crops are mainly spring wheat, soybeans, maize, sorghum, millet and some early-ripening rice. The other crops are mainly sugar beets and flax. There is little wasteland suitable for reclamation in the central and southern parts of the Songnen Plain since these areas have a long history of cultivation. The northern part of the plain was only opened in a later period, and so part of the wasteland there can still be reclaimed.

3. Transformation and Utilization of the Natural Environment

(1) Establishment of a Commodity Grain Base

Heilongjiang Province has recently become a key reclamation area as well as the largest marketable grain base in the country. The province has large tracts of reclaimable land that could be put to use with the appropriate coordination of water and heat resources, as well as fertile soil.

The Northeast Region as a whole has rich climatic resources. Despite its severe cold in winter, it has a higher temperature in summer in comparison with the marine climatic areas of the same latitudes in western Europe. Take Huma for instance. Although this city has a higher latitude (51°43′ N.) than Paris or London, its average temperature in July is greater than it is in the two European cities. The abundant heat and ample water resources of the Northeast Region have created favourable conditions for growing one high-yield crop each year. However, as the growing period is short, the harvest is greatly reduced in years when the frost period comes ten days earlier than usual. The time of the arrival or retreat of the monsoon changes from year to year, and so the length of the frostless period is quite unstable. This being the case, research on early ripening and cold-resistant plant species is of particular importance to the growing of high-yield crops in this region.

This region has vast expanses of marshland with flat terrain and fertile soil which can be opened to agricultural production. In the Sanjiang Plain, for instance, 1.3 million hectares of land have been reclaimed, but there are still about 2 million hectares of wasteland to be developed. Thus, research into the transformation and utilization of marshes is of great significance.

The main defects of marshes are excessive water, low temperature and the uneven distribution of nutrients. The utilization and transformation of marshes needs to begin with water drainage in order to improve the air-containing and hydrological conditions in the soil to raise the soil temperature. In this respect, a number of effective measures have been put into practice in recent years.

The marshes on the Sanjiang Plain developed mainly because there is a clay layer on the underlying surface that precludes smooth drainage. Therefore, in addition to digging canals and ditches to drain the water, wells must be dug to penetrate the clay layer and drain surface water. Furthermore, incorporating earth and sand to improve the peat soil and turning over the soil to expose it to the sun are measures that aid in the development of arable land. Peat soil has a high organic content and soft texture, but few quick-acting nutrients. Thus spreading earth to incorporate it into the peat soil is a most effective means of changing it into arable land. After five to seven years, the output from land thus improved can reach that of ordinary paddy fields.

(2) Regeneration of Forest Resources

Before Liberation, random timber felling caused havoc in the forests in northeast China. It created a number of waste mountains. And the frequent occurrence of forest fires, as well as water and soil erosion, also damaged forest resources. After Liberation, planned felling was combined with forest regeneration and protection against fires. However, with the development of the timber industry, the problem of forest regeneration has taken on increasing importance in this Northeast Region, the largest base for timber resources in China. This afforestation is conducted by selecting different tree species to fit different land conditions. For instance, Dahurian larch and Manchurian ash can be grown in humid valleys; Korean pine, Siberian spruce (*Picea obovata*), Dahurian larch and Manchurian walnut in valleys with good drainage conditions; Korean pine, yeddo spruce and Amur linden (*Tilia amurensis*) on humid slopes; and Mongolian pine and mono maple (*Acer mono*) on dry steep slopes. After drainage, marshland can be used to grow Dahurian larch, Korean pine and Manchurian ash.

Chapter VIII

THE NORTH CHINA REGION

The North China Region lies between Latitude 32° and 42° N., and is mostly in the warm-temperate zone of eastern China. In the north, it borders the Northeast Region and the Inner Mongolian Region roughly along the cumulative temperature isopleth of 3,000°C. active temperature. In the west, the border extends from Qingtong Gorge of the Huanghe River to Wuxiaoling Mountain and then along the eastern base of the Qilian Mountains, west of the Taohe River, down to the Bailong River. The southern boundary lies along the northern base of the Qinling Mountains, passes through Funiu Mountain and follows the Huaihe River all the way east to the Yellow Sea. The region spans more than 20 degrees of longitude from west to east. Apart from the latitudinal variations, it shows marked longitudinal differences. The region occupies an area of one million sq. km., accounting for about 10 per cent of the nation's total area.

The Qinling Mountains are an obvious physical boundary between north and central China. They not only form one of the major divides between the Huanghe and Changjiang River basins, but they also prevent the passage of the southeast monsoons in summer. Areas to the north of the Qinling Mountains are insufficient in water and have an aridity exceeding 1.0. For example, Xi'an has an annual precipitation of only 557 mm., whereas Hanzhong, south of the Qinling Mountains, enjoys 841 mm. of rainfall per year. The amount of humidity also varies greatly in the two places. And this affects plant growth and soil development.

The North China Region was the cultural centre of ancient China. Feudal dynasties entrenched themselves in this area and launched large-scale land reclamation projects that brought about tremendous changes in the physical environment. Under the rule of the Kuomintang and during Japanese occupation, the natural environment was disastrously plundered. After Liberation, the people in this region mounted a tenacious struggle to conquer floods, waterlogging, sand storms, salinization and alkalinization, soil erosion and other natural disasters. They accumulated a wealth of experience in transforming the physical environment of north China on a large scale.

1. Warm-Temperate Semi-Humid to Semi-Arid Loess Landscape

(1) Distribution and Formation of Loess

The most distinguishing geographical feature in the North China Region is the extensive distribution of loess and loess-like deposits. Loess is a term that refers to yellowish silt deposits with high-porosity vertical joints and rich carbonates. Such deposits are distributed widely throughout Shanxi, Shaanxi and Gansu provinces, to form the Loess Plateau. Due to relocation, loess-like deposits are yellowish silt deposits with bedding, sand and gravel, which are distributed on old diluvial plains, old alluvial plains and modern terraces. Such loess-like deposits are a common sight on the North China Plain and on the Liaohe Plain.

According to statistics compiled by the Geological Institute of the Chinese Academy of Sciences, the loess regions in China occupy 440,000 sq. km., and the areas of loess-like deposits come to 190,000 sq. km. They are basically distributed north of the Qinling, Qilian and Kunlun mountains (Fig. 18). The most concentrated loess region is in the middle reaches of the Huanghe River, an area called Loess Plateau, which

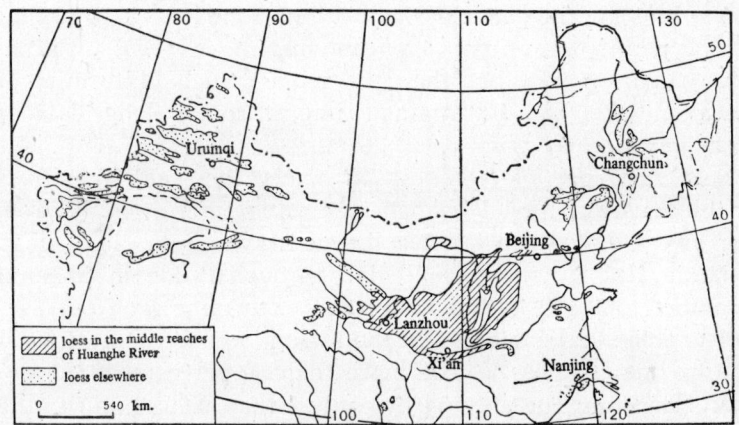

Fig. 18 Distribution of Loess in China

roughly starts from the Great Wall in the north, extends to the Qinling Mountains in the south, goes to Riyue Mountain in the west and to the Taihang Mountains in the east. The Loess Plateau covers an area of about 300,000 sq. km. Within these limits, the loess forms a continuous overburden, mostly 100 to 200 m. thick. The elevation of loess distribution can reach as high as 3,000 m. above sea level on mountain slopes, such as the summits of Liupan and Lüliang mountains. The loess layer on the Loess Plateau is composed of two parts: an upper part with buff colour and soft texture called Malan loess, which originated in the Late Pleistocene Epoch; and a lower part with red bands, called red loess, which originated in the Middle or Early Pleistocene.

In the past there were several hypotheses as to the source of the loess. But in recent years, a host of research data testifies to the fact that the loess on the Loess Plateau (including Malan loess and red loess) is chiefly the product of wind.

1) The particle composition of the loess is highly homogeneous, chiefly coarse silt (grain size 0.05 to 0.01 mm.) and little coarse or fine sand (larger than 0.1 mm.). On the vast

Loess Plateau, the particle composition of the loess is so similar that it points to a unitary agent moving the material, an agent that can be none other than the wind. Such uniformity of loess material can be attained only through long-distance transportation by wind.

2)   The particle composition of the loess also manifests an obvious directional change, becoming finer roughly from northwest to southeast. If a line is drawn from Haiyuan in Ningxia Hui Autonomous Region through Suide in Shaanxi Province to Jingle in Shanxi Province, the fine sand particles (0.1 to 0.05 mm.) contained in the Malan loess to the northwest of this line compose a little more than 30 per cent of the deposits, whereas the clay particles (less than 0.005 mm.) to the southeast of this line exceed 15 per cent. This change in loess particle composition shows that the loess was blown here from the vast desert area in the northwest by northwesterly winds, and that, owing to the gradual weakening of the wind from northwest to southeast, the particle composition tends to become finer in this direction.

3)   The mineral composition of the loess is highly uniform, both in its components and in its distribution. But the underlying bedrock varies greatly. This also shows that the loess material is not a local product, but has been transported from far away by the wind.

The above facts prove that the loess on the Loess Plateau is a product of the wind. Of course, after the loess has accumulated, flowing water may remove it from higher places of deposit to lower ones.

Loess-like deposits are generally distributed in lowlying locations. Lithologically there is a certain change of phase from watershed to river valley, sandwiched by gravel deposits. This shows that such deposits were formed under the action of flowing water. For instance, along big rivers on the Northeast Plain and the North China Plain, there are natural dykes of coarse silt near the banks that were formed by flooding because of the large amount of silt and loess carried in the river water. In the depression on both sides of these dykes are deposits of loess-like material.

(2) Influence of Loess on the Landscape

1) The loess landform has its own peculiar features and process of development. The chief geomorphical feature of the Loess Plateau is the existence of loess *yuan* (flat highlands) and loess hills. A loess *yuan* is the surface of a plateau accumulated by loess, which is flat with a gradient of less than one degree, and marked slopes only at its edges. The Dongzhi *yuan* in the middle reaches of the Jinghe River and the Luochuan *yuan* in the middle reaches of the Luohe River are among the larger loess highlands. Loess hills may be divided into two types according to their shape: long-shaped ones are called *liang* (elongated ridges) and oblong or spherical ones are called *mao* (knolls). They have small tops but large slopes, with 10 to 35 degrees of gradient.

At present, the surface of the vast loess *liang* and *mao* area is disintegrated by many gullies. The heads of these gullies continue to stretch upwards, nibbling away at the *yuan*, *liang* and *mao*. A *yuan* gradually becomes a *liang*, and a *liang* gradually becomes a *mao* owing to the gully erosion.

Since loess has vertical joints, the gully slopes are often steep, forming vertical cliffs. Loess particles are cemented together by calcium, but groundwater carries away the soluble salts, which gives rise to sinkholes and causes the collapse of the earth, thus facilitating the extension of the gully heads.

On the Northeast Plain and the North China Plain, the loess is mostly distributed on piedmont plains, marginal low mountains or medium mountains, and it is not very thick. Owing to water erosion, the surface is also broken and dissected by gullies. Where there are loess-like deposits the surface is flat lowland or terrace.

2) Rivers in the loess region carry a tremendous amount of silt. The Huanghe River carries as much as 1,600 million

tons of silt a year past the Shaanxian Station. The Yongding River carries 76 million tons of silt past the Guanting Station, and the Liaohe River carries 47 million tons of silt past the Tieling Station. About 90 per cent of the silt carried by the Huanghe comes from the Loess Plateau. This soil erosion links the Loess Plateau to the North China Plain, making the two parts of an organic whole in terms of physical geography.

Only about 30 per cent of the silt carried by these rivers is estimated to empty into the sea, and the rest is deposited on the plains. Over a long period of time, the Chinese people erected dykes to prevent floods, and a large amount of silt was deposited inside the dykes. This caused the river beds to rise and form above-ground rivers. Since Liberation, the main river course of the Huanghe has been rising at an annual rate of 10 to 20 cm. per year. At present, the river bed is much higher than the flatland along its banks, more than 10 m. in some places. Since the river flows above the ground, no tributary can join it and the dykes often become the "watershed" for the flat fields on both sides of the river course. This results in a peculiar pattern for the drainage network and regional runoff. In the event of torrential rains, the river swells and is prone to overflow the dykes and flood the banks. The silt pours out of the river bed, along with the floodwater, and is deposited on the plains. This gives rise to vast tracts of sandy inundated area. Historical records show that before Liberation the Huanghe overflowed on 1,593 occasions, and changed its course on 26 occasions (Fig. 19). The breaching at Dongwaxiang in 1855 and at Huayuankou in 1938 both resulted in large inundated areas. Only after Liberation was this problem brought under control, and the summer and autumn floods have now passed without causing any damage for several years running.

3) The wide distribution of loess in the North China Region has exerted a profound influence on soil development. First, soil erosion in the Loess Plateau region has greatly altered the natural soil-forming process, and, in some cases, the

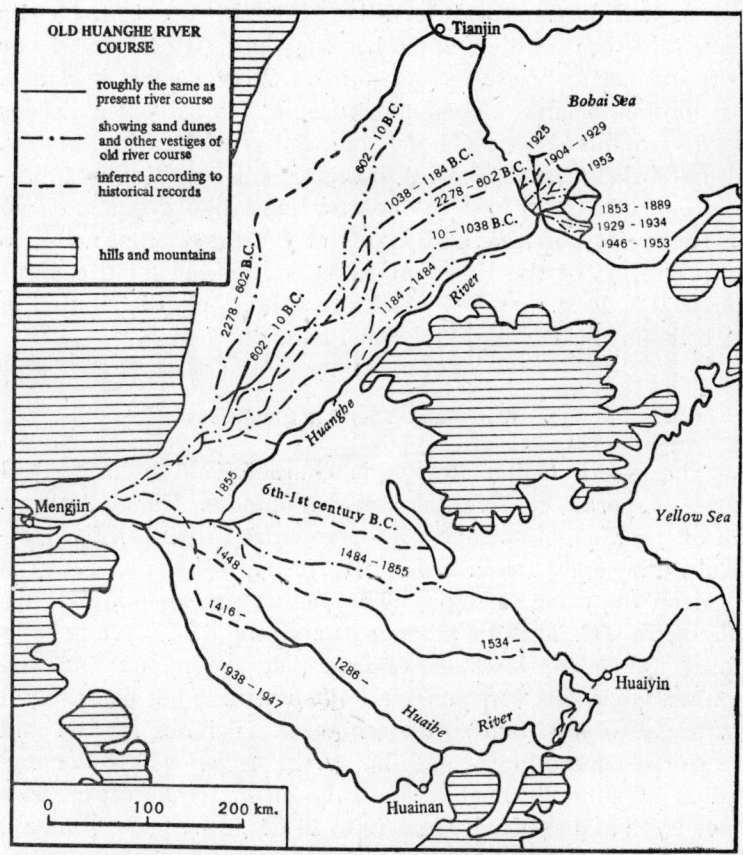

OLD HUANGHE RIVER COURSE

————— roughly the same as present river course

—·—·— showing sand dunes and other vestiges of old river course

—————— inferred according to historical records

hills and mountains

Tianjin

Bobai Sea

602 – 10 B.C.

1038 – 1184 B.C.

2278 – 802 B.C.

10 – 1038 B.C.

1925

1904 – 1929

1953

1853 – 1889
1929 – 1934
1946 – 1953

184 – 1484

River

2278 – 602 B.C.

802 – 10 B.C.

Huangbe

1855

Mengjin

6th–1st century B.C.

1484 – 1855

1448

Yellow Sea

1416 –

1534 –

1938 – 1947

1286 –

Huaiyin

Huaibe   River

0   100   200 km.

Huainan

Fig. 19 Migration of the River at the Lower Reaches of the Huanghe

oil has not been able to develop properly. Second, because loess and loess-like materials are loose sediments, they do not have to undergo weathering in order to grow plants and undergo the soil-forming action. Third, in chemical composition loess contains a large amount of calcium carbonate and some magnesium carbonate so that the calcium content in the loess is very high. Besides, it has rich amounts of potassium, sulphur and phosphorus. Loess thus contains many crop nutrients, and has natural fertility. Fourth, apart from its mechanical composition, loess has high porosity (39 to 54 per cent) and vertical fissures and joints. When soaked in water, it is prone to sink. Thus moisture in the soil easily seeps downward and also rises along the capillaries. In arid climates, salt rises along the capillaries to the topsoil, resulting in salinization. Soils developed in loess or loess-like deposits often form a variety of new carbonates at certain depths owing to the migration of the carbonates, especially carbonate concretion, that is, loess nodules, which are extensively distributed in the soils on the Huang-Huai-Hai Plain.

(3) Water and Thermal Conditions

The North China Region is characterized by a typical warm-temperate continental monsoon climate. Under the control of the Mongolian high pressure centre in winter, the temperature becomes much lower than it is at other places in the world on the same latitude. The January mean temperature falls below 0°C., and the passage of a strong cold wave usually chalks up record lows at various places. In summer, the summer monsoons can penetrate deep within the continental low pressure area, and so the temperature climbs rapidly and the North China Plain and the Weihe River valley become centres of summer heat. The July mean temperature rises above 26°C. and gradually lowers to 24°C. on the Loess Plateau. Influenced by the foehn effect of the descending summer monsoons over the Qinling Mountains, the Weihe River valley receives extremely high temperatures in summer. Xi'an, for example, has an absolute high of 45.2°C.

The North China Region is an important farming centre for China. Judging from the agricultural index for temperatures, the growing period in the year is long and the heat resources are abundant. Because of its large area, the recorded heat varies greatly from place to place, gradually reducing from north of the Huaihe River to the western part of the Loess

Plateau. The agricultural index of temperatures in various places is listed in Table 10.

Table 10.   Stable Duration When Average Daily Temperature
in the North China Region Is Equal to or
Above 0°C., 5°C., 10°C., 15°C.

Area	Stable duration (days) of average daily temperature				Accumulated temperature (°C.)	
	≥0°C.	≥5°C.	≥10°C.	≥15°C.	≥5°C.	≥10°C.
Huaibei-Central Henan Plains	270	239	201	158	4,750-5,000	4,250-4,500
North China Plain, Fenhe-Weihe Valley	254	228	181	145	4,000-4,750	3,750-4,250
Liaodong Peninsula, Liaohe Plain, Northern Hebei Mountains	231	199	163	116	3,500-4,000	3,250-3,750
Loess Plateau	214	174	136	—	<3,500	<3,250

Except in mountains, the thermal regime of the North China Region generally satisfies the needs of crops in their growing periods. But, attention must also be paid to the effect of frost on the crops.

The annual precipitation in the North China Region is less than 800 mm., generally reducing from south to north and from east to west, with the Taiyue Mountains having the greatest amount of precipitation. The distribution of precipitation in the middle reaches of the Huanghe River decreases from the southeast to the northwest, the southeast having about 400 to 600 mm. and the northwest about 400 mm. The amount of precipitation on the Weihe River Plain is between 500 and 700 mm., because the Qinling Mountains act to retard and prevent cold fronts. This is a rainy area in the North China Region, as are the coastal and mountainous areas. The plain area east of Shijiazhuang in central Hebei Province is a relatively rainless area, with less than 500 mm. of precipitation a year. The Xianxian-Shenze-Hengshui area (in the middle reaches of the Ziya River) has even less rain, under 400 mm.

The aridity for most parts of the North China Region is between 1.0 and 1.5, increasing roughly from east to west. It is under 1.0 on the shores of the Liaodong Bay, Jiaozhou Bay and Bohai Sea, and somewhere between 1.25 and 1.5 on the Loess Plateau. The Zhengzhou-Luoyang-Kaifeng area in northern Henan is particularly dry, with an aridity of above 1.5.

The yearly distribution of rainfall is uneven in this region. Spring and autumn witness frequent weather fluctuations, but the air-mass contains little moisture and so cannot produce a large amount of precipitation. The rainfall in spring accounts for about 10 per cent of the year's total. In winter it is entirely controlled by the polar continental air-mass, and snowfall is scarce. Thus over 60 per cent of the precipitation in this region occurs in summer. On the Hebei Plain, the precipitation in summer makes up three-quarters of the year's total, this being the area with the greatest concentration of summer precipitation. Statistics show for most years the North China

Region has no less than 400 to 500 mm. of precipitation during the growing period (April to October). This concentration of rainfall is good for agricultural production.

However, the lack of rainfall in spring leads to frequent spring droughts and poses a threat to the growth of wheat. In spring, the rapid increase in temperature, strong winds, relative low humidity and precipitation variability combine to aggravate the spring droughts, sometimes causing a decrease in the harvest. Torrential rains in summer, strong soil wash, and insufficient effective rainfall all have an effect on farmland improvement and water and soil conservation.

(4) Vegetation and Soils

The long history of farming in the North China Region has greatly altered the properties of natural soils, and natural vegetation has mostly been replaced by cultivated crops. However, what remains of the natural vegetation and soils manifests zonal characteristics of a longitudinal nature. These result from the decrease in water from east to west and appear in this order: humid deciduous broadleaf forest with brown earth zone; semi-humid deciduous broadleaf forest with drab soil zone; semi-humid forest grassland with dark loessial soil zone, and semi-arid steppe with sierozem zone.

1) The humid deciduous broadleaf forest with brown earth zone is distributed on the Liaodong and Jiaodong peninsulas, where there is a warm and humid climate. The deciduous trees here are chiefly Liaodong oak (*Quercus liaotungensis*), mixed with Japanese red pine (*Pinus densiflora*), which sometimes form dominant species. Besides, there are Mongolian oak (*Quercus dentata*) oriental oak (*Q. variabilis*), glandbearing oak (*Q. glandulifera*) and sawtooth oak (*Q. acutissima*). This zone also contains a number of subtropical thermophilous species, such as Chinese elm, Chinese hackberry, Japanese pagodatree, Chinese sumac and other deciduous broadleaf trees; *Lespedeza bicolor* and other shrubs; pueraria thunbergia and

other vines; and *Pteris multifida, Cyrtomium falcatum* and
other ferns.   The soil is mainly developed from weathered
residual gneiss and granite. It is loose in texture and has good
drainage with fine leaching. The soil is low in soluble salts and
so is neutral or slightly acid. Under the deciduous broadleaf
vegetation, organic substances account for about 5 to 8 per cent
of the soil. This zone is a well-known tussah breeding area in
China and also a major apple and pear growing area. The cultivated crops are mainly kaoliang (sorghum), maize, peanuts,
wheat, paddy rice and cotton. The hills in this zone, which have
a thin layer of soil, are the most suitable sites for planting
deciduous fruit trees and toothed oaks.

2)   The semi-humid deciduous broadleaf forest with drab
soil zone includes the North China Plain, northern Hebei mountains, southern part of the Shanxi plateau and Weihe River
valley. Most of the deciduous broadleaf plants are oaks (*Quercus*), which have many species to the east of the Taihang
Mountains.   But the oaks to the west of the mountains are
mainly Liaodong oaks. The needle leaf trees are chiefly Chinese pines (*Pinus tabulaeformis*), oriental arborvitaes (*Biota
orientalis*) and lacebark pines (*Pinus bungeana*). The deciduous
broadleaf trees other than oaks are the northern species,
such as betula, populus, acea and tilia, which form mixed
woods in the low mountains and hills or are scattered on the
plains.   Of the semi-cultivated and cultivated deciduous broadleaf trees, the most common are the ulmus species, Japanese
pagodatree, tree of heaven jujubes, pears, persimmons and
walnuts.   The soil is chiefly formed from various carbonates,
and tends to be calciferous, neutral or slightly alkaline.   But
as a result of leaching, the carbonates often subside markedly
to form obvious caliches in the soil.   This distinguishes drab
soil from brown earth, and reflects the variation in humidity
in the two zones.   The drab soil has a moderate texture, holds
moisture well and is fertile.

3)   The semi-humid forest grassland with dark loessial
soil zone is distributed in the eastern part of the Loess Plateau,

including northern Shanxi, northern Shaanxi and eastern Gansu. Here the elevation is 1,000 to 1,500 m. above sea level, and the temperature is low. For instance, the accumulated temperature at Xifeng, in Gansu, comes to just 2,700°C. The forest grassland is chiefly composed of *Bothriochloa ischaemum, Themeda triandra* and a few other kinds of grasses. Because much of the Loess Plateau is under cultivation, natural vegetation can be found only in isolated sections. On the mountains at about 1,400 m. above sea level are distributed open forests of Liaodong oaks, aps (*Populus davidiana*) Sichuan poplars, Chinese pines and oriental arborvitaes. They are generally low trees, locally called elfin forests. Nanniwan to the southeast of Yan'an was formerly an elfin forest. These forests look like green islets standing in the vast "ocean" of dark loess.

The dark loessial soil, so named because of a thick layer of humus (as deep as 100 cm.), developed under the forest grassland and grassland vegetation. It is classified under the black soil series, together with black soil and chernozem. It is mainly distributed in the flat and lightly eroded loess *yuan* areas and valley terraces. Its parent material, loess, is loose and porous, and exhibits a strong calciferous reaction when a thick soil profile is tested. The soil profile is characterized by a layer of cultivated soil (about 20 cm. thick) greyish brown in colour, under which there is a humus layer and then a layer of carbonate illuvium. Because of the cultivated layer, some people regard dark loessial soil as a grassland soil that has matured through long cultivation. Yet thick as this layer is, its content is not rich, only 1.0 to 1.5 per cent.

4) The semi-arid steppe with sierozem zone is distributed in the western part of the Loess Plateau, roughly including the area to the south of the Huanghe in Ningxia and the section between Lanzhou and Pingliang in Gansu. The natural vegetation belongs to a transition type including both that of grassland and desert steppe. Generally, the desert steppe type occupies the southern slopes of the hills, while the northern

slopes are grassland. The grassland vegetation here is chiefly *Stipa bungeana* and *S. breviflora*, which grows to a height of 20 cm. The desert steppe vegetation here is short grass and semi-shrubs, chiefly *Stipa breviflora* and *Ajania fruticulose*, which grow sparsely to a height of only 10 to 20 cm. Since the Loess Plateau has long been cultivated, the natural vegetation is confined to steep slopes and hill tops. Isolated mountains on the Loess Plateau, such as Xinglong and Maxian mountains, have picea and aps forests because of their high elevation (more than 3,000 m.) and humidity.

The soil, sierozem, is often related to its loess-like parent material and occupies a relatively limited area. It still exhibits the process of humus accumulation and calcification of grassland soils. But, owing to scanty rainfall (generally 400 mm.), the grass is short and sparse and the humus layer is thin and light in colour (light yellowish grey). As a result of weak leaching, the differentiation in the soil profile is not as marked as it is in ordinary grassland soil, with caliche appearing at a depth of between 15 to 30 mm. Sierozem contains few nutrients, and can be used, when properly fertilized, to plant leguminous green manure. Thus, by rotating grain crops with fodder crops, it can be used for both farming and livestock breeding.

There are also large tracts of azonal soils in the North China Region, chiefly meadow soils and solonchaks. The vast alluvial plain areas in the lower reaches of the big rivers are flat and have inadequate drainage. The groundwater generally runs 1.5 to 3.0 m. deep, and it may rise to the surface along capillaries to form a special light meadow soil. With the change of seasons, the groundwater rises and drops frequently and the resulting oxidization and reduction in the soil gives rise to large amounts of cutans and mottling along the soil pores and fractures. The process also leaves fine-grained iron-manganese concretions and lime nodules where the groundwater rises and drops alternately. Most of the light meadow soil area is farmed. Soon after the loessial wash is deposited on the Huanghe-Huaihe-Haihe Plain, it is cultivated and becomes cropped soil (dry cultivated soil), called "yellow *chao* soil". It has a uniform texture, is slightly alkaline to alkaline and contains 1 to 2 per cent of organic substances. Thus it is quite fertile and widely adaptable to growing various crops.

As the region has an arid climate, salinized soil and saline soil are widely distributed where the groundwater is shallow and the ascending of capillary action is predominant. This is the case in the depression between rivers on the North China Plain, on both banks of the Huanghe dykes and in coastal areas. The salt in the soil of the North China Plain tends to accumulate through evaporation. The shallower the groundwater, the more serious is the salinization of the soil. The coastal saline soil, distributed along the Bohai shore, is formed as a result of soaking by sea water.

2. Regional Differentiation of the Natural Landscape

The natural landscape of the North China Region is rather varied. Thermally, the plains and hills in the eastern portion belong to the warm-temperate zone, but much of the Loess Plateau (including areas to the northwest of the Taiyuan-Yan'an-Pingliang line) belongs to the temperate zone and can only grow one crop a year. This is because of the high elevation of the Loess Plateau and the fact that the accumulated temperature there is less than 3,000°C. This plateau occupies a vast area (at least 200,000 sq. km.). Like the Yunnan Plateau, this plateau does not merely have vertical zonation, but it has horizontal zonation as well.

The water conditions vary greatly in this region. It includes a humid area, with an aridity of less than 1; a semi-humid area with an aridity of 1.0 to 1.25, and other areas, with aridities of 1.25 to 1.5. Some belong to the dry semi-humid category and others to the semi-arid category. Judging from investigations of the natural vegetation and soils, most sections of the North China Region should fall into the semi-humid classification.

It is thus quite difficult to delineate the boundaries of the North China Region in strict accordance with the values of accumulated temperature or aridity. Because this region has been subject to the extensive influences of human activity, there is little natural vegetation left, and the three longitudinal zones of humid forest, semi-humid forest grassland and semi-arid steppe are not markedly reflected on the landscape. On the other hand, the wide distribution of loess, an azonal factor, plays a significant role in the formation of the landscape in the North China Region. Enormous gully erosion on the Loess Plateau is closely related to the river silt and sediment on the plains in the lower reaches of the Huanghe River, and the water and soil conservation in the middle reaches of the Huanghe is inter-related to the control of drought, waterlogging and alkalinization on the plains. Thus the whole Loess Plateau comes under the category of the North China Region, and its western portion includes the areas to the south of Wuxiaoling Mountain and to the east of Riyue Mountain in Qinghai Province.

The vicinity of Lanzhou is in part of the plateau where the loess is upwards of 200 m. thick. The Huangshui River valley around Xining is a dry farming region of loess, which is markedly different from the Qinghai-Tibetan Plateau steppe pastoral region to the west of Riyue Mountain, both in natural landscape and agricultural use. The Minxian-Lintao area, in southwestern Gansu, is also a dry farming region of loess. It is vastly different from the livestock breeding region in the Xiahe-Zuoni area to its west, the two being divided by the contour line marking 3,000 m. above sea level. The valley of the Bailong River, a tributary of the Jialing River, belongs to the Central China Region, but the section beyond the watershed (Dieshan Mountain) between the Bailong and the Taohe rivers up to Minxian belongs to the Loess Plateau.

The northern boundary of the North China Region coincides with the topographical line on the southern rim of the Inner Mongolian Plateau, that is, it includes the areas south of Zhangjiakou. The agricultural differences between Bashang and Baxia, both in Hebei Province, have since ancient times provided an obvious natural boundary. The southern rim of the Inner Mongolian Plateau is locally called "Batou" and the elevation difference between its upper part (Bashang) and lower part (Baxia) is more than 700 m. The thermal difference is also great. Zhangbei on Bashang has a cumulative temperature of 2,140°C. and belongs to the temperate zone, whereas Zhangjiakou at Baxia has a cumulative temperature of 3,300°C. and belongs to the warm-temperate zone. The Bashang area has an elevation of 1,300 to 1,600 m. above sea level, with only 90 to 100 frost-free days. It is a steppe with chestnut soil region, entirely different from the North China Region. Maize, sorghum and paddy rice can grow at Baxia, but not on Bashang.

The North China Region is vast in area, and can be divided into the following physical regions in accordance with variations in the thermal, water, and geomorphical conditions, and variations in agricultural use:

II_A Liaodong Peninsula and Jiaodong Peninsula Subregion

II_B North China Plain Subregion

II_{B1} Lower Liaohe River Plain Area

II_{B2} Huanghe-Huaihe-Haihe River Plains Area

II_{B3} Northern Hebei Mountains Area

II_{B4} Central Shandong Mountains Area

II_C Loess Plateau Subregion

II_{C1} Shanxi Plateau Area

II_{C2} Shaanxi-Eastern Gansu Plateau Area

II_{C3} Western Gansu Plateau Area

(1) Liaodong Peninsula and Jiaodong Peninsula Subregion

Though separated by the Bohai Sea, the Liaodong and Jiaodong peninsulas are similar in geological structure and climatic humidity, with an aridity of less than or equal to 1.0. Thus they are combined to make one subregion.

The topography in this subregion is chiefly that of rolling hills, mostly below 500 m. in elevation, and the plains are quite narrow. The hills often extend into the sea, forming a zigzag coast and giving rise to deep-water harbours, such as Dalian and Qingdao. The Qianshan Mountains form the backbone of the Liaodong Peninsula, their peaks rising more than 1,000 m. above sea level. Granite on the Jiaodong Peninsula forms a number of high ridges, such as Laoshan Mountain near Qingdao (1,130 m.).

Thanks to its seaside geographical location, this subregion enjoys more favourable water and heat conditions than do the Liaohe and North China plains, and it experiences a relatively small temperature variation between winter and summer. In January the average temperature is above 0°C.; in July, around 25°C., and the frost-free period lasts from 165 to 250 days. The coast of the southern part of the Jiaodong Peninsula has the warmest climate in the North China Region. The cumulative temperature there may reach 3,900°C., and the annual precipitation is between 600 and 700 mm. The rainfall even reaches more than 800 mm. on the windward eastern side of the Liaodong Peninsula and 1,000 mm. in the isolated windward mountainous areas of the southern Jiaodong Peninsula. About 85 per cent of the annual rainfall occurs during the period when the average daily temperature is equal to or above 10°C. With an aridity equal to or less than 1.0, this subregion is the most humid portion of the North China Region. Moreover, owing to the small precipitation variability and high relative humidity (upwards of 70 per cent at Dalian and Qingdao), the spring drought is not serious. This is an important difference between this and other subregions in the North China Region.

The vegetation and soils also reflect the characteristic humidity of this subregion. Very little of the natural vegetation has been preserved, owing to agricultural development in this area over thousands of years. Only in the Qianshan Mountains are there some well-preserved forests, chiefly of Mukden pine (*Pinus tabulaeformis var. mukdensis*) in places of higher elevation and Liaodong oak in places of lower elevation. The forests on Laoshan Mountain are of Japanese red pine at higher elevations; mixed woods of oak, elm, chinaberry and Japanese red pine at lower elevations, and deciduous broadleaf trees in the foothills and river valleys. This suggests that the original natural vegetation in this subregion would have been warm-temperate deciduous broadleaf forests, dominated by the oaks and pines. Chief among these pines is Japanese red pine. Mukden pine can only be found in the Liaodong area, and not in the Jiaodong areas, whereas pony-tail pine is seen in the Jiaodong area only, and not in the Liaodong area. This reflects the thermal differences between the Liaodong and Jiaodong peninsulas.

The soil in this subregion is brown earth, also called brown forest soil. Because it has a long warm season and the land is not deep-frozen in winter, the soil clayization is stronger than in the temperate humid region of northeast China. Soluble salts and carbonates are leached from the soil to form an illuvial clay layer (B horizon). Owing to the warm and humid climate, bacterial action may continue throughout the year, decomposing and destroying most of the organic substances so that the brown earth doesn't contain much humus.

Two crops can ripen in the year in this subregion. The chief farming system presently used here is intercropping of winter wheat and soy beans or maize. Fruit growing is broadly developed, with pears, apples and grapes as the most important varieties. The apple trees grow mainly on hill slopes, concentrated near Yantai, Fushan and Mouping in the northern Jiaodong Peninsula, and near Fuxian and Gaixian in the western Liaodong Peninsula. The main pear production centre is at Laiyang on Jiaodong Peninsula. Breeding of tussah with the leaves of toothed oaks is also done in this subregion.

(2) North China Plain Subregion

This vast plain includes the Northern Hebei Mountains —
composed of mountains in northern Hebei, western Liaoning
and the southeastern part of the Inner Mongolian Autonomous
Region — as well as the Central Shandong Mountains. It can
be divided into four areas: the Lower Liaohe River Plain, the
Huanghe-Huaihe-Haihe River Plain, the Northern Hebei
Mountains, and the Central Shandong Mountains.

Climatically, the North China Plain Subregion is in the
warm-temperate semi-humid zone. Compared with the Liaodong and Jiaodong Peninsulas Subregion, it has a higher aridity, greater precipitation variability, more serious spring
drought and shorter frost-free period. Three crops are reaped
in two years in most parts of this subregion. The natural vegetation is mesophytic deciduous broadleaf forests and xerophytic deciduous broadleaf forests, and the underlying soil is drab
soil. As a result of leaching, the carbonates in the soil settle
downward to form a caliche in the soil profile.

Geomorphologically, the North China Plain adjoins the
Changjiang and Huaihe Lower Reaches Plain in northern Anhui
and Jiangsu in the southeast. Here the North China Region is
more or less separated from the Central China Region by the
southern bank of the Huaihe River and the abandoned Huanghe
River course. The boundary between these two regions roughly
coincides with the isometric line of 4,500°C. cumulative temperature, January mean temperature of 0°C., annual precipitation of 900 mm. and aridity of 1.0.

The physiographical features of the four areas of this
subregion are:

1)   Lower Liaohe River Plain. This is separated from the
Huanghe-Huaihe-Haihe River Plains area at Shanhaiguan Pass.
Because this area also belongs to the warm-temperate zone,
it is delineated as a physical area of this subregion. The plain
belongs to the Bohai depression in geological structure, and is
gradually subsiding, causing the watershed between the

Songhua and the Liaohe rivers to move northward. The present watershed has already moved about 150 kilometres to the north of its original site (the Faku-Tieling area) since this subsidence began.

Meander bends are well developed and accumulation is extensive in the lower reaches of the Liaohe River, where there are many bars in the shifting river course. The Panjin Prefecture on the lower reaches of the Liaohe used to suffer waterlogging nine out of ten years, earning it the name "Southern Wilderness in the Northeast". Since 1958, however, the area has become a paddy rice producer and a marketable grain base thanks to the efforts in controlling floods and developing irrigation.

2) Huanghe-Huaihe-Haihe River Plain. This is one of China's major farming areas and population centres. Beijing, the capital of the People's Republic of China, lies in this region. The northern part is the Haihe Plain; the central part, the Huanghe Plain; and the southern part, the Huaihe Plain. There have been frequent changes in the course of the Huanghe over the centuries, and this river once flowed as far north as Tianjin and as far south as Huaiyin. Its alluvial deposit is therefore distributed throughout most parts of the Huanghe-Huaihe-Haihe Plain area.

The area is relatively flat in relief, generally below 50 m. above sea level. But its micro-geomorphical structure is rather complex. And with the micro-geomorphical changes, the surface materials, chemical composition of groundwater, soil, vegetation and agriculture change accordingly. The topography of the plain inclines mainly from west and southwest to east and northeast, and the natural landscape is correspondingly divided into three landscape sections: piedmont diluvial-alluvial fan plain, alluvial plain, and coastal plain. The landscape spreads in semi-circles from the foothills to the sea (Fig. 20 and 21).

Piedmont Diluvial-Alluvial Plain. This is 30 to 100 m. above sea level, has a 1/200 to 1/2,000 gradient, good drainage,

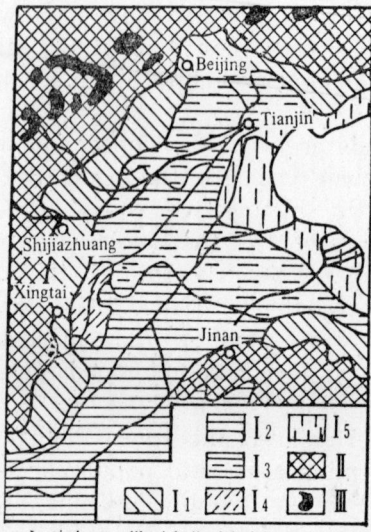

I₁ piedmont diluvial-alluvial plain

I₂ alluvial plain

I₃ poorly-drained low alluvial plain

I₄ depression with surface waterlogging

I₅ coastal saline low land

II low mountains with oak and Chinese pine
   forests and shrubs as well as drab soil

III middle mountains with vertical structure

**Fig. 20 Landscape Types on the North China
Plain and Adjacent Mountains**

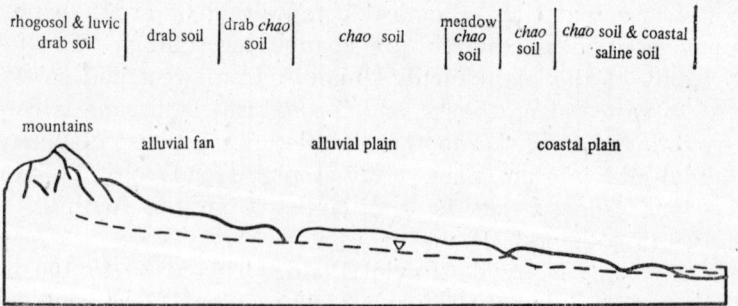

Fig. 21 Cross Section of Soil on the North China Plain

groundwater mineralization of less than one g/l, fine-quality and abundant water. The soil is free from salinization or alkalinization. For example, Beijing is on the alluvial plain of the Yongding River, the top of which is in the vicinity of Shijingshan and which expands and inclines towards the east, northeast and southeast. At present, Beijing is using the rich underground water resources to supply the needs of the urban population as well as the needs of industry and agriculture.

Alluvial Plain. This is mostly below 50 m. above sea level and has about a 1/5,000 to 1/10,000 gradient. Its micro-landform is quite complex, having many elongate mounds with gentle slopes and relative heights of 1 to 5 m. The mounds are often flanked by banded sand dunes and are always interlaced with depressions. Between the depressions and the mounds there is a slightly inclined flatland (locally called "secondary slope land"). In accord with the changes in the micro-landform, the deposits also change in a regular pattern. The deposits on the gentle mounds are mostly sandy, those in the depressions are clay, and those on the slightly inclined flatland are silt sandwiched in with clay. The quality of the ground-water changes accordingly too. The groundwater in the mounds is mostly freshwater, and that in the depressions is highly mineralized, always reaching 2 to 5 g/l. Along the natural dykes and old river beds and mounds, the soil is generally light in texture, easy to cultivate, free of salt and highly fertile. In the clayey shallow depressions, owing to seasonal water-logging, the soil is locally gleized and salinized to varying degrees. On the "secondary slope land", there is salinized yellow *chao* soil if the groundwater is high because of the existence of a clay layer. These micro-geomorphical units present obvious differences in the utilization of agriculture owing to the variations in soil texture and groundwater. In Fengqiu County, Henan Province, for instance, two crops can ripen in one year on the mounds and three crops in two years on the slightly salinized *chao* soil of the "secondary slope land". Salt-enduring *Tamarix chinensis* and *Kochia scoparia* can be planted in the heavily salinized depressions, whereas only one crop, peanuts or soy beans, can ripen in a year on the sandy land formed by the abandoned river bed of the Huanghe.

The elongated mounds with gentle slopes are the old channels of the Huanghe and Haihe rivers. These rivers carried much silt that raised their river beds rapidly and formed a "hanging river" that stood above the surface of the flatland on both banks. At present, the channel of the Huanghe already rises several to a dozen metres higher than the land surface on its banks. This is also true with the Zhanghe River, whose bed stands 3 to 4 m. above the land outside its dykes. Because of frequent changes in the channels of the Huanghe, the Zhanghe and the Hutuo, this area has overlapping and intersecting sections of abandoned channels, most of which have become elongated gentle mounds. We see this in the Heilonggang Prefecture in southern Hebei, where the abandoned channels total more than 12,000 sq. km., accounting for nearly 1/3 of the prefecture's area. On these elevated old river beds and at the places of modern breaching of huge rivers, the deposits are mostly fine sand which, when windblown, often forms sand dunes. This is how the huge groups of sand dunes, rising as high as 30 m., on the southern bank of the Huanghe in the Zhengzhou-Kaifeng area were formed.

On the plain are also many lakes, such as the lake group centred around Baiyang Lake in central Hebei and the Dongping-Nansi Lake group in western Shandong.

Coastal Plain. This is the section that extends up to the contour line of 4 m. in the west and meets the Bohai Sea in the east. The surface gradient is less than 1/10,000. Its formation was influenced by marine deposition in addition to fluvial alluviation. The surface component material is chiefly clay and the groundwater highly mineralized, reaching 20 g/l. The soil is solonchak, the topsoil containing 1 to 3 per cent salt, chiefly chlorides. The coastal saline area along the Bohai Sea may reach upwards of 60 km. at its widest point. In this section grow halophytes and salt-enduring plants, mainly

Aeluropus littoralis and *Suaeda glauca,* occasionally mixed with halophilous shrubs such as *Tamarix chinensis* and *Nitraria schoberi.* This area includes the Haihe River Delta and the Huanghe River Delta. The present Huanghe River Delta, covering an area of 5,400 sq. km., was formed in 1855 after the Huanghe breached its channel at Tongwaxiang and entered the old channel of the Daqing River to empty into Bohai Sea. Because the Huanghe carries much silt into the sea (1,170 million tons of silt passes Lijin each year), silt accumulates at the river mouth rapidly and the sand spit is extending into the sea at an annual rate of some 3 km.

3) Northern Hebei Mountains. These include the Yanshan Mountains and the mountains in western Liaoning, with an elevation exceeding 1,000 m. above sea level at their highest point. They run mostly in an west–east or northeast direction. Within these mountains are some rift basins, such as Miyun and Huailai basins. The end of the Yanshan Mountains protrudes into Bohai Sea. The eastern section of the Great Wall, totalling 6,700 km., was erected to take advantage of the topography of these Northern Hebei Mountains. The wall starts in the east at Shanhaiguan Pass by the Bohai Sea. In the Qianan, Zunhua and Xinglong area to the west, Sinian hard quartzite forms a high ridge that extends in an west–east direction and along which was built a section of the Great Wall. The Luanhe River and its tributaries dissect this ridge to form the Xifengkou, Dongjiakou and other gateways. To the northwest of Beijing, the Great Wall rises against the Yanshan Mountains and snakes along the contour of the rolling mountain ridges, presenting an awesome view. The upper reaches of the Chaobai and Yongding rivers flow past the Miyun and Huailai basins in the interior of the Yanshan Mountains, where two reservoirs, Miyun and Guanting, have been built to store and supply water for Beijing and for industrial and farm use.

The Northern Hebei Mountains are an enormous inclined surface between the Inner Mongolian Plateau and the North

China Plain. Some high sections of this area show obvious
vertical zones of vegetation. For instance, on Xiaowutai
Mountain (2,870 m. above sea level) to the northwest of Beijing the vegetation zones are as follows: below 1,600 m. —
deciduous broadleaf forests, mainly oaks, birches and lindens;
1,600 to 2,000 m. — spruce forests, and also Wilson spruce
(*Picea wilsonii*) and Khingan fir; 2,000 to 2,500 m. — forests
of Prince Rupprecht larch (*Larix principis-rupprechtii*); above
2,500 m., already exceeding the upper limit of tree distribution — subalpine meadows, chiefly short grasses.

4) Central Shandong Mountains. These include Taishan
Mountain, Yishan Mountains and Mengshan Mountains, with
the highest peaks surpassing 1,000 m. above sea level. Taishan
Mountain, for instance, stands 1,524 metres above sea level,
the highest peak on the North China Plain. The rest of the
mountains are generally 500 to 600 m. above sea level. They
are mostly composed of pre-Sinian metamorphic rock covered
by Cambrian-Ordovician limestone. In southern Shandong, the
limestone is distributed almost horizontally on the mountain
tops, forming the steep, flat-topped "mesa" landforms. The
limestone region abounds in karst limestone springs, the most
famous of which is the Baotu group in Jinan, known as a
"city of springs".

The climatic conditions in the Central Shandong Mountains are roughly the same as they are on the Jiaodong Peninsula, but there is an occasional drought in spring. The soil
here is virtually free from waterlogging and salinization,
which is different from the situation in the Huanghe-Huaihe-
Haihe Plain area. The natural vegetation is chiefly pines and
oaks. The bio-habitat on the northern slopes is more humid
and there are better forests than on the dry southern slopes
where there is sparse vegetation. On the Taishan, Yishan and
Mengshan mountains there are forests of Chinese pine and
mixed forests of Chinese pine and oaks. Oak trees are also
scattered on the hills and lower sections of the mountains.

(3) Loess Plateau Subregion

The varying terrain and loess overburden results in marked variations of landscape within this subregion, which may be divided into three areas: the Shanxi Plateau, the Northern Shaanxi-Eastern Gansu Plateau and the Western Gansu Plateau. In Shanxi and northern Shaanxi, this subregion adjoins the Inner Mongolian Region roughly along the Great Wall, the boundary of which is equivalent to the isopleth of 3,000°C. cumulative temperature and more than 1.5 aridity. The subregion is mostly between 1.25 and 1.5 in aridity, having a semi-humid climate with a dry tendency.

1) Shanxi Plateau. This area includes the land between the Luliang and Taihang Mountains. Instead of being a flat plateau, it is a highland composed of a series of folded block mountains and rift basins. It is called a plateau because it has steep slopes on the eastern and southern flanks. The mountains run mostly in a north-northeast direction, and some of them have peaks that exceed 2,000 m. above sea level in height. Bedrock is exposed on the upper part of these mountains, while the lower sections are covered by loess. But on the 2,500-metre summit of Lüliang Mountain there is also some loess among the exposed rocks. Many of the intermontane basins on the plateau contain thick loess deposits. That is why the Shanxi Plateau is categorized under the Loess Plateau subregion even though there are many rock mountains and ridges. Loess *yuan, liang* and *mao* are mostly distributed in the middle and upper reaches of the Zhanghe and Qinhe rivers. The Fenhe River valley is the biggest of these intermontane basins. It lies 400 to 500 m. above sea level and contains some of Shanxi's major cities, such as Taiyuan and Linfen.

Another characteristic of the Shanxi Plateau is its broad limestone outcrop area, amounting to more than 60,000 sq. km. and being northern China's largest karst region. Huge karst springs, such as Taiyuan's Jinci Spring, often flow in the incised valleys and piedmont belts and are important sources for irrigation.

The climatic conditions here vary with elevation. The intermontane basins, with lower elevation, have more heat, their cumulative temperatures generally topping 3,200°C. Although the natural vegetation is largely destroyed, some mountains still contain semi-natural residual forests displaying vertical zones. On Lüliang Mountain, for instance, in the area below 1,300 m. above sea level there is piedmont grassland; between 1,300 and 1,800 m., deciduous broadleaf forests of pine and oak; between 1,800 and 2,700 m., subalpine needleleaf forests composed of Prince Rupprecht larch, and dragon spruce; and on the summit or windblown cold slopes, subalpine meadows.

2) Northern Shaanxi-Eastern Gansu Plateau. This lies between the Lüliang and Liupan mountains. It lies about 1,000 m. above sea level and contains a wide distribution of loess. In between there are very few low bedrock mountains protruding above an "ocean of loess", like isolated islets, such as Mount Ziwu, between the Jinghe and Luohe rivers; Mount Huanglong, between the Luohe and Huanghe rivers; and Mount Laoshan, southwest of Yan'an (1,452 m. above sea level). In the southern part of the plateau, the loess *yuan* are well preserved and the surface is quite flat; the northern part is mainly composed of dissected and disintegrated loess hills, that is, loess *liang* and *mao*.

The cumulative temperature on the Loess Plateau is generally less than 3,000°C. For example, the town of Xifeng has a cumulative temperature of only 2,700°C., and thus should belong to a temperate zone in terms of heat conditions. Only the valleys in this area have higher heat, but they are few. The annual rainfall is between 400 and 500 mm., and it is mostly concentrated in summer and autumn, with frequent torrential rains. Owing to little vegetative cover, there is a huge difference between the amount of water in rivers during the high and low-water seasons. For instance, the maximum flow of the Yanhe River reaches 2,800 cu. m./sec., while its minimum flow is only 0.001 cu. m./sec. Mount Ziwu and some of the other mountains contain secondary young forests (elfin forests). Nanniwan to the southeast of Yan'an was formerly a dense elfin forest, composed of Liaodong oak, aps and oriental arborvitae.

The Weihe Plain, between the southern flank of the plateau and the Qinling Mountains, was called Guanzhong in ancient times. It is a graben plain and can be viewed as a huge intermontane basin within the Northern Shaanxi Loess Plateau. Its northern limit is the Weihebei Mountains, a series of limestone block mountains, and its southern limit is the grand fault cliff on the northern slopes of the Qinling Mountains. The Weihe Plain is low in elevation and its water and heat conditions are similar to those on the Huanghe-Huaihe-Haihe Plain. Two crops can be reaped annually, and so it is one of China's major wheat and cotton producers.

3) Western Gansu Plateau. This is divided by the Liupan Mountains from the Longdong Plateau. The Liupan Mountains were called the Longshan Mountains in the old days, and so the area to their east is generally called Longdong and the area to their west, Longxi. They are a narrow mountain range running in a north-northwest direction. Their main peak is over 2,900 m. above sea level, and their eastern slopes are steep while their western slopes are gentle. West of the Liupan Mountains, the Loess Plateau rises about 2,000 m. above sea level and the landform is chiefly loess hills.

The Western Gansu Plateau has lower heat because of its high elevation. For most of the plateau areas (Yuzhong, Dingxi, etc.) the cumulative temperature is less than 2,500°C., or colder than the Northern Shaanxi-Eastern Gansu Plateau. The precipitation is 400 to 500 mm., and the aridity is lower than on the other plateau. On this plateau there are some valley plains, such as those surrounding upper Weihe River near Tianshui and the Huanghe River near Lanzhou. Because of the lower relief of these valley plains, they receive a higher amount of heat. The plain in the vicinity of Lanzhou receives little rain but has a great amount of evaporation. The dry fields there are often covered by a layer of pebbles in order to reduce the evaporation. The higher mountains on the plateau still preserve a few residual forests. For instance, above 2,000 m. on the Liupan Mountains, there are pine and oak forests composed of Chinese pine, oriental arborvitae, aps, Asian white birch, and Liaodong oak. Xinglong Mountain to the south of Lanzhou contains forests of dragon spruce, aps and Liaodong oak. Very little other natural vegetation is preserved in this area, and soil erosion is serious.

3.   Utilization and Transformation of the Natural Environment

The North China Region has a long history of agricultural production and livestock breeding, and it is one of China's most important farming areas. But owing to the irrational utilization of the natural environment over a long period before Liberation, coupled with shortcomings in this natural environment, we find that there are a number of major problems related to the development of agriculture here. These are mainly four — drought, waterlogging, salinization and alkalinization, and soil erosion.

(1)   Control of Drought

The cause of drought in the North China Region does not lie in the amount of annual precipitation, but in its uneven distribution throughout the year. The amount of precipitation for most years comes to less than the average value, while that in isolated years exceeds the average. The summer precipitation often consists of torrential rains that occur only on a few occasions, resulting in an extreme shortage of rainfall. Furthermore, high temperatures and strong evaporation make the effective precipitation inadequate and the surface runoff scanty. The lack of rain, high temperatures, low humidity and dry winds during the growing period combine to create dry spells in North China that greatly affect the harvesting of farm crops. Spring (March to May) is the season when the autumn-sown crops develop and ripen, and it is also the time when spring crops are planted. But the amount of precipitation at this time is only about 10 per cent of the year's total. In April and May the rainfall comes to a mere 5 to 15 mm. (75 per cent guaranteed rate).

The rapidly rising temperatures, low relative humidity and the high wind velocity make it impossible for the little amount of rainfall to compensate for the loss of moisture through evaporation. Thus the upper layer of soil dries quickly, deteriorating the conditions for crop growth. The most arid area is in the northern part of the North China Plain and on the Shanxi Plateau. This is followed by the middle and lower reaches of the Huanghe River and the Weihe River basin. The average precipitation variability in April on the Haihe Plain is as high as 70 to 80 per cent, and there may be a three to five-fold difference in the amount of precipitation from one year to the next.

After Liberation, great efforts were made to expand the water sources and to develop irrigation on the North China Plain. The first step was to tap the groundwater. The Hebei Plain abounds in old river channels, with rich reserves of freshwater in shallow layers only 20 to 50 m. below the surface. This water is stored in huge volumes and is of high quality (mineralization less than 2 g/l). The wells dug by the people on the Hebei Plain in recent years have contributed much to the development of agricultural production in this region.

A project is under study to divert the water from the Changjiang River in the south up to the plain. If implemented, this should meet many of the needs of industry, agriculture and urban consumption.

(2) Prevention and Control of Floods

Precipitation in the North China Region is highly concentrated in summer torrential rains (June to August). When these occur, they may last for several days. These rains plus the large amount of silt carried by the rivers threaten the North China Region with floods and waterlogging. The major tributaries of the Huanghe River, such as the Weihe, the Fenhe, the Yiluo and the Qinhe, all empty into the Huanghe near Tongguan. In the event of a torrential rain in the area of the middle reaches of the Huanghe, the waters of the Huanghe and its tributaries converge to form a flood peak. Since the Huanghe in its lower reaches already "flows above the ground", every breach in its dykes inevitably leads to inundation of the land. In serious cases, the floodwaters destroy villages and much farmland. At the same time, silt left in old river channels may be swept up by the wind and distributed across the fields, causing a sandy waste and much damage. Historically, the Huanghe has changed its course several times. The breach of its dyke at Huayuankou in 1938 resulted in a vast inundated area between the Huanghe and Huaihe rivers.

The Haihe River system consists of five big tributaries: the North Grand Canal, the Yongding, the Daqing, the Ziya and the South Grand Canal. Most of these flow through the loess region and across the eastern slopes of the Taihang Mountains to meet the Haihe in the vicinity of Tianjin. The eastern slopes of the Taihang Mountains are a centre for torrential rains, and whenever flood peaks of the tributaries meet, a big flood peak develops near Tianjin. Furthermore, the low land between the rivers on the Hebei Plain is prone to suffer waterlogging, and the area is not easy to drain.

After Liberation large-scale water-conservancy works were undertaken by the people of the North China Region. The dykes along the lower reaches of the Huanghe were repaired, heightened and fortified. Flood control reservoirs were built at Sanmen Gorge and elsewhere. Flood detention and diversion areas were opened at Dongping Lake and at some other places, so that there has been no breaching of the Huanghe during the high-water season for 30 years running. This has ensured the safety of vast regions near the lower reaches of the river.

(3) Control of Salinization and Alkalinization

There are large tracts of solonchak on the North China Plain. Patches of solonetz are distributed in between the tracts of solonchak. Besides, many localities divert river water to irrigate fields without arranging proper outlets for drainage. This causes salinization and alkalinization of the soil. Except for that on the coastal plain area, the salinization and alkalinization of the North China Plain are chiefly due to inadequate drainage, high water table, arid climate and strong evaporation.

But in recent years people have done much to prevent and control soil salinization and alkalinization and to improve the solonchak and solonetz. They have adopted measures suited to the local conditions and resources of the North China Plain. For example, the hinterland areas along the banks of the Huanghe and other big rivers are lowlying and prone to waterlogging. Thus they have become mostly saline or alkaline depressions. Taking advantage of the rich amount of silt carried by the rivers, the people have diverted the floodwaters into the depressions so that silt is deposited and the soil improved.

The North China Plain is rich in shallow-layer groundwater. Pumped wells are used for both irrigation and drainage, and to control drought, waterlogging, salinization and alkalinization. Besides, many localities use such methods as overt ditches to drain and irrigate fields, washing away the saline content in the soil. And the farmers plant green manure to ameliorate the soil. It has long been a practice to grow rice on solonchak or solonetz to improve the soil. This combines improvement with utilization, and produces quick results and high yields. Big coastal farms, such as the ones at

Lutai and Qinghe, are now growing paddy rice over wide areas, yielding 6,000 kg. per hactare.

(4) Water and Soil Conservation

Soil erosion is a serious problem on the Loess Plateau. About 1,600 million tons of silt are carried downstream by the Huanghe each year through Shaanxian, of which 90 per cent comes from the Loess Plateau. With the silt, about 30 million tons of nitrogen, phosphorus and potassium are lost. Erosion has thus reduced the soil on the Loess Plateau to infertility, resulting in very low crop yields. And the huge amount of sediment carried downstream silts up the river courses to cause floods.

Although soil erosion is a natural process, human beings in the old society did much to aggravate the loess problem. The natural cause is first of all the property of the loess itself, which is loose, homogeneous, and free of granular structure. Although it contains a high percentage (5 to 15 per cent) of carbonates, it lacks organic matter. The soil particles are cemented together merely by calcium, so the loess is easily dispersed in water and incapable of resisting erosion.

Often one torrential rain may erode more than 70 per cent of the total amount of soil eroded from an area in one year. For instance, a torrential rain in the Jinghe River Basin may account for about 50 per cent of the annual precipitation. The soil loss from such a rain on the surface of farmland with a gradient of 5° is 0.02 cu. m. per sq. m. The Yuntaishan basin (upper reaches of the Yanhe River) in Ansai County, Shaanxi Province, received 143 mm. of rainfall in one downpour on July 5 to 6, 1977, and the silt washed into the Yanhe was nine times the average annual amount.

Unlimited reclamation of the land for farming and grazing in the old days largely destroyed the natural vegetation and exposed the loess. Data collected at the Huanglong Water and Soil Conservation Station in Shaanxi shows that on the wooded land the runoff is reduced by 78.4 per cent and river silt by 94 per cent.   The annual amount of soil loss on the elfin forest grassland comes to only 4 per cent in comparison with that of farmland on the slopes. Therefore, the destruction of the natural vegetative cover has greatly aggravated the problem of water and soil erosion. Owing to the reasons mentioned above, at least one-third of the Loess Plateau is now composed of gullies that serve as a passageway for the transportation of silt on the plateau.

After Liberation, a large-scale campaign was launched to improve the Loess Plateau. Over a period of 20 years or so, soil erosion has been brought under control in an area of several millions of hectares. Forests for water and soil conservation were planted on the loess hills in the Yulin Prefecture of Shaanxi Province. This has controlled soil erosion. As a result, the prefecture is now self-sufficient in food grain.

Chapter IX

THE CENTRAL CHINA REGION

The Central China Region is roughly situated between the Qinling Mountains and the Nanling Mountains, starting from the east margin of the Qinghai-Tibetan Plateau in the west and reaching the sea in the east. The region is located between Latitude 24° to 34° N. and Longitude 103° to 123° E., comprising chiefly the middle and lower reaches of the Changjiang River and Zhejiang and Fujian provinces, with a total area of 1.8 million sq. km.

Lying within the scope of China's subtropical zone, the region borders on the North China Region in the north and extends to the southern foot of the Nanling Mountains in the south. The southern boundary stretches from south of Fuzhou through the north of Guangzhou and Nanning to the neighbourhood of Bose in Guangxi.

Topographically, the Sichuan Basin and the lower Changjiang River act as the main axis of the Central China Region, which slants towards the Changjiang valley from north and south and lowers its heights step by step from west to east. With the exception of the Qinling and Daba mountains and the Guizhou Plateau, the region is composed of low mountains and hilly areas alternating with basins and plains. Roughly speaking, the Qinling and Daba mountain areas exceed 2,000 m. above sea level, the Guizhou Plateau averages 1,000 to 1,500 m. above sea level and the Sichuan Basin is about 500 m. above sea level. The Changjiang Delta Plain and the Qiantang and Minjiang River estuary plains are only 10 to 20 m. above sea level.

The Central China Region is a transitional area between

the country's north and south, and its natural landscape also has transitional features. It belongs to that of a subtropical humid forest zone. It is a rich agricultural area with a great production potential.

1. Monsoonal Subtropical Landscape

In terms of its latitude, the Central China Region is in the sphere of a subtropical high pressure zone. But owing to the strong East-Asian monsoons, the planetary wind circulation systems are altered near the earth's surface. Consequently, the Central China Region is not only spared the arid climate that prevails in other subtropical high pressure zones of the same latitude (such as the Sahara Desert), but it is warm and humid, with a manifest monsoonal subtropical landscape.

(1) Subtropical Humid Climate

In the Central China Region, the winter and summer monsoons change clearly and there are four distinct seasons. This is one of the major characteristics of the climate in this region. Controlled by the strong continental air mass, the winter in this region is rather long, lasting generally 3.5 to 4 months, except in the southernmost part where it lasts only 1 to 2 months; summer also lasts 3 to 4 months.

As the Central China Region lies in the transitional zone between the country's north and south and is affected by the Tibetan Plateau in the west, the region's atmospheric circulation takes on a unique transitional form. A winter cyclone frequently passes through this region, causing an extraordinary amount of cloudiness and rain. Precipitation in winter accounts for about 10 per cent of the year's total, which creates an extremely favourable situation for the growth of winter crops. In early summer, owing to the presence of two jet streams over Japan, the passage of further continental cyclones is blocked.   Meanwhile, beginning in May, summer monsoons entering the Central China Region from the south meet the polar front to form frontal rain.   This occurs continuously in a given area over a certain period of time, and because such rains come when the plum trees ripen they are called "plum rains".   They are an extraordinary phenomenon in the climate of the Central China Region.   With the northward advance of the summer monsoons and the northward retreat of the polar front, the plum rains gradually advance northward. They make their appearance along the Fuzhou-Hengyang line in late May, push forward into the Changjiang valley by mid-June and arrive in northern Jiangsu and southern Henan at the end of June.   The plum rain season at a single location generally lasts 20 to 30 days, and becomes shorter farther to the north.   The characteristics of the plum rain period are: a great frequency of rainy days, huge amounts of average rainfall and high relative humidity.   It forms a striking contrast to the days before and after the plum rain season.

The plum rains constitute an important component of the precipitation in the Central China Region.   The average plum rain precipitation in Shanghai, Nanjing, Wuhu, Jiujiang and Hankou is 123 mm., accounting for 70 per cent of the total precipitation at these five places in June and July.   Too long or too short a plum rain period often is followed by a flood year or a drought year.

In July and August, after the plum rain front has moved northward, a Pacific subtropical high pressure air mass overhangs and, with the exception of the southern slope of the Qinling Mountains, the weather in the whole region becomes clear and hot.   There is little rainfall and farmland lacking in irrigation suffers from drought.   As the summer monsoonal climate is rather humid, hot thunderstorms or cold frontal thunderstorms may emerge, under the circumstance of convective instability, to help alleviate the summer drought.   In early September, the Mongolian high pressure system in the north takes shape and its high pressure wedge extends southward.

But the Pacific subtropical high pressure ridge at this time has not yet completely withdrawn. Thus, in September and October, the two high pressures overlap and result in clear autumnal weather that is centred in the Poyang and Dongting lake basins. At this time, there are typhoons and storms in the coastal areas while autumnal rains occur in the Sichuan and Guizhou areas in the west, as the cold air from the north moves southward and the front is obstructed by the orographic conditions.

The Central China Region has abundant rainfall, two or three times as much as north China does. The precipitation increases gradually from north to south, with the Huaihe River basin registering more than 750 mm. annually; the lower reaches of the Changjiang River, about 1,000 mm., and the middle reaches about 1,200 mm.; and Hunan, Jiangxi, Zhejiang and Fujian provinces reaching 1,500 mm. The windward slope of mountains have more rainfall. For instance, the Guling at the upper part of Lushan Mountain registers 2,528.7 mm., while Jiujiang at the foot of the mountain registers only 1,433.1 mm. Mount Emei in Sichuan Province registers 1,960 mm., while Emei County at its foot registers only 1,638 mm.

It is thus clear that with the advance and retreat of the monsoons in the Central China Region, there are frequent frontal and cyclonic activities. Although precipitation is abundant and its distribution in a year rather even, there is still considerable interannual variability because of the late or early arrival of the summer monsoon and the different durations of the plum rain front. For example, in 1954 the rainfall in the Changjiang River area was twice or even three times greater than average. In July of that year the precipitation in Huaiyin was 216 per cent greater than the monthly average, while in Wuhu it reached 316 per cent.

The region has rich heat resources, with active accumulated temperatures reaching 4,500° to 6,500°C. The average temperature in the coldest month is 0°C. As the region straddles

10 degrees in latitude from north to south, the average temperature difference in the coldest month is 10°C. The distribution of the isotherm is rather even. With the exception of the Sichuan Basin, which is sheltered by the Qinling and Daba mountains in the north, the absolute lowest temperature of all places in the middle and lower reaches of the Changjiang River can fall below 0°C. In places farther to the north, the absolute lowest temperature can drop to -10°C. and even to -20°C. The extreme lowest temperature of Shouxian County in Anhui Province has reached -24.1°C. and Chuxian County -23.8°C.

Summer in the region is rather hot. The July average temperature in the middle reaches of the Changjiang River and central Sichuan can stand at 30°C., with the highest temperature averaging above 34°C. Chongqing, Wuhan and Nanjing, all along the Changjiang River, are known as the "three big fireplaces" of China. With its cold winter and hot summer, the Central China Region is unique in comparison with other places in the world on the same latitude.

In central China there are generally more than 165 days in which the average temperature is higher than 15°C., with the Minjiang and Oujiang River basins and the valleys in the Nanling Mountains averaging 190 days, and the Sichuan Basin and the middle and lower reaches of the Changjiang River averaging 175 days. The abundant heat resources provide favourable conditions for the growth of two crops of rice, cotton or other subtropical crops. Citrus and sugarcane can be grown in the Sichuan Basin and areas south of the Changjiang River, while tea trees can be cultivated in areas of this region north of the river.

In summary, the climate of the Central China Region is characterized by four clear-cut seasons and winters and summers of equal length. It is thus distinct from the South China Region, where there is no winter all year round, and the North China Region, where the winter is long and the summer short. Along with the transitional nature of the climate, the vegetation, soil and other physiographical elements also have transitional features. Thus the region is included in the subtropical zone, which is a transitional area between the temperate and tropical zones.

(2) Water Resources and Hydrological Features

The rivers in the Central China Region are abundantly supplied with water and there is a dense drainage system in this region. The Changjiang River is one of the biggest rivers in the world, with an average annual flow of over 30,000 cu. m. per sec., or 17 times that of the Huanghe River. The flow of its main tributaries, such as the Minjiang, Jialing, Yuanjiang, Xiangjiang, Hanjiang and Ganjiang rivers, all surpass that of the Huanghe River. The drainage area of the Minjiang River, for example, is less than one-fifth that of the Huanghe, yet its average flow is twice as much as the latter. Although the Minjiang and Oujiang rivers are short and swift and have small drainage areas, they have a rich runoff, with the runoff modulus reaching 35 litre per sec. per sq. m. They are thus important rivers on China's southeast coast.

The average runoff modulus of the entire Changjiang River basin is 17 litres per sec. per sq. m., 9.5 times that of the Huanghe River basin. The figure for the Nanxiang Basin on the north bank of the Changjiang and the upper reaches of the Jialing River is only 5 to 7 litres. On the south bank of the Changjiang the runoff modulus increases greatly, with that of the mountainous and hilly areas reaching 40 litres and that of the Nanling Mountains 30 to 35 litres.

The seasonal changes in runoff also differ in the north and the south as the summer monsoons advance. In the southern part of Hunan, Jiangxi and Fujian provinces, flood waters appear in April and May. This time is put off until June in Hunan and Hubei, to July and August in the Sichuan Basin and to September in the upper reaches of the Hanjiang River. When the flood peak appears in the Hunan-Hubei

Basin, it does not pose a menace since the water level in the basin is still low and the rivers and lakes in the basin can play a regulating role.   But when the flood peak appears in the Sichuan Basin and the Hanjiang River basin, the rainy season is at its height and the water level of the lakes has also risen. In such cases, flood waters sometimes cannot be discharged smoothly, and the rivers and lakes retain their high water level for a comparatively long time.   In these circumstances, the water in the rivers is abundant and the water level stable. This is most favourable to navigation and irrigation.   But in certain years, the flood waters still pose a threat.

The lakes along the Changjiang River are huge natural reservoirs.   To a great extent they play the role of regulating and conserving flood waters.   They are also rich storehouses for China's fresh-water acquatic resources.   The Poyang and Dongting lakes are the largest in China, and they have enormous flood regulation and conservation power.   They are of great importance to the development of the national economy.

The waters of Poyang Lake flow into the Changjiang River in one direction and, as a rule, the flood waters of the Changjiang do not flow back into the lake.   Hence the main function of Poyang Lake is to conserve the flood waters in the Poyang Lake drainage system (the Ganjiang, Xiushui, Fuhe, Xinjiang and Pojiang rivers).   Take the biggest flood peak in June 1954, for instance.   After going into Poyang Lake, the maximum outward flow of the five rivers at Hukou, the outlet of the lake, was reduced by half.   This clearly shows the role played by the Poyang Lake in weakening the flood peak from the upper reaches of the rivers.

Dongting Lake also plays an important regulating role in the flood season.   It not only receives all the flow of the Xiangjiang, Zishui, Yuanjiang and Lishui rivers but also conserves water diverted during the flood season from the Changjiang River.   This greatly reduces the burden of flood drainage for the Jingjiang River channel and also delays the flood waters of the four rivers flowing into the Changjiang.   During summer and autumn, the water level of Dongting Lake is at its highest because of the heavy flow of water into the lake. In ordinary years such flood waters pose little threat, as the flood peak in the Dongting Lake appears before that in the upper reaches of the Changjiang River. In years when the flood peaks of the lake and the Changjiang occur at the same time, such as 1954, a catastrophic flood took place in the Dongting Lake area and the middle and lower reaches of the Changjiang River. According to data compiled on July 30, 1954, Dongting Lake reduced the flood waters of the Changjiang by 39.7 per cent. From this one can see the immense regulating and conserving power of Dongting Lake.

As a huge amount of sediment is carried into the lake annually by the Changjiang River and by the other four rivers, Dongting Lake has gradually silted up. Moreover, reclamation of the lake banks over the years has steadily reduced the size of the lake. The average annual inflow of silt reaches 168 million cu. m., 84 per cent of which comes from the Changjiang River. The outflow of silt at Yueyang comes to only 40 million cu. m. Therefore the annual amount of silt filling in the lake is 128 million cu. m., and 200 million cu. m. in high-flood years. As a result of this silting, the bottom of the lake is rising an average of 4.6 mm. a year. Through this process and others Dongting Lake, the biggest in China, has been divided into many big and small lakes. The largest of these are East Dongting, West Dongting, South Dongting and Datong lakes. East Dongting Lake is the deepest of any of these.

(3) Transitional Vegetation and Soil

The natural vegetation in the Central China Region north of the Changjiang River and the Daba Mountains are deciduous broadleaf forests with evergreen broadleaf trees. In the northern part of this region are also some warm-temperate trees. Between the Changjiang River and the Nanling Mountains are subtropical evergreen broadleaf forests. And south of the

Nanling Mountains are also some species of tropical trees as the vegetation gradually changes to that of the quasi-tropical zone of south China.

The deciduous broadleaf forests containing evergreen broadleaf trees are distributed in cloudy mountainous areas. Most of these trees are somewhat cold-resistant evergreens mixed with some temperate deciduous broadleaf trees. Such forests are called mixed evergreen broadleaf and deciduous broadleaf forests. They have a complex form with three layers of species. The first layer consists of deciduous broadleaf trees, while in the second and third layers are evergreen broadleaf trees. On the forest ground grows the somewhat cold-resistant *Sinarundinaria chungii*. The deciduous broadleaf trees are mainly of the beech family, which reflects the extreme humidity of the local atmosphere. The evergreen broadleaf trees are *Cyclobalanopsis glauca* of the beech family, *Phoebe bourpei* of the laurel family and *Schima superba* of the tea family.

The subtropical evergreen broadleaf forests are mainly distributed on low mountains below 1,100 m. The forests take on a green look all year round and contain an arbor layer, a shrub layer and a herbaceous layer. In damp areas there are many vines and epiphytes, but not as many as are found in tropical rain forests. The trees are mainly *Cyclobalanopsis glauca* and *Castanopsis eyrei* of the beech family and associated deciduous trees of the beech, walnut and maple families.

On the Nanling Mountains below 1,200 m. and south of the Nanling Mountains in the southern part of the Central China Region are evergreen broadleaf forests with some tropical trees. The trees in these forests are mainly thermophilic ones, such as *Castanopsis hystrix* and *Castanopsis carlesii,* and a few cold-resistant ones, such as *Cyclobalanopsis glauca.* In the first arbor layer of these forests are also trees of the laurel and tea families.

Masson pine and China fir forests are the most representative coniferous ones in the Central China Region. Although

The Northeast Plain stretches to the horizon; many
mechanized farms were built here after Liberation.

The marshland on the Northeast Plain.

Heavenly Pond, a crater lake atop Baitou Mountain.

The Songhua River.

Plain on the lower reaches of the Huanghe River.

The Loess Plateau near Huajialing in central Gansu.

Sheer cliffs on the West Peak of Mt. Huashan.

The Jiangdu irrigation works in central Jiangsu.

Shelterbelt at Minquan, Henan Province.

The Jianghan Plain in southern Hubei.

The red basin of central Hunan.

China fir forest in southern Hunan.

Terraced fields in the Sichuan Basin.

A plantation of the famous Longjing green tea in Hangzhou.

A bamboo forest in the Wuyi Mountains, Fujian Province.

An ancient Chinese irrigation project, the Lingqu Canal, in Guangxi.

Guangxi has many famous limestone caves; Lu Di Yan (Reed Flute Cave) has beautiful stalactites and stone pillars.

The Zhujiang Delta in Guangdong.

The mangrove forest on the sea shore of Leizhou Peninsula.

The eastern sea shore of Taiwan.

most of them are secondary forests or semi-natural forests formed after cultivation, they are distributed according to a regular pattern, that is, in the eastern part of the subtropical region where there is no obvious drought in winter. Masson pines can stand dry and infertile soil, while China firs grow well only on deep soil and a humid environment. Both make good timber, particularly China fir, which is grown only in China and forms an excellent building material. The Central China Region also boasts of the world-famous Tertiary relic plants dawn redwood (*Metasequoia glyptostroboides*) and *Cathaya argyrophylla*. Mixed dawn redwood and China fir forests were discovered in Shuishanba, Lichuan County, Hubei Province, growing by the side of valleys 950 to 1,150 m. above sea level. Mixed *Cathaya argyrophylla* forests now exist only in Huaping longsheng of 1,420 m. above sea level in Guangxi and on Jinfo Mountain in Sichuan Province.

There are many kinds of bamboo forests, the most extensively distributed being the moso bamboo forests. Moso bamboo (*Phyllostachys pubescens*) is an important commercial timber that has many uses. The scope of distribution of Moso bamboo forests and the environment in which they grow are similar to those of China fir forests. Aside from pure Moso bamboo forests, there are also mixed Moso bamboo and China fir forests.

The soil in the Central China Region is composed mainly of yellow brown earth, red earth and yellow earth. The yellow brown earth is distributed in the northern part of the subtropical zone, that is, in areas to the north of the Changjiang River and on the hills and low mountains of northern Hubei, southern Shaanxi and southwestern Henan. Both its distribution and generation show manifest features of transition from north to south. The ratio between humid acid and fulvic acid in the humus of yellow brown earth in forest areas is generally about 0.5 and the pH is usually between 5.5 and 7.0, or between that of brown earth and red earth. As the climate in this region is warm and humid, the weathering of the primary minerals that form the yellow brown earth is rather fast. The clay minerals in the soil are mainly hydromica-vermiculite-kaolin. The clay accumulation forms a layer of clayish brown subsoil in the profile and even a clay pan which is apt to perch ground-water. The iron and manganese content in the soil also leaches out, often forming a layer of iron-manganese concretion. It can readily be seen that yellow brown earth has some of the char-acteristics of brown earth as well as of yellow earth.

The red earth and yellow earth are mainly distributed in the southern part of the subtropical zone. The red earth is mainly distributed in the low mountain and hilly areas to the south of the Changjiang River. Its allitic weathering is ob-vious, the siallitic ratio of its clay particles is between 2.0 and 2.2, and its clay minerals are mainly composed of kaolin with a certain amount of hydromica. Its whole profile presents an acid reaction, pH 4.5 to 5.5. On the forest ground in moun-tainous areas, the organic materials of the surface layer may reach 4 to 6 per cent. The surface soil is greyish brown, called dark red earth, and the soil fertility is rather high. When forests are destroyed, the organic content in the soil rapidly declines so that grassland red earth has only 1 to 2 per cent organic content. In low hilly areas not covered by natural vegetation, the soil erosion is serious and the organic content is less than 1 per cent. The soil is too clayish for cultivation and must be improved.

The yellow earth is mainly distributed in areas that are cloudy and humid and enjoy little sunshine. It is distributed over large areas in Guizhou Province and in the southern mountainous areas of the subtropical zone. Under the humid climatic conditions in which dry and rainy seasons are not clearly defined, the yellow earth has a high water content. Its free iron oxide is hydrated and so its profile presents a yellow colour. Its allitic weathering is weaker than that of red earth, its siallitic ratio is slightly higher (about 2.5) and its pH is 4.5 to 5.5. Under natural vegetation, the organic content of yellow earth is higher than that of red earth; under a forest it is 5 to 10 per cent, and even under bushes it is about 5 per cent.   Because yellow earth has a rather high natural fertility, it is suitable for the development of forestry and agriculture.

In the Central China Region, limestone is extensively distributed throughout Guangxi and Guizhou provinces, while in the Sichuan Basin Mesozoic purple sand and shale are widely distributed.   Thus all kinds of limestone soil and purple soil have developed in these areas and their character and form are distinctly different from that of red and yellow earth.   Besides, paddy rice is grown extensively on the alluvial plains and on river banks in the Changjiang River Delta Plain, which is the area in China covered most widely by paddy soil.

The timber forests in this region are subtropical in nature, reflecting the north-south transition zone.   The timber trees include moso bamboos, China firs, lacquer trees, Chinese sapiums, tea trees, tea-oil trees, tung-oil trees, citrus, red bayberries and loquats.   But warm-temperate fruit trees, such as persimmons, Chinese chestnuts, pears, peaches and apricots, can also be grown in this region.

2.   Regional Differentiation of the Natural Landsc.pe

The northern border of the Central China Region is the boundary between the subtropical zone and the warm-temperate zone, with the Qinling Mountains and the Huaihe River forming the line.   This border is also the area where the accumulated temperature reaches 4,500°C.   The Qinling-Funiu mountains are high and precipitous.   The natural landscape (climate, vegetation, soil and agricultural vegetation) of the Hanzhong and Nanyang basins to the south of these mountains and the Guanzhong and Yuzhong plains to the north of them are completely different and so the boundary is conspicuous. Many subtropical plants, such as Moso bamboos, tea trees, China firs and citrus trees, grow south of the Qinling Mountains and are not seen north of this range. The exceptions, if any, are limited to places where the microclimate is especially favourable.

The northern part of Anhui and Jiangsu provinces forms a vast plain where the boundary of physical geography is not so obvious. The general view at present is that the northern border of the subtropical zone should be drawn roughly along the line of the Huaihe River-northern Jiangsu general irrigation canal. But climatically, Suxian, Sixian, Boxian and Fuyang counties to the north of the Huaihe River in Anhui Province all have an accumulated temperature of some 4,700°C., similar to that of Bengfu and Shouxian County, south of the river. Xuzhou and Qingjiang to the north of the Jiangsu general irrigation canal also have an accumulated temperature above 4,500°C. It is thus clear that in these plain areas it is very difficult to divide the boundary of physical regions with any strict climatic figure. Moreover, the plains in this area have been turned into farmland for a long period of time. The main soil there is paddy soil, and little natural vegetation has been preserved. Hence it is a debatable question as to where to draw the northern border of the Central China Region.

Zonal factors play a dominant role in the regional differentiation of natural landscape in the Central China Region. As the whole region lies in the humid zone, the amount of heat is the leading factor for the regional differentiation. Consequently, the Central China Region can be divided into a northern subregion and a southern subregion. These correspond to the deciduous broadleaf forests with yellow brown earth in the northern part and evergreen broadleaf forests with red earth and yellow earth in the southern part. The boundary between the two starts roughly from the northern rim of the Sichuan Basin and extends southeast through the southern slopes of the Daby Mountains, then east along the south bank of the Changjiang River through the Yili Mountain area and the south bank of Taihu Lake in Jiangsu, until it reaches the north bank of the estuary of the Qiantang River. This boundary approximately amounts to the active accumulated temperature of 5,000°C., or the isopleth of 4°C. January average temperature.

The Central China Region has a complicated terrain and the different geomorphic units have marked landscape differences. Hence relief often constitutes an important factor for differentiation of the natural landscape in the two subregions. For instance, the Sichuan Basin area and the middle and lower Changjiang plain and hill areas have similar latitudes. Sheltered by the Qinling and Daba Mountains in the north, the Sichuan Basin is warm in winter and is covered extensively by tall evergreen broadleaf trees. Sugarcane and citrus can be grown in this basin, which also has a long history of cultivating two crops of rice each year. Accordingly, the basin belongs to the southern part of the subtropical zone. On the other hand, the middle and lower Changjiang plain area has low temperatures in winter and is covered extensively with deciduous broadleaf trees. It belongs to the northern part of the subtropical zone.

Another example is that of the average annual temperature of the Guizhou Plateau. Though this is situated south of the Sichuan Basin, the annual temperature is lower than that elsewhere south of the Changjiang River, because the average altitude of the plateau is over 1,000 m. above sea level. However, because the cold front has little effect on the plateau, the drop in winter temperature there is not fast as elsewhere. The land surface is covered with large areas of carbonate rock, karstification is strong and lithology plays an important part in the shaping of the natural landscape. Therefore, the plateau is a special physical area in the southern part of the subtropical zone.

According to the quantity of heat, we divide the Central China Region into two subregions and further divide the subregions into eight areas in accordance with their terrain.

III$_A$ The Jianghan-Qinling Subregion (Northern Part of Central China)

III$_{A1}$ The Changjiang Detla Plain Area

III$_{A2}$ The Middle and Lower Changjiang Plain and Hill Area

III$_{A3}$ The Qinling and Daba Mountains Area

III$_B$ The South Changjiang-Nanling Subregion (Southern Part of Central China)

III$_{B1}$ The South Changjiang Low Mountain, Hill and Basin Area

III$_{B2}$ The Sichuan Basin Area

III$_{B3}$ The Guizhou Plateau Area

III$_{B4}$ The Nanling Mountain Area

III$_{B5}$ The Northern Guangxi Area

(1) Jianghan-Qinling Subregion (Northern Part of Central China)

This subregion is located in the northern part of the subtropical zone. It has an accumulated temperature of 4,500° to 5,000°C., with a January average temperature of 0°-4°C. The soil does not freeze, but when a cold wave moves in there is a drastic fall in temperature, with the absolute lowest temperature reaching somewhere below -10°C. The frostless period usually extends from 210 to 250 days. The first frost sometimes appears in late October and the last frost may be put off till late March or early April. Unprotected by mountain shelters, the eastern part of this subregion in winter is colder than the western part.

The annual precipitation generally stands between 800 and 1,300 mm., with the Daba Mountains receiving 1,200 mm.; the Dabie Mountains, 1,500 mm.; and the Hanzhong Basin, 800 mm. However the precipitation variability is high. In some years the aridity can be larger than 1.0. Shanghai, for instance, has had an aridity of between 1.0 and 1.25 in 32 per cent of the past years in which records were made.

The vegetation mainly consists of deciduous broadleaf forests with evergreen broadleaf trees. Only in lower valleys do there grow scattered evergreen broadleaf trees. As the subregion has a long history of agriculture and a dense population, little forest vegetation has been preserved. The remnant forest vegetation comprises mainly trees of the oak family, such as oriental oak (*Quercus variabilis*) and sawtooth oak (*Q. acutissima*) which often form the first layer arbor with Chinese sweetgum (*Liquidamba formosana*) and Chinese pistache (*Pistacia chinensis*). The lower layer usually includes hornbeam, Chinese elm and trident maple, sometimes mixed with privet, *Cyclobalanopsis glauca* and other evergreen trees.

In regard to the composition of plant species, this subregion has a distinct transitional nature. For example, this subregion includes birchleaf pear (*Pyrus betulaefolia*), Chinese white poplar and a number of other warm-temperate plants that grow farther north, while subtropical trees such as China fir, masson pine, tea-oil tree, tung-oil tree, Chinese sapium, Moso bamboo, palm tree, Chinese sweetgum, which grow farther south, also grow here. This transitional nature is reflected in the growth of cash crops. On the Jianghuai Plain, which has good water conservancy conditions, two crops of rice and wheat or wheat and cotton are reaped annually, while on the Taihu Plain two crops of rice can be grown. Subtropical fruits such as citrus and loquat can be grown around Taihu Lake. But when loquat and citrus are introduced to areas north of Xinghua, they die of cold in winter. Although tea-oil trees, tea trees and tung-oil trees have been introduced into areas north of the Changjiang River, they cannot be planted extensively there and do well only where the topographical conditions are quite favourable.

Except on hills and mountains where there is yellow brown earth, paddy soil is the main soil on the vast alluvial plains of this subregion. There are small areas of alluvial and marsh soil along both banks of the Changjiang River, around lakes and on low land of the plains. In the coastal areas of northern Jiangsu Province there is saline soil.

This subregion has vast plains, chiefly the Middle and Lower Changjiang Plain and the Changjiang Delta Plain with thick Quaternary alluvial deposits. With fertile soil, numerous lakes, anastomosing drainage network and convenient irrigation, it is the richest agricultural area in China.

The major mountains north of the Changjiang include the Qinling, Daba and Huaiyin mountains, which all stretch in a west-east direction. The Qinling and Daba mountains in the western section have high altitudes, obstructing the winter and summer monsoons. The northern slopes are cold in winter and hot in summer and enjoy little precipitation, while the southern slopes are warm in winter and have sufficient rainfall. The southern foot of the mountains below 800 m. has subtropical characteristics. Here citrus and eucalyptus can be grown. The Huaiyin Mountains in the eastern section have little undulations. In winter they are noticeably influenced by the cold wave, and evergreen trees are rarely seen there.

The soil in this area is yellow brown earth. As the eastern part is close to the sea and more humid than the western, the eastern soil experiences more leaching and is different from the western. For example, the Xiangfan area in Hubei Province and the Nanjing area in Jiangsu Province are located on the same latitude, but the former has a higher average annual temperature, less precipitation and yellow brown earth with conspicuously different characteristics (Table 11).

Table 11. Regional Differences in Yellow Brown Earth

Place	pH	Clay particles SiO_2/R_2O_3
Xiangfan area	6.5-7.5	2.3-2.8
Nanjing area	5.5-6.4	2.0-2.2

This subregion comprises the following three physical areas.

1)   The Changjiang Delta Plain Area

This area has Zhenjiang as its apex. It extends to the northern Jiangsu general irrigation canal in the north and the north bank of Hangzhou Bay in the south. Its western border roughly takes the Grand Canal as its boundary. West of Zhenjiang and Danyang are the Ningzhen Hills and Maoshan Mountains with a natural landscape that is obviously quite different from that in this area. The area is 80,000 sq. km. in size, but only 22,800 sq. km. are part of the Changjiang River Delta, judging from the composition of sediments. North of Taizhou and Haian, in northern Jiangsu Province, there is a gradual transition to the alluvial plain of the Huanghe and Huaihe rivers.

This area has an extremely flat relief. As there are no mountains to provide shelter in the north, its winter temperature is rather low and the frostless period rather short. Shanghai in the southern part of this area has only 234 frostless days. Hanzhong, whose latitude is almost two degrees higher than that of Shanghai, has much heat because it is sheltered by the Qinling Mountains. As the climate gradually changes from north to south (Table 12), the vegetation also changes. North of the Huaihe River, tea and bamboo are difficult to grow; south of the river bamboo and tea can be grown in some areas. But north of Latitude 33° N. China fir and masson pine are scarcely grown because they are prone to damage from freezing. South of Latitude 33° N. masson pine and China fir can grow normally, and bamboo, tea and common China fir (*Gunninghamia lanceolata*) can also be grown. Furthermore, the East and West Dongting Hills near Taihu Lake have a history of several hundred years in growing evergreen fruit trees, such as loquat and citrus. This reflects the local microclimate conditions. Despite the preservation of natural vegetation, the Dongting Hills have no typical subtropical evergreen broadleaf forests.

Although the delta plain has a flat surface, the microrelief is quite complicated. The microgeomorphic features deeply af-

Table 12. Differences in Climate on the Changjiang Delta Plain

Place	Average annual absolute minimum temperature (°C.)	Annual precipitation (mm.)
North of the Huaihe River	-13 to -14	850-900
South of the Huaihe River	-8 to -12	900-1,100
South of the Tongyang Canal (about Latitude 32.5° N.)	-8 to -10	1,150

fect the composition of sediments, nature of soil and hydrological conditions, and this, in turn, affects the way of land use. Also a number of island-shaped relic hills below 200 m. in height are scattered on the plain. The best-known are Huqiu Hill near Suzhou and the Huishan Hill near Wuxi.

The major microgeomorphical units on the plain include: (a) Coastal sandbars that run parallel to the coastline in a northwest-southeast direction. Composed mainly of sand and shells, they stand above the nearby land by 1 to 2 m. They were inhabited by human beings in ancient times, and on them are found many ruins and tombs, some dating back to the Neolithic Age. (b) Lagoon plains, behind the coastal sandbars, that are generally 2 to 5 m. above sea level and have a dense network of waterways and numerous lakes. The lagoon plains average 1.5 to 3.0 km. of river for each sq. km. of land. In fact the water area of six counties and three municipalities, including Suzhou and Wuxi, accounts for 28 per cent of the total land area. There are 128 lakes each larger than 66 hectares of land. The lakes of Wujiang County account for 38.2 per cent of the total area of the county. That's why this region, the Taihu region, has long been known as China's "water country". The major lakes here are Taihu, Yangcheng and Gehu, all of which have very shallow water. Taihu Lake is one of China's five big fresh-water lakes. It has an area of 2,250 sq. km. and an average depth of only 1.29 m., the deepest point being only 4.87 m. All lands on the Taihu Plain have been turned into paddy fields. The paddy soil here has the characteristics of that in the yellow brown earth region. The leaching is weaker than that of the paddy soil in the red earth region. It generally shows a neutral reaction, the pH being 6.0 to 7.0 and it is clayish with good water preservation and penetration characteristics and a high capacity for preserving and supplying fertilizer. On top of this, the area has convenient irrigation facilities and is known for its intensive cultivation. Three annual crops are produced, two of rice and one of winter wheat (or rape or green manure) with very high per-hectare yield. (c) The Changjiang levee that has a high terrain, sandy soil and strong water penetration, but weak water preservation capacity. The way of land use here is entirely different from that on the lagoon plain. In the Tongyang area on the north bank of the Changjiang River, the crops are mainly dry land crops, such as cotton, wheat, peanuts and food grains other than wheat and rice.

The North Jiangsu Plain to the north of the Changjiang River Delta is a vast low-lying plain, high on four sides and low in the middle. It is known as the Lixiahe district, and covers an area of 14,000 sq. km. from the Grand Canal in the west to the Chuanchang River on the east, and from the general irrigation canal in the north to the Tongyang Canal in the south. The centre of this low-lying Lixiahe district is dotted with lakes, such as Sheyang and Dazong, which are less than 2 m. above sea level, while the perimeter of the low-lying land is 3 to 5 m. above sea level. During torrential rains, this kind of cauldron-bottom-shaped land is prone to waterlogging, as flood waters are not easily discharged. Although the climate in this Lixiahe district allows of two crops a year, only one crop of early rice was grown here annually before Liberation because of problems in discharging accumulated water. In recent years all kinds of water conservancy projects have been built, and large areas of low-lying land have been turned into dry land. Thus three crops per year can now be grown here, including two crops of rice. As a result, agricultural production has greatly increased.

The coastal section in northern Jiangsu to the east of the Chuanchang River is the vast littoral plain that has a natural landscape and ways of land use that are also conspicuously different from that of other sections. The plain is 20 to 60 km. wide and generally 2 to 5 m. above sea level. It was formed of deposits on the beach placed there within the historical period. The famous Fangong Embankment, for instance, was built during the Song Dynasty (960-1279) as a dyke against tidal waves. Now it is 50 to 60 km. from the sea. As the land was formed relatively recently, the soil has a salt content and belongs to the category of coastal saline soil. In accordance with the amount of salt content, the soil is divided into desalted soil, light saline soil (containing 0.1 to 0.2 per cent of salt), moderate saline soil (containing 0.2 to 0.4 per cent of salt), and heavy saline soil (containing 0.4 to 0.6 per cent of salt). Desalted soil and light saline soil are distributed roughly in an area between the Chuanchang River and the Yellow Sea highway, which is now an important cotton and grain growing area. East of the Yellow Sea highway are distributed chiefly light saline soils and moderate saline soils on which salt-resistant cotton can be grown. East of the new sea embankment is heavy saline soil.

The estuary of the Changjiang has a complicated landform, dotted with shoals and sand isles. One of these, Chongming Island, is the third largest island in China. With an area of 1,083 sq. km., it was formed at the end of the Ming Dynasty and the beginning of the Qing when many small shoals at the mouth of the Changjiang linked up. After Liberation more than 26,600 hectares of land were reclaimed on the beach of this island. It stretches alongside the mouth of the Changjiang and divides the river into two branches. In recent years, the northern branch has gradually silted up so that the main stream of the river empties into the sea from the southern branch. To the south of Chongming Island, there are a group of sand isles, such as Changxing and Hengsha, all of which came into being in the past few decades. These sand isles divide the southern branch of the Changjiang River into north and south channels. Shanghai, the biggest city in China, is situated at the place where the Huangpu River flows into the mouth of the Changjiang. It is the hub of commerce for the vast Changjiang basin area.

2) The Middle and Lower Changjiang Plain and Hill Area

This area includes the vast region to the west of Zhenjiang and east of Yichang. Its northern boundary follows the Funiu Mountains and the Huaihe River and includes the Nanyang Basin in Henan Province and the Xinyang-Gushi Plain to the south of the Huaihe River. The region roughly has the Hanjiang and Changjiang rivers as its southern boundary.

Topographically the lands on both banks of the Changjiang and Hanjiang rivers are alluvial and lacustrine plains, and south of the Huaihe River is the Huanghe and Huaihe alluvial plains. The Funiu, Tongbai and Dabie mountains are the most important mountains in this area. They are an eastern extension of the west-east tectonic belt of the Qinling Mountains. South of the Funiu Mountains is the Nanyang Basin. On the eastern side of this basin the Funiu Mountains are broken and low. Near Fangcheng, there is a wide and low pass (<200 m. above sea level). Through this pass the Central Henan Plain is linked to the Nanyang Basin, leading to Xiangfan in the south. This is the Nanyang Pass, historically an important point for north-south traffic. The Tongbai and Dabie mountains on the border of Hubei and Henan provinces are low and broken, mostly less than 1,000 m. above sea level. Hence the Wuhan area is strongly affected by the cold waves in winter. The absolute lowest temperature at Wuhan is -14.9°C. The highest part of the Dabie Mountains is located in the border area between Hubei and Anhui provinces, with the highest peak being 1,774 m. above sea level. The high peaks here play a remarkable shelter role against cold waves. The Foziling area on the northern slope of the Dabie Mountains has an annual average temperature of 14.6°C., with 222 frostless days. Taihu, on the southern slope, has an annual average temperature of 16°C., with 255 frostless days. This has an impact on differences in the distribution of vegetation and soil on the north and south slopes.

Although Yuexi, Tongcheng (Anhui Province), Yingshan (Hubei Province) and other places south of the Dabie Mountains are located north of the Changjiang River and their latitudes are higher than that of Wuhan, their cumulative temperature is greater than 5,000°C. Thus they belong to subtropical evergreen broadleaf forest with reddish-yellow earth area. Farther east, the mountain turns into a group of hillocks that stand less than 200 m. above sea level. Consequently cold waves can sweep down onto Nanjing, which becomes quite cold in winter. Winter also lasts there for four and a half months (the same as Dongtai and Huaiyin), with the frostless period being less than 240 days (the same as Dongtai). Accordingly, the Nanjing-Wuhu area south of the Changjiang River still belongs to the mixed evergreen broadleaf and deciduous broadleaf forest with yellow brown earth region. The Tongbai and Dabie mountains and the Zhangbaling Ridge between Nanjing and Bengfu are together called the Huaiyang Mountains because they are situated south of the Huaihe River. The tectonic strike runs first from northwest to southeast, and then, near Huangmei in Hubei Province, from southwest to northeast, thus forming an arc protruding southward. This is the famous Huaiyang Arc. The section of the Changjiang River from Wuhan to Nanjing, affected by this arc, turns in a similar direction.

Since there is no topographical barrier between the sections south and north of the Huaihe River and the plains are linked up, the Huainan and Huaibei plains have similar climates. The winter on these plains is long, the frostless period short and the absolute lowest temperature below -20°C. The Huainan Plain is covered with farmland. It is only on hilly areas south of this that the vegetation shows the characteristics of transition from a warm-temperate zone to a subtropical one. The vegetation of the Jianghuai hills and northern Hubei Province is mainly composed of deciduous broadleaf forests interlaced with some evergreen broadleaf trees. This is a transitional type between China's warm-temperate deciduous broadleaf forests and subtropical evergreen broadleaf forests.

Owing to the influence of cold waves from the north, the trees are mainly deciduous broadleaf trees with a small number of cold-resistant evergreen trees, such as evergreen *Castanopsis sclerophylla, Cyclobalanopsis glauca* and Chinese ilex. The composition of the vegetation also clearly reflects the characteristics of the transitional belt. There are species of North China flora, such as Korean hackberry (*Celtis koraiensis*), oriental white oak and Mongolian mulberry (*Morus mongolica*), but the East China and Central China flora still dominates. With regard to forest vegetation, coniferous forests take up large areas. The main coniferous trees are masson pine, China fir and Huangshan pine (*Pinus hwangshanensis*), all subtropical trees. There are no confierous trees of the North China flora, such as the Japanese red pine and the Chinese pine. The masson pine and China fir are mainly distributed in areas below 600 to 800 m. Above this Huangshan pines grow. On the low mountains and hills often grow chestnuts, tung-oil trees, Moso bamboos, tea trees and Chinese sapium. The tea of Liuan and the chestnut of Shucheng in Anhui Province are well-known. But fruit trees, mainly pears and apples, are also grown.

As the weather gets hotter from north to south, the vegetation of this area changes. The northern section is mainly comprised of deciduous broadleaf forests and evergreen broadleaf trees, while the southern part mainly consists of mixed deciduous broadleaf and evergreen broadleaf forests.

The plains are covered mainly with paddy soil, and the hills and low mountains with yellow brown earth or mountainous yellow brown earth. As the climate changes from north to south, the characteristics of the yellow brown earth also undergo changes. In the Sihong section in Jiangsu Province, on the north rim of this area, sajong (lime concretion) can be found about 2 m. below the earth's surface. Near Liuhe, however, rock sajong is found 4.5 m. below the surface. In the Maoshan hills, in the southern part of this area, scattered oval-shaped sajong is seen 8 m. below the surface. Thus, with the increase of precipitation from north to south, soil leaching also gradually increases.

Hongze and Chaohu are the biggest lakes in this area. With a size of 2,590 sq. km., Hongze Lake is the third largest fresh-water lake in China. Its bottom is 10 to 11 m. above sea level, 4 to 8 m. higher than the North Jiangsu Plain to the east of the lake. Thus Hongze Lake is a "hanging lake" towering over the North Jiangsu Plain. A big dyke has been built on the eastern side of this lake to hold back the water and protect the Lixiahe area from flooding. Hongze Lake was originally one of a group of lakes on the lower reaches of the Huaihe River. In 1194 breaching in the Huanghe River resulted in much of its water flowing into the Huaihe, and huge amounts of silt were soon deposited in the lower reaches of the Huaihe to raise the water level. The many original lakes thus merged to form the huge Hongze Lake.

In recent years, a series of water conservancy projects have been built, such as the Sanhe sluice gate and the Erhe sluice gate along the Honghu Dyke, the north Jiangsu general irrigation canal and the waterway by which the Huaihe River flows into the Changjiang River. These projects have controlled the drainage in the Huaihe and in Hongze Lake, removing the menace of Huaihe River floods, facilitating irrigation and power supply, and turning the North Jiangsu Plain into an agricultural area with high and stable yields.

3) The Qinling and Daba Mountain Area

This area includes the Qinling and Daba mountains, the Hanzhong Basin between them, and the middle and lower reaches of the Bailong River in southern Gansu. The Qinling Mountains are an important geographical boundary in China. They stand 2,000 to 3,000 m. above sea level, and the Baoji-Xi'an section, south of the Guanzhong Plain in Shaanxi Province, is very precipitous. The main peak, Mount Taibai, rises 3,767 m. above sea level, the highest peak in the Central China Region. In geological structure, the Qinling Mountains are a tilted block. The north slope consists of huge, magnificent fault cliff. Huashan Mountain, one of the five famous mountains in China, is noted for its steepness. Along the fault line are hot springs, such as the Lishan hot spring which has been well-known since ancient times. Thus the north slope of the Qinling Mountains is short and steep, while the south slope is long and gentle. The main ridge of these mountains lies on the northern side. The rivers on the north slope cut down into the earth violently, creating deep valleys called the "seventy-two ravines" of the Qinling Mountains. The gentle south slope is an important agricultural centre. Before highways and railways were built, the main traffic routes between the north and south followed the river valleys of the north slope. The routes were steep and difficult, known historically as "plank roads".

The Qinling Mountains have played a sheltering role climatically. In winter the Guanzhong Plain on the north slope has a much lower temperature than the Hanzhong basin on the south slope, while in summer there is not much difference. For instance, when a strong cold wave struck in January 1955, the lowest temperature in Xi'an was -20.6°C., while in Ankang it was only -7.6°C.

Sheltered by the Qinling Mountains, the Hanzhong Basin is warm and has similar frostless and crop-growing periods to

Wuhan, which is 2° lower in latitude. The western section of the northern border of the Central China Region stretches to Latitude 33° N., about 1° higher than the Huaihe River line. The section of the Qinling Mountains between the Weihe River valley in southern Gansu Province and the upper reaches of the Jialing River is rather dissected and is of low altitude. However, the difference in climate between the south and north slopes is remarkable. The Tianshui area belongs to a warm-temperate zone while the Wudu area belongs to a sub-tropical zone.

The vertical spectrums of the north and south slopes of Mount Taibai in the Qinling Mountains are clearly different. The south slope has mixed evergreen broadleaf and deciduous broadleaf forests with yellow brown earth, while the north slope has deciduous broadleaf forests with brown earth. In regard to agricultural vegetation, the Hanzhong Basin on the south slope mainly produces two annual crops, paddy rice and winter wheat. However, in recent years, successful experiments have been made with three crops, including two crops of paddy rice. On the Guanzhong Plain of the north slope, two crops of winter wheat and food grains other than wheat and rice are produced. In the Hanzhong Basin (mainly at Chenggu), high-quality citrus trees are grown over large areas. This is the northernmost citrus-producing area in China. Sugarcane is grown on both banks of the Hanjiang River, which is the northernmost area of the country to cultivate sugarcane. Recently, *Eucalyptus robusta* has been introduced into this area and is doing well. This obviously has something to do with the fact that the Hanzhong Basin is sheltered in winter by the Qinling Mountains. Consequently its agricultural vegetation shows the characteristics of the southern part of a subtropical zone. On the hills and low mountains are planted tea, tea-oil trees, tung-oil trees, masson pine, China fir, etc. The deciduous broadleaf trees on the Guanzhong Plain are mainly warm-temperate poplars, willows, elms and Chinese

scholar trees.   The fruit trees are mainly apples and walnuts.
Masson pine is not grown in this area.

The height of the Hanzhong Basin averages 500 m. above
sea level.   Like the Guanzhong Plain, it is an intermontane
rift basin.   Stretching some 80 km. from north to south, it is
an important agricultural centre in south Shaanxi and is
known as the granary of Shaanxi Province.   The basin has
diversified agriculture and an enormous potential for comprehensive development.   Besides, east of Hanzhong and along
the banks of the Hanjiang River there are the Hanyin and
Ankang basins, which are also important rice-growing areas.

South of the Hanzhong Basin are the towering Daba
Mountains (western section called the Micang Mountains)
which stand 2,000 to 3,000 m. above sea level.   These include
extensive limestone areas, with a variety of karst landforms
such as karst depressions, dolines and karst springs.   On the
south slope is found a kind of earth indicating a transition
from mountainous yellow brown earth to mountainous yellow
earth.   The natural landscape undergoes a gradual transition
until it reaches the Sichuan Basin in the southern part of the
subtropical zone.

The eastern section of the Daba Mountains, known as
Shennongjia, thrusts into the northwest of Hubei Province.
The main peak there stands 3,052 m. above sea level, being the
highest peak of the Daba Mountains.   Here the mountains are
higher than 1,800 m. above sea level and are constantly shrouded in mists.   The snow period lasts more than six months,
from September to the end of March.   The weather is cold
and humid.   The vegetation basically retains its primitive
state, having a clear vertical spectrum; below 1,000 m. are
mainly subtropical forests of tung-oil trees, eucommia and
Chinese sapium; from 1,000 to 1,700 m. are mixed evergreen
broadleaf and deciduous broadleaf forests composed mainly of
Paulownia fortunei, oriental oak and *Castanea sequinii;* from
1,700 to 2,200 m. are mixed coniferous and deciduous broadleaf forests, mainly armand pines (*Pinus armandii*), *Quercus*

alienas and beeches; and above 2,200 m. is a dark coniferous
forest belt consisting chiefly of fir trees, some 100 years old.
This section is one of the major forest areas of central China.

(2) South Changjiang-Nanling Subregion (Southern Part of Central China)

This subregion, which includes the Sichuan Basin, the
Guizhou Plateau, Hunan, Jiangxi, Zhejiang and Fujian provinces, and the northern part of Guangdong and Guangxi
provinces, belongs to the evergreen broadleaf forest with red
and yellow earth belt of the southern part of the subtropical
zone. Compared with the northern part of the subtropical
zone, this subregion receives much more solar heat, with the
active accumulated temperature standing at between 5,000° and
7,000°C. It is warm in winter and hot in summer. From north
to south, the average temperature in January increases from
4°C. to 8°C., with the July temperature standing mostly between 28° and 29°C., and the absolute highest temperature
reaching more than 40°C. Because of its high altitude it is
cooler in summer on the Guizhou Plateau, where the July
average temperature is about 25°C.

The annual precipitation in all parts of this subregion
surpasses 1,000 mm. The windward slopes of the mountains
in the eastern part, such as the Wuyi Mountains, have a rainfall measurement of 1,800 mm., with a lot of torrential rains
and rich surface runoff. In the Sichuan and Guizhou provinces in the western part of this subregion, the annual precipitation reaches about 1,000 mm., but the air is humid. Sichuan is cloudy and Guizhou rainy, both having relatively
short durations of sunshine.

Thanks to the ample rainfall and adequate conditions to
live through the winter, the natural vegetation consists of
evergreen broadleaf forests. In these forests are liana and
epiphyte, most of the former also being evergreen. On the
ground grow evergreen ferns, such as *Dicranopteris linearis*

and bush rhododendron. The northern part of this subregion is close to the northern part of the subtropical zone. The evergreen broadleaf forest trees there are mainly *Castanopsis sclerophylla, C. eyrei, C. carlesii.* In the southern part of this subregion Chinese cryptocarya, Ceylon evergreen chinkapin (*Castanopsis concinna*) and camphor trees grow well, and there are some tropical trees. Masson pines, China firs and bamboos are extensively cultivated for their economic value. Subtropical forests of the subregion also have a long history of cultivating two crops of rice annually.

Red earth and yellow earth are the forms of zonal soil here. Yellow earth is distributed on all humid mountains with the exception of the Guizhou Plateau, where it is distributed horizontally over large areas. At the foot of mountains and hills is red earth. The lower limit for the distribution of yellow earth depends on the humidity. As there is abundant rainfall in the southeast coastal areas, the lower limit of yellow earth generally stands at 500 to 600 m. above sea level, while in western Hunan, northern Jiangxi and northern Guangxi it rises to 700-800 m. On the western rim of the Sichuan Basin, where the climate is particularly humid, the lower limit for the distribution of yellow earth is 500 m.

The Nanling Mountains was regarded as a boundary between the subtropical and tropical zones of China, and between the South China and Central China regions. But the Nanling Mountains are now so eroded that there are many low, flat passes through which cold waves can move southward. Thus Guangxi and northern Guangdong to the south of the Nanling Mountains have clear-cut winters and it can become rather cold there. The average temperature in January is less than 10°C. and the absolute lowest temperature can drop below -4°C. The natural landscape here is similar to that of the southern part of the subtropical zone. Therefore, its southern limit, located north of the Nanning-Guangzhou line, roughly corresponds to the boundary between lateritic red earth and red earth.

The differentiation of the third-order natural landscape in this subregion is to a large extent identical to the major topographical units. It can be divided into five areas.

1)   The South Changjiang Low Mountain, Hill and Basin Area

This area includes Hunan, Jiangxi, Zhejiang, the northwestern part of Fujian and the southern part of Hubei and Anhui. It is a typical subtropical area of China, namely a subtropical evergreen broadleaf forest with red earth region.

Evergreen broadleaf trees predominate in the natural vegetation. In the Yixing mountainous region of Jiangsu on the north rim of this area, evergreen broadleaf trees account for 70 to 80 per cent of the total number of forest trees. In addition, there are *Pasania glabra, Castanopsis myrsinaefolia*, camphor tree, *Machilus thunbergii* and *Phoebe sheareri* which are not seen in the northern part of the subtropical zone. Among the coniferous trees are golden larch and Chinese torreyas. On the ground in these forests grow *Dicranopteris linearis,* a typical ground vegetation in the southern part of the subtropical zone. China fir and Moso bamboo forests are widely distributed, as are tung-oil trees and tea-oil trees. This is markedly different from the northern part of the subtropical zone. But in the northern rim of this area, such as in the Yili Mountains of Jiangsu and in the mountains in southwest Anhui, there are mixed deciduous broadleaf and evergreen broadleaf forests, which indicates the gradual transition from north to south. Hunan and Jiangxi have lower latitudes and better heat conditions. Consequently citrus and camphor trees are more extensively planted there.

Owing to different parent materials, terrain and climatic conditions, the red earth in this area can be divided into three subgroups. The soil which developed from Quaternary red clay is called red earth. This kind of soil has thick soil layer, high clay particle content (60 per cent fine particles <0.01 mm.), good water permeability, and poor aeration. It is widely distributed and there are still large expanses of cultivable red

earth wasteland. Dark red earth is distributed in the mountainous areas. As forest vegetation grows well in this soil,
the surface layer has an organic content of 4 to 7 per cent,
with high natural fertility and humidity. All this facilitates
the growth of trees. In the northern and western margins
of this area where the heat is slightly lower, the soil is a transition type called yellow red earth. The topsoil is brown or
yellow brown, but the subsoil and lower subsoil remain red
in colour. The soil here is less developed than is red earth,
and its siallitic ratio of the particles is rather high, being 2.5
to 3.5. Among the clay minerals in yellow red earth are kaolin,
hydromica and some montmorillonite. Base saturation and
exchangeable calcium-magnesium contents are slightly higher
than in red earth, showing that its degree of leaching is slightly
less.

This area has many medium mountains 1,500 to 2,000 m.
above sea level, with clear vertical spectrum. Take Huangshan
Mountain (1,873 m.) in Anhui Province, for example. Below
600 m. there is red earth and an artificial cultivation area of
tea plantations, tea-oil, tung-oil and Chinese sapium. Between
600 and 1,000 m. there is yellow earth with evergreen broadleaf forests composed mainly of *Castanopsis sclerophylla* and
Cyclobalanopsis glauca, and in some areas there are mixed
deciduous broadleaf trees. Between 1,000 and 1,600 m. there
is mountainous yellow brown earth with deciduous broadleaf
forests, the major trees including English beech (*Fagus eng-
leriana*), sequin chinkapin, Japanese linden and *Magnolia cylindrica.* Above 1,600 m. is mountainous meadow soil with
mountainous meadows, mainly *Arundinella hirta, Calamagrostis pseudo-phragmites* and *Parnassia foliosa.*

Topographically, the northern part of this area is the
middle and lower Changjiang alluvial plain. As part of this
plain, the Jianghan Plain west of Wuhan and south of the
Hanjiang River and the plain around Dongting Lake to its
south are low and flat, rising less than 35 m. above sea level.
With crisscrossing waterways and a cluster of lakes, this is a

well-known lake area in China. For instance, the water-covered area of Qianjiang County in the central part of the Jianghan Plain accounts for more than a quarter of the county's total lake-water area. According to incomplete data, there are more than 600 lakes larger than six hectares on the Jianghan Plain.

In geological history this area has been sinking since the Cretaceous Period. But owing to sedimentation of the Changjiang and Hanjiang rivers and land reclamation, most of the former lakes have become dry land and the one major lake left is Dongting Lake. As this is linked to the Changjiang River, every flood season a large amount of silt is deposited in the lake and gradually a west-east sandbank (the Nanxian County and Caowei area) is being formed. It has divided the original lake into the East Dongting, South Dongting, West Dongting and Datong lakes. This, in addition to constant reclamation, has reduced the lake area by 40 per cent since 1937 until it is now 2,820 sq. km. in size. The lakes on the Jianghan Plain are generally small and shallow ones with flat bottoms. Honghu Lake, one of the larger ones with an area of 438 sq. km., was a well-known revolutionary base before Liberation.

In agriculture, the Jianghan Plain and the Dongting Lake Plain are important grain-producing areas. They annually produce two crops of rice and cotton.

South of the Middle and Lower Changjiang Plain, the terrain alternates between low mountains, hills and basins. Hunan Province, for example, has the Xiangjiang River and Dongting Lake area as the centre of its depression. On the west side are the Wuling and Xuefeng mountains and on the east side are the Luoxiao and Jiuling mountains. The terrain of Jiangxi Province is similar to that of Hunan Province, with the Ganjiang River and Poyang Lake area as the centre of its depression. On the western side are the Luoxiao and Jiuling mountains and on its east, the Wuyi Mountains. These mountains generally stand 1,000 m. above sea level, their

highest peaks being 1,500 to 2,000 m. in elevation. They run
in a northeast direction.   There are many rift basins in these
mountains composed of upthrusted red sedimentary rock. After
erosion, most of these red beds have become hills and mounds
with relative heights of less than 100 m. The Changsha and
Hengyang basins in Hunan and the Jian and Ganzhou basins
in Jiangxi cover wide areas, and are population and agricultural centres.   The Changsha Basin is intermittently surrounded by low mountains and hills on which are many red
clay and red-bed mounds.   Such mounds account for 59 per
cent of the land of the whole county.   Valley plains account
for only 17 per cent.   The Shaoshan district in Hunan Province belongs to such a terrain.   This area was the birthplace
of Mao Zedong.   On the hills grow bamboo, masson pine and
China fir forests.   Tea plantations and citrus groves are also
widely distributed.   The climate here is warm and the frostless
period extends for 280 days.   Annual precipitation is ample,
reaching 1,300 to 1,500 mm., but the rainfall is concentrated
in April, May and June, accounting for 45 per cent of the year's
total.   After June, the rainfall sharply declines.   In the hottest months of July, August and September, water received
in the form of precipitation equals only half that of the
evaporation, and drought appears.   This is particularly unfavourable to the growth of two crops of rice in a year.   Recently, the Shaoshan irrigation district has been established.
It uses water of the Lianshui River, a tributary of the Xiangjiang River, to irrigate some 67,000 hectares of farmland in
Changsha, Xiangtan and four other counties.   This has greatly
extended the area that can produce two crops of rice per year.

The Wuyi and Huangshan mountains are the watershed
between the Changjiang River drainage system and the drainage systems of Zhejiang and Fujian provinces (the Qiantang,
Wujiang and Minjiang rivers).   East of the Wuyi Mountains,
except in the Jinqu Basin (Jinhua and Quxian County) which
covers a wide section, most of the land is composed of low
rolling mountains and hills, and the alluvial plains are rather

narrow. The coastal mountains, such as Tianmu, Tiantai, Kuocang and Jiufeng, run in a northeast direction. The coasts are tortuous and dotted with harbours. There are also many nearby islands formed of bedrock. The Zhoushan Islands of Zhejiang Province are the biggest of these. They are also one of China's most famous fishing grounds.

Although the mountains of this area are not high, there are many well-known ones, such as Lushan Mountain in Jiangxi Province, Huangshan Mountain in Anhui Province, Yandang Mountain in Zhejiang Province and Hengshan Mountain in Hunan Province. The Jinggang Mountains in the centre of the Luoxia range on the Hunan-Jiangxi border were a well-known revolutionary base before Liberation.

2) The Sichuan Basin Area

With striking physical features and definite regional boundaries, the Sichuan Basin is a special area of the Central China Region. The basin is topographically a complete entity. Surrounded by high mountains and plateaus, 2,000 to 3,000 m. above sea level, it has the Daba and Longmen mountains to the north, the Qionglai and Daliang mountains on the rim of the Qinghai-Tibetan Plateau to the west, the Dalou Mountains to the south and the Wushan Mountains to the east. These mountains are the natural boundaries of this area, and the basin itself is composed of plains and hills 300 to 700 m. above sea level.

Rectangular in shape, the basin is high in the northwest but low in the southeast. Consequently the tributaries of the Changjiang River on the northern side are relatively big rivers. These are the Minjiang, Tuojiang, Fujiang and Jialing rivers from which Sichuan (meaning "Four Rivers") gets its name. The tributaries on the southern side are relatively small and include the Wujiang and Chishui rivers. These rivers constitute an asymmetrical drainage system converging in the centre of the basin.

The Changjiang River cuts across the Wushan Mountains at the eastern edge of the basin to flow eastward, forming the famous Three Gorges of the Changjiang. With a total length of 180 km., these gorges include Qutang, Wuxia and Xiling, all located in the limestone region. The Wuxia Gorge is particularly magnificent and the Twelve Peaks of the Wushan Mountains that can be seen from this Gorge are known throughout the country (Fig. 22). In some sections of these gorges, the precipitous cliffs on both banks are 500 m. above the surface of the river, which is only 100 m. wide at these places.

The physical features of the Sichuan Basin result from the topography of an enclosed basin and the rock formations of which it is composed.

(a) Warm winter. The January average temperature is 2 to 4°C. higher than it is in the middle reaches of the Changjiang River. Sugarcane, in addition to typical subtropical plants, is grown in the basin, with Neijiang as its centre. Fig trees are widely distributed, and are the most common "shading tree" in the area. Tropical fruit trees, such as the litchi and longan, grow in the Changjiang valley in southern Sichuan. The double shelters of the Qinling and Daba mountains in the north prevent the intrusion of cold air in winter, and so the Sichuan Basin has very few frost days and plants can grow all year round. The city of Chongqing, for instance, has a frostless period of 349 days. Winter is very short, lasting only 30 days in Yibin and 80 days in Chongqing. The accumulated tem-

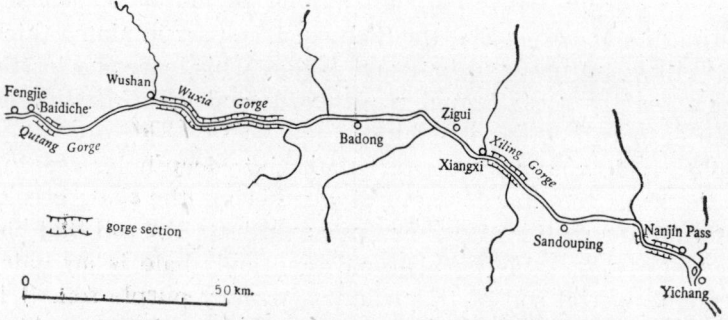

Fig. 22 The Three Gorges of the Changjiang River

perature, equal to or above 10°C., is about 5,000° to 6,000°C., increasing gradually from northwest to southeast. In addition to two crops of rice each year, agricultural vegetation on the Chengdu Plain is characterized by the growing of three crops of spring maize, paddy rice and wheat per year.

In summer the air from the south crosses the Dalou Mountains and settles down in the basin, producing a foehn. Hence there is a long and hot summer. In the Changjiang River valley there the summer lasts about four and a half months. Chongqing becomes even hotter than Wuhan and has recorded an absolute highest temperature of 44°C.

2) Cloudy and foggy. Because the Sichuan Basin is located on the eastern side of the Qinghai-Tibetan Plateau, the wind forces are relatively weak. This, combined with the prevailing temperature inversion on the ground in cold seasons, makes it easy for local radiation fog to form, and the high humidity and abundant clouds make it difficult for the fog to disperse. Therefore there are many foggy days in the Sichuan Basin. Chengdu and Chongqing, for instance, have more than 100 foggy days a year, particularly in winter. The Sichuan Basin, in fact, is the most cloudy centre in the country. Chengdu has an average of 244 overcast days a year and Chongqing has an average of 219 days. The annual sunshine percentage is less than 30 per cent, and in winter only 15 per cent.

3) Purple soil. Through a long period of subsidence during the Mesozoic Era, the Sichuan Basin accumulated thick deposits of purple sandstone and shale. This loose and brittle stone readily goes through weathering and disintegration to turn into soil with rich mineral nutrients. The process is quite rapid as seen by the fact that when deep holes are dug in the shale to allow for natural weathering, the shale breaks into soil in a matter of two or three months. The soil that has developed from this purple sandstone and shale is an independent special soil of this country, namely purple soil. It is extensively distributed throughout the Sichuan Basin, making

it a unique pedogeographical region distinctly different from the red earth region south of the Changjiang River.

There is no marked humus layer in the profile of purple soil; immediately under the surface layer is the parent material layer. As the sandstone and shale often contain calcium carbonate, some of the soil layers may contain as high as 10 per cent calcium carbonate. The pH of this soil is 7.5 to 8.5. Purple soil is rich in phosphorous and potassium, with a full phosphorus content of 0.15 per cent and full potassium content of 2 per cent and above. Therefore it is quite fertile and fit for the growth of many crops. With this fertile soil, rich terrestrial heat and abundant rainfall, the Sichuan Basin has great potential for agricultural production. The area has always been known as "the land of abundance".

The different terrains in the Sichuan Basin have resulted in a secondary differentiation of the natural landscape, namely the Chengdu Plain, the Central Sichuan Basin and the parallel valleys of eastern Sichuan. The Chengdu Plain is the only big plain in the Sichuan Basin. It is mainly composed of the Minjiang River alluvial fan, having an area of some 6,000 sq. km. The terrain slants from northwest to southeast. The land surface has an average slope of 0.4 per cent with its apex in the neighbourhood of Guanxian County. The plain there stands 750 m. above sea level. It drops to 520 m. at the rim of the alluvial fan (near Chengdu). This gently slanting terrain is most favourable to the development of irrigation by gravity flow. Back in 250 B.C., during the Qin Dynasty, the Dujiangyan water conservancy project was built to channel the water of the Minjiang River onto the farmlands of the Chengdu Plain. In recent years, irrigation canals have been constructed to lead this water to the Mianyang district east of the Chengdu Plain and, cutting across the Longquan Mountain, to irrigate Renshou and Jianyang counties. The irrigation acreage of the Dujiangyan project has thus greatly expanded, being today four times what it was in the early days after Liberation.

Winter on the Chengdu Plain is rather long because of its high altitude. The city of Chengdu, for instance, has a winter of three months with 288 frostless days in a year, 61 days less than Chongqing. And Chengdu is also cooler than Chongqing in summer. Its average temperature in July is 2° less than that in Chongqing. The soil here is chiefly fertile paddy soil. With convenient irrigation facilities, the plain has become a stable, high-yield agricultural area. In addition to grain, it is a rich production area for silk and sun-cured tobacco.

Longquan Mountain on the eastern boundary of the Chengdu Plain rises 1,000 m. above sea level. Between Longquan Mountain and Huaying Mountain (1,580 m.) is the Chuanzhong Basin with large expanses of mesa-like hills that rise 350 to 450 m. above sea level, with a relative height of dozens of metres. These undulating hills are in stark contrast to the flat Chengdu Plain. With the gradual increase of the dip angle of the purplish red sandstone rocks towards the edge of the basin, cuestas and hog-back ridges have appeared.

Intensive cultivation is practised in the Chuanzhong Basin. With thick soil, good water and fertilizer, two crops of rice and another one of winter wheat or rape can be harvested on the flat land. And on terraced fields on the slopes of hills, two crops of paddy rice and wheat (or rape) are harvested. On the top of hills, where the soil is thin, a dryland two-crop system has been adopted — sweet potatoes or peanuts in summer and peas or wheat in winter. On the slopes of hills where the soil is thicker, wheat or rape is planted in winter. Before they ripen, maize is interplanted; and before the maize ripens, sweet potatoes are interplanted. Thus time and space are fully utilized to reap three harvests a year. This interplanting system (interplanting thermophilic maize and sweet potatoes) makes full use of the superior heat conditions in the Sichuan Basin. The >10°C. temperature duration in the Chuanzhong Basin lasts ten to ten and a half months. The average daily temperature rises to more than 10°C. in the

Changjiang River valley after early February and in the Chuanzhong Basin after mid-February.

The Chuanzhong Basin has an annual precipitation rate of some 1,000 to 1,200 mm. The western rim of the basin, located on the eastern slope of the Qinghai-Tibetan Plateau, also has abundant rainfall. Ya'an, for instance, has 1,800 mm. a year, while Mount Emei has more than 2,000 mm. Thanks to the abundant rainfall and intense humidity, large areas of yellow earth are distributed on the low mountains and hills of the western rim of the basin. The lower limit for the distribution of yellow earth is 500 m. above sea level, while the upper limit is 1,100 m. The east slopes of Daliang and Qionglai mountains, which are on the western rim of the basin and lack a clear dry season, have a combination of humid evergreen broadleaf forests (chiefly *Cyclobalanopsis glauca* and *Schima confertiflora*) and masson pine and China fir forests. In contrast, the mountainous areas of Lijiang and Yanyuan, in the Southwest Region where the dry season is quite obvious, have a combination of dry evergreen broadleaf forests (chiefly *Castanopsis yunnanensis* and *Cyclobalanpsis glancoides*) and Yunnan pine (*Pinus yunnanensis*). The upper limit of the evergreen broadleaf forest belt is 2,000 to 2,400 m. on the east slope of Daliang Mountain and 3,000 m. in the Lijiang-Yanyuan area in the Southwest Region. Such a change obviously results from the greater humidity and lower temperature in winter on the western rim of the basin.

The main peak of Mount Emei, on the western rim of the basin, is Wanfo Peak. This stands 3,099 m. above sea level and rises 2,500 m. above the plain with steep precipices that present a spectacular view. The mountain has preserved many Tertiary relic plants such as the gingko, *Davidia involucrata* and Chinese larch (*Larix potaninii*). As the mountain has special cool and humid climatic conditions, the lower limit of fir forests has been reduced to 1,900 m. These fir forests are often mixed with evergreen broadleaf forests to produce a characteristic feature of the vertical spectrum of Mount Emei.

On the western side of Huaying Mountain is a big fault which separates it from the Chuanzhong Basin. East of Huaying Mountain is a series of roughly parallel comb-like folds running from northeast to southwest. Their anticlines are narrow and steep and their synclines are broad and flat. There are altogether more than 20 anticlines. Mount Geluo, near Chongqing, is a low mountain which is the southward extension of the anticline of Huaying Mountain. The Jialing River cuts across the southern section of this anticline of Huaying Mountain three times between Hechuan and Chongqing, forming a "small Three Gorges" of the Jialing River. These syncline valleys are topographically local plains and gentle hills. Because of their excellent climatic conditions, they are agriculture and population centres in eastern Sichuan.

3) The Guizhou Plateau Area

The Guizhou Plateau embraces most parts of Guizhou Province. Situated between the Sichuan and Guangxi basins, it slants in the east to the Xiangxi hill and basin area. The plateau averages 1,000 m. above sea level. Its northwestern part is higher, reaching 1,500 to 2,000 m., with the Wumeng Mountains standing at some 2,500 m. above sea level. In the west it links up with the Yunnan Plateau to form the surface of the Yunnan Plateau. The Guizhou Plateau has a complicated landform, with mountains, hills, valleys and intermontane basins interlocking each other. The major mountains include the Dalou Mountains in the north and the Miaoling Mountains in the south, with the main peaks rising 2,000 m. above sea level and a number of intermontane basins standing at some 1,000 m. above sea level. The Zunyi area north of the Wujiang River is a series of northeast folds alternating mountains with valleys. Limestone covers vast areas of this plateau, accounting for about 70 per cent of the total land of Guizhou Province. Karst landforms here are highly developed. Many of the intermontane basins, such as Pingba, Anshun and Guiyang, are large karst depressions. They are also population and agricultural centres.

At the rims of the plateau, the rivers fall along slopes, forming torrents and waterfalls. Valleys often cut down to a depth of only several hundred metres above sea level. The noted Huangguoshu Waterfall, located at the edge of the plateau in the southwestern part of Guizhou Province, is a huge waterfall on the upper reaches of the Dabang River, a tributary of the Beipan. It is 60 m. high and over 20 m. wide. During the flood season it has a flow of 2,000 cu. m. per sec. The Chishui River, a tributary of the Changjiang, cuts across the northern rim of the plateau to flow into the Sichuan Basin. The valley in the lower reaches of this river is very low. Here litchi and longan are grown. Maotai town on the bank of Chishui River is where Mao Tai, a liquor known throughout the world, is produced. This town is also where the Red Army crossed the Chishui River during the Long March.

The Guizhou Plateau has a humid climate all year round. Its natural landscape is distinctly different from the other areas of this subregion.

1) Rainy all year round. In the winter half of the year the Guizhou Plateau is affected by the polar continental air mass that arrives from the northeast and remains as a stationary front. In the summer half year it is affected by the polar front and equatorial front. As a result, the plateau is humid and rainy all year round. Guiyang has an average of 188 rainy days a year. Even in December, when there is the least rain, it has 13 rainy days. However, most of the rain comes as a drizzle. Sixty per cent of the rainfall in Guiyang between March and August is a drizzle of less than 5 mm. a day. Every month the rainfall exceeds evaporation and so there is no dry season during the year. The aridity is 0.50, and the relative humidity of Guiyang for the whole year surpasses 70 per cent.

Due to its high altitude, most parts of Guizhou are colder than is the Sichuan Basin in winter. The January average temperature for Guiyang is 5°C., a temperature similar to that at Hengyang on the same latitude, but it is cooler in summer with an average temperature in July of less than 25°C. Thus there is no bitter cold in winter and no sweltering heat in summer. The cumulative temperature on the plateau is lower than that of the Sichuan Basin or in Hunan or Jiangxi provinces, and this is unfavourable to the growth of two crops of rice. However two crops of rice can be grown in the valleys and intermontane basins less than 800 m. above sea level.

2) Yellow earth. Under the humid climate of Guizhou, most of the soil is yellow earth. This is found in areas higher than 600 to 800 m. above sea level, and the Guizhou Plateau is where yellow earth is most extensively distributed in China. In valleys and basins below 600 to 800 m., there is red earth such as that found at Luodian in southern Guizhou. The clay mineral composition of this yellow earth, because of the low quantity of heat, is different from tropical mountainous yellow earth (in which kaolin predominates). It is composed mainly of vermiculite and secondarily of kaolinite and hydromica, which reflects the characteristics of subtropical soil. In areas where limestone emerges, there is also black limestone soil and yellow limestone soil.

3) Vegetation. The regional vegetation consists mainly of humid evergreen broadleaf forests, chiefly of *Castonopsis tibetana* and *Cyclobalanopsis glauca*. On Qianling Mountain in Guiyang there are remnant camphor trees, and in the mountainous area near Pingba, which rises 1,500 m. above sea level, there are evergreen broadleaf forests of *Cyclobalanopsis glauca*. But because limestone is widely distributed in this area, the vegetation is affected by the lithology. Most of the rocks on the limestone mountains are exposed, and only in stone gullies and rock fissures is there a thin cover of soil. In addition, limestones leak water and the rock surfaces absorb and radiate heat quickly so that there is great difference between day and night temperatures. As a result, the soil is dry. The limestone soils are mostly composed of calcium and contain 2 to 3 per cent calcium oxide. Accordingly, the

vegetation has lithophyte, xerophyte and calciphilous characteristics, which makes it quite different from non-limestone
region vegetation. Lithophytes are those plants whose roots
can penetrate deep into stone fissures, plants such as the
small-leaf buckthorn (*Rhamnus parvifolia*). Xerophytes are
those plants that can readily adapt to a dry environment, such
as the small-leaf *Myrsine africana* and *Origanum vulgare*;
the hard-leaf glandbearing oak, and chylophylly (common
nightblooming cereus); and the thorny bank raspberry. Calciphilous plants are those that like calcium, such as Chinese
elm and Chinese hackberry of elm family; the *Platycarya
strobilacea* and *Engelhardtia chrysolepis* of the walnut family;
the Chinese pistache and Chinese sumac (*Rhus Chinensis*) of
the cashew family; the Chinese honeylocust and lebbek albizzia
of the pea family; the hornbeam of the maple family, and the
coniferous mourning cypress.

After the virgin forests in the limestone area were destroyed, the conditions of water preservation rapidly dete-
riorated. Most of the forests were replaced by thorny bushes
and grass. Almost 80 per cent of the vegetation in Guizhou
today is of this secondary type. The restoration of forest
vegetation on the mountain slopes is a slow process, requiring
the closing off of some hillsides to facilitate afforestation in a
planned way.

4) The Nanling Mountain Area

The Nanling Mountains are on the border of Hunan, Jiangxi, Guangdong and Guangxi provinces. From east to west
they include the Dayu, Qitian, Mengzhu, Dupang and Yuecheng
ridges, known as the "Five Ridges". Most of them are low
mountains and hills that rise less than 1,000 m. above sea
level, but the main peaks are as high as 1,600 to 2,200 m. As
the west-east tectonic line in this area is interrupted by the
Cathysian northeast tectonic line, the strikes of these mountains are in disorder. Some run northeast, some west-east
and some reveal indistinct strike direction. Topographically
they form an expanse of broken mountains, quite distinct from

the high and integrated Qinling Mountains. The rivers here flow deep into the mountains, forming many low and flat valleys. There are chiefly five of them, the Zhenshui and Wushui rivers in northern Guangdong and the Hejiang and Gongcheng rivers and Lingqu Canal in northern Guangxi. All have been communication arteries between north and south over many centuries, as well as channels through which cold air currents intrude into the south in winter. The Lingqu Canal, also called the Xingan Canal, is situated in the Hunan-Guangxi corridor between the Yuecheng and Dupang ridges in northern Guangxi. It is a man-made canal that was dug 2,000 years ago. Here the valley is low and flat, part of the watershed between the sources of the Xiangjiang and Lijiang rivers. It is an expanse of low tableland, rising only 6 m. above the valley plain. The 34-km. canal is mainly used for irrigation, and waters some 2,700 hectares of farmland.

Some medium mountains in Guangdong Province, such as the Yaoshan, Qingyun and Luofu mountains, are topographically linked to the Nanling Mountains and their vegetation belongs to the type of evergreen broadleaf forests with tropical trees, so that they are included in the Nanling Mountain Area. The mountains from Fuzhou to Gutian in central Fujian Province are also included here because their natural landscape is similar to that of the Nanling Mountains, though topographically they do not belong within their scope. But the northern part of Guangxi composes its own area because of the extensive distribution of limestone there. Administratively, the Nanling Mountain Area includes northern Guangdong Province, central Fujian Province and the southern rim of Hunan and Jiangxi provinces.

In the mountainous regions of this area, there are many intermontane basins that are agricultural and population centres. Nanxiong and Pingshi are in an area composed of red rocks. The thick conglomerates are often eroded into sheer precipices and strange peaks known as Danxia landforms (the name is derived from Danxia Mountain in Renhua, Guangdong

Province, where this landform is typical). Lianxian County (Guangdong) and Linwu (Hunan) are limestone basins where karst landforms have developed. The famous Jiuyi Mountain is composed of nine similar karst pinnacles rising 800 to 900 m. above sea level. The 2,100-year-old "map of the southern part of the Changsha State in early Han Dynasty", unearthed recently in the Mawangdui tomb at Changsha, depicts the karst pinnacles of Jiuyi Mounain.

This area has a warm climate. The valleys and basins have an accumulated temperature of 5,700° to 6,500°C., with an average annual temperature of some 20°C. But in winter, affected by cold waves, the absolute lowest temperature may drop to -7°C. There is a short period of frost, snow and freezing and a short winter (about two weeks). Therefore, this area still belongs to the subtropical zone.

The winter temperature varies considerably from place to place because of the local relief. Generally speaking, the northern slopes of the Nanling Mountains are colder than the southern slopes. Jianghua and Yizhang (in Hunan) on the northern slopes have a January average temperature of less than 7.5°C. while at Lianxian, Shaoguan and Nanxiong (in Guangdong) it is around 10°C. There is a differene of 2°C. in temperature between the south and north slopes. For this reason, the Nanling Mountains are taken as the boundary between the Central China Region and the South China Region. In summer the air currents from the south cross the Nanling Mountains and move along the north slope, producing a foehn. Therefore places like Yizhang and Dayu on the north slope are hot in summer, with the temperature higher than it is on the south slope. As the Nanling Mountains have a broken terrain and cold waves can pass through the mountain passes to move southward, places on the south slope of the Nanling Mountains near the mountain passes have low temperatures in January. For example, the January average temperature at Pingshi is only 7.5°C. and at Luochang only 9.3°C. On the other hand, the January temperature of Nanxiong, which is on the same latitude with Luochang but is sheltered by the Dayu Ridge, is as high as 11.7°C.

The Nanling Mountains are one of the rainy centres of China, with an average annual precipitation rate of 1,500 mm., and as much as 2,046 mm. at Ruyuan on the southern slope. In winter the cold air moves southward but is blocked by the north slope. This brings a long period of cold wind and drizzle, known as "cold wave rain".

As a result of these climatic characteristics, the natural vegetation of this area is one of transition from a subtropical zone to a tropical zone. The vegetation consists mainly of evergreen broadleaf forests intermixed with tropical trees. The leeward, humid and hot gully areas under 500 to 700 m. above sea level have subtropical rain forests. Many of the plants are ligneous vines with rich elements of tropical flora such as *Fissistigma oldhami, Uvaria microcarpa, Artocarpus hypargyra, A. bicolor, Gnetum indicum, Alocasis odora, Alpinia chinensis* and *Cyathea spinulosa*. On slopes 700 to 1,400 m. above sea level there are mountainous evergreen broadleaf forests, mainly composed of *Cyclobalanopsis glauca, Castanopsis myrsinaeflolia* and *Castanopsis sclerophylla*. The lower slopes have some tropical species such as *Exbucklandia tonkinensis*. Above 1,400 m. there are mixed coniferous and broadleaf tree forests composed mainly of subtropical mountainous coniferous trees, such as Chinese hemlock, Guangdong pine and Fujian cypress. The second layer is composed of broadleaf trees, chiefly evergreen broadleaf trees such as *Castanopsis eyrei* and *Schima superba*. On mountain ridges above 1,600 m. there are mountainous brushwood forests, composed mainly of evergreen broadleaf trees such as *Quercus oxyodon var. fargesii* and *Castanopsis carlesii*. As the mountain tops are buffeted by strong winds and constantly shrouded by mist, the trees there are short and twisted, usually below 15 m. in height. There is abundant underwood, such as *Enkianthus chinensis* and *Sasa sp.*, and bryophytes abound on tree trunks.

The eastern section of the Nanling Mountains is close to

the sea, and therefore more humid. From east to west the humidity gradually decreases and the composition of the tropical flora in the vegetation also decreases. But even in the Jianghua area of Hunan, there are still many tropical elements in the vegetation. Owing to differences in water and heat conditions, the heights of the vertical zones on the north and south slopes of the Nanling Mountains are markedly different (Fig. 23).

On lower hills and slopes, masson pine, China fir and Moso bamboo forests are extensively distributed, showing the characteristic landscape for a subtropical zone. Chinese sapium and

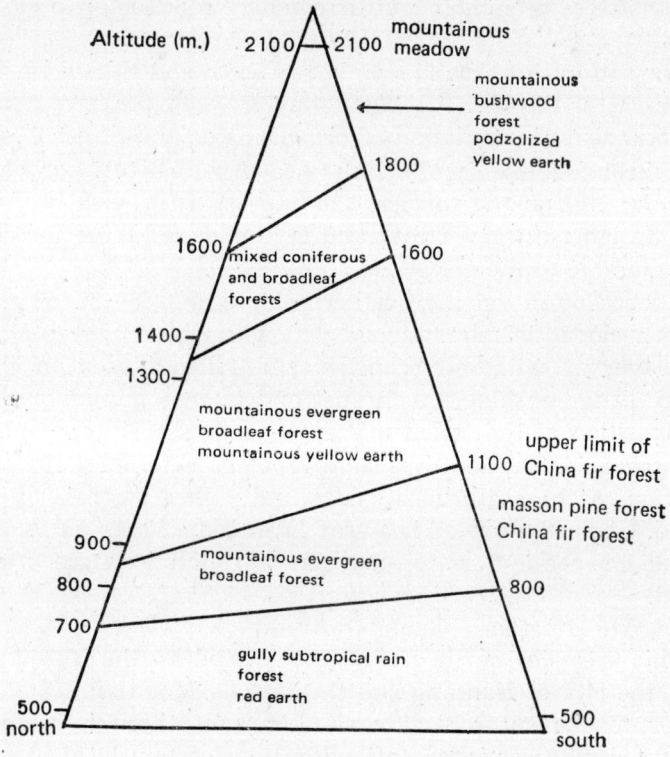

Fig. 23 Vertical Zonation in the Nanling Mountains

tea-oil trees are also widely distributed. China fir is produced in the Nanling Mountains where, because the climate is warm and humid, the tree grows fast. The Jianghua forest area in Hunan Province (Latitude 25° N.) is located on the north slope of the Nanling Mountains. Chinese firs here reach 20 m. in height, with circumferences of 25 to 35 cm., in 25 years. On the other hand, in the Huitong China fir area of southwestern Hunan, which is at Latitude 27° N., China firs grow to a height of only 13.6 m. in 19 years. Oranges, pomelos and citrus fruits also grow well in this area. Although there are tropical fruits, such as longan and Chinese quince, in the basins on the south slope, the trees bear their fruit irregularly and it is of inferior quality.

The soil in this area is mainly red earth and yellow earth. The forests of the Nanling Mountains are well preserved and there is a rich accumulation of organisms on the forest floor. The soil consists mainly of dark red earth with 4 to 7 per cent organic matter on the surface. The top soil is greyish brown. It has a high natural fertility and is humid. All these factors are favourable to the growth of trees.

Above 700 m. on the northern slopes and 800 m. on the southern slopes is mountainous yellow earth. As there is a thick layer of withered branches and fallen leaves on the ground, little sunshine, much mist and intense humidity, the decomposition of the fallen matter engenders a large amount of organic acid. The soil thus shows the characteristics of podzolization. At high altitudes, podzolized yellow earth is often formed. Under the topsoil is a grey layer some 10 cm. in thickness, and beneath this iron-manganese concretions are often formed.

5) The Northern Guangxi Area

This area lies north of the line formed by the Youjiang River, the city of Nanning and the Darong Mountains, and it belongs to the subtropical zone. Limestone here is widely distributed whereas it is confined only to certain local basins in the Nanling Mountain Area. However, Guangxi is topographically a basin of low altitude and the limestone landscape here is different from that forming the Guizhou Plateau. That is why it is classified as a separate area.

North of the Guangxi Basin is the Guizhou Plateau; west of it is the Yunnan Plateau. In the northeast are the Nanling Mountains and in the southeast are the Shiwan, Darong and Yunkai mountains. The basin slants from northwest to southeast. The Youjiang, Hongshui and Guijiang rivers all flow into the Xijiang River along this slant. In the basin are rolling mountains, chiefly the Guangxi arc-shaped mountains. The east wing consists of the Dayao and Haiyang mountains running in a northeast direction, and the west wing consists of the Daming and Duyang mountains running in a northwest direction. The tip of the arc lies to the south of Litang. The highest peak of the arc-shaped mountains in Guangxi is more than 1,500 m. above sea level, while some karst depressions and valley basins are less than 100 m. above sea level. The karst landforms are highly developed, with karst pinnacles and karst depressions interspersing each other. There are more than 40,000 karst depressions in the Guangxi region, mostly in this area. The landscape at Guilin and Yangshuo is quite famous; both cities are noted tourist sites for Chinese and foreigners.

A large number of gaps in the Nanling Mountains northeast of the Guangxi Basin provide for the entry of cold waves into Guangxi. Hence the isotherm of the basin turns southward here in the eastern part of the country. Facing the Hunan-Guangxi corridor, Guilin experiences strong winds in the winter, which lasts 55 days with the average temperature in January of only 8°C. As the Hunan-Guangxi corridor is wide and flat, the cold waves sweep into Guangxi with strong force. In areas not sheltered by mountains, the boundary of the subtropical zone extends further south — all the way south to the Litang-Guixian line, or half a degree lower than the latitude of Guangdong. Because of the varied heat conditions, there are corresponding differences in the cultivated plants of the subtropical zone in north Guangxi and the tropical zone in south Guangxi. For example, moso bamboo forests are confined to north Guangxi, and China fir forests grow far more vigorously there. The species of tung-oil trees in north Guangxi are confined to *Aleurites fordii* (a subtropical species), while in south Guangxi are found *Aleurites montana* (a tropical species); the fruit trees in north Guangxi are mainly citrus trees, while in south Guangxi they are mainly tropical fruit trees, such as jack fruit and mango. But in the Hechi and Huanjiang areas in the north, where the Guizhou Plateau acts as a shelter, bananas and litchi can be grown.

The annual precipitation of the province stands at between 1,000 and 2,000 mm., reducing gradually from east to west. Most of the areas east of the Dayao Mountains have an annual precipitation of more than 1,500 mm., while west of them it is only 1,000 to 1,100 mm. For this reason, the vegetation differs from east to west. In the eastern part are mainly *Cyclobalanopsis glauca, Platycarya strobiacea, Engelhardtia chrysolepis, Schima superba,* masson pine, and *Castanopsis eyrei,* while in the western part are mainly xerophyte plants such as *Cyclobalanopsis glaucoides, Platycarya glandulosa, Engelhardia colebrookiana* and *Schima wallichii.* The Yunnan pine is a characteristic species of the Southwest Region. In Guangxi it is distributed mainly in the dry northwest corner. Near the Lingyun-Leye line is an area of mixed masson pines and Yunnan pines.

The natural landscape in this area of limestone and nonlimestone mountains and hills is of two vastly different types, depending on the bedrock. The landscape of the limestone mountains is mostly composed of karst pinnacles with steep slopes, while most of the slopes of sandstone and shale mountains are gentle. The primary vegetation on the limestone mountains is mixed evergreen broadleaf and deciduous broadleaf forests, chiefly *Cyclobalanopsis glauca* or *C. glaucoides, Sapium rotundifolium, Celtis sinensis, Pistacia chinensis,* and *Platycarya strobilacea.* The soil here is mainly brown lime soil, its pH being 6.0 to 7.5. The karst depressions are generally covered with layers of sediment. The soil in these depressions is red earth, but its nature is affected to some extent by the limestone. The primary vegetation on the low mountains and hills of sandstone and shale is evergreen broadleaf forests, composed mainly of plants of beech, tea, witchhazel and laurel families. The soil here is red earth. Thus *Cyclobalanopsis glauca* and *Sapium rotundifolium* trees with brown lime soil and castanopsis forests with red earth represent the two types of natural landscape in the subtropical north Guangxi area. And the two are often interspersed on the same plane.

Farmland improvement and water conservancy projects in this area have been greatly developed in recent years. In Duan, for instance, an underground river has been diverted for use in irrigation, and at other places underground reservoirs have been built (using karst caves and underground river channels) to provide excellent conditions for agriculture.

3. Utilization and Transformation of the Natural Environment

With a warm and rainy climate, four distinct seasons, widely distributed plains and basins, and numerous rivers and lakes, the Central China Region provides excellent natural conditions for the development of agriculture, forestry, animal husbandry and fishing. The area of cultivated land in this region accounts for a quarter of the country's total cultivated land, and because it is rich in paddy fields, the region turns out more than two-thirds of the country's rice. In addition, wheat, cotton, rape and other crops are grown, and high yields of timber from tung-oil trees, tea-oil trees, tea trees, China firs, masson pines and bamboo are harvested. Although the region has a long history of cultivation, the natural resources for agriculture still have great potential and large areas of red earth hills are yet to be improved and fully utilized.

(1) Role of Thermal and Water Resources

This region has rich heat and water resources and relatively even rainfall throughout the year, which is favourable to the growth of crops.   Thermophilic crops, such as paddy rice and cotton, grow well in an average daily temperature surpassing 15°C., and generally the duration of above 15°C. temperatures in the Central China Region is more than 165 days. The Minjiang River, the Oujiang River and the valleys of the Nanling Mountains have an average of 190 such days, and the Sichuan Basin and the middle and lower reaches of the Changjiang River have 175 such days.   In areas north of the Changjiang, there are 230 to 250 days in which the average daily temperature is equal to or above 10°C., with an accumulated temperature of 4,500°C.   In the southern part of Hunan and Jiangxi and the northern part of Fujian and Guangdong there are 270 to 300 such days, with an accumulated temperature of 5,000° to 7,000°C.   It should be noted that the full growing period* for two crops of rice is generally 220 days.   In southern and eastern Zhejiang, southern Jiangxi, eastern Hunan and the central part of the Sichuan Basin, there are 230 to 250 suitable days for the growing of crops.   These areas are the best for growing two crops of rice, and the output here is stable.   In central Zhejiang, southern Anhui, northern Jiangxi, the central part of the Hunan-Hubei Basin and most parts of Sichuan, there are 220 to 230 days fit for the growing of crops.   The heat conditions in these areas are suitable for two rice crops, but efforts must be directed against the early arrival of the autumn cold.   In northern Zhejiang, southern Jiangsu, central Anhui and western Hunan, there are 210 to 220 days fit for the growing of crops.   However, the output of two crops of rice in these areas is restricted be-

---

* Calculated in terms of agroclimate, the full growing period for crops refers to the average number of days between the period fit for the sowing of early rice and the safe flowering period of late rice plus the average number of days between the flowering and ripening of late rice, the latter being about 45 days.

cause of cold waves and unstable weather in spring, and because of the early arrival of cold in autumn.

In the Central China Region, early frost generally arrives in mid-November, with it coming to the northern part 15 to 20 days earlier than it does to the southern part. The last frost generally comes in early March, with the northern part receiving it 15 to 20 days later than the southern part. Except for the areas near the Nanling Mountains and in the Sichuan Basin, there is not only frost in March but the temperatures also fall below 0°C. For instance, in March 1952 the temperature in Jiangsu Province at Nantong stood at -3.4°C. and at Changzhou, at -3.6°C. And if the "plum rains" come early, the temperature may drop below 5°C. even in April. These low temperatures in late spring and early summer are unfavourable for the ripening of wheat, the sowing of rice and the nurturing of rice seedlings. Therefore, expanding the acreage planted in two crops of rice will not necessarily increase production in the transitional areas between the northern and southern parts of the subtropical zone. And, in the introduction of a three-crop system, including two crops of rice and one of wheat, it is impossible to use fine varieties that require a longer period of growth because each growing season is too short. For this reason, two crops of semi-late rice and wheat will yield more than a three-crop system of two rice plantings and one of wheat.

(2) Comprehensive Utilization of the Changjiang River

The Changjiang River is a long-winding river with many tributaries. It has a vast drainage area of 1.8 million sq. km. and a particularly rich flow that accounts for 37.2 per cent of the total runoff in the country. In terms of average flow, the Changjiang has a water resource reserve of 230 million kw., or 42.5 per cent that of the whole country. The Changjiang valley has a dense drainage network with the river and its tributaries having a navigation mileage of more than 70,000 km., or 70 per cent of the navigation mileage for the whole country. A total of 2,900 km. of navigation channel below Yibin in Sichuan Province are navigable by steamship throughout the year. After Liberation, the conditions for navigation greatly improved because the navigation channel at the Three Gorges and other places were dredged, dangerous shoals were removed and navigation marks established. In recent years, the tortuous Jingjiang River channels between Zhijiang in Hubei Province and Chenglingji in Hunan Province have been straightened, shortening the navigation route of the Jingjiang River by 58 km. In addition the capacity of the river's flow discharge has been increased and the flood-water level reduced.

The Changjiang River's flood season starts in April and ends gradually in October. The flood peak during this time is high and the flow enormous. The runoff accounts for more than 60 per cent of that for the whole year. The flood waters of the river are derived mainly from rainstorms over wide areas. In cases when the flood waters in the upper reaches meet those in the middle reaches, disastrous flood damage can occur. Before Liberation, the flood waters often breached the dykes. After Liberation, the 3,100 km. of dykes along the river were heightened and strengthened. In addition, the Jingjiang River and Hanjiang River flood diversion projects were completed, and big, medium-sized and small reservoirs, such as the one at Danjiangkou on the Hanjiang River, were built. All these have raised the flood prevention capacity enormously.

Tens of thousands of large, medium-sized and small reservoirs also were built since Liberation, and the irrigated acreage in the middle and lower reaches of the Changjiang River has rapidly increased. Moreover, scores of big and medium-sized hydroelectric power stations were constructed. One of these, the Gezhouba key water conservancy project, is the largest hydroelectric power station in the country. As part of the Changjiang Three Gorges project, this power station has a total generating capacity of 2.7 million kw., and an average annual power generation capacity of 13,800 million kwh. This is more than three times the total power generating capacity for the whole country in 1949. With the building of this key project, the water level of the Changjiang has been raised, with its water flowing back over 100 km. This has effectively improved the dangerous river channel of the Three Gorges and promoted navigation in the Changjiang.

(3) Utilization of the Red Earth Hills

Red earth is distributed extensively throughout the southern part of the subtropical zone south of the Changjiang River, covering about half of the total area. However, red earth has the following defects: It contains only a small amount of organic matter and has a high degree of acidity; it has weak water and fertility preservation power, and few plant nutrients; it is not easily replaceable or cultivable, and it is apt to be washed away or dried up. But the climate south of the Changjiang is warm and humid. The organic matter in the soil decomposes rapidly and the nutrients leach out of the earth quickly, but they also accumulate quickly. Many red earth hills and low mountains now suffer from serious soil erosion, and large expanses of wasteland have yet to be reclaimed.

As red earth hills and low mountains have different thicknesses of soil, fertility conditions and varying amounts of soil erosion, they must be improved according to local conditions. Roughly speaking, gentle slopes of less than 10° gradient and valleys where soil erosion is infrequent are suitable for growing food and other cash crops. Slopes of 10° to 20° gradient are suitable for growing tea, tea-oil trees, tung-oil trees, citrus groves and other marketable plants. Steep slopes of more than 20° gradient and hills, mounts and soil erosion areas need afforestation to conserve water and soil. In recent years, after overall planning and comprehensive improvement, a number of red earth areas that were low-yielding in the past have taken on a new look.

Chapter X

THE SOUTH CHINA REGION

The South China Region lies in the southernmost part of China and consists of the southern parts of Guangdong, Guangxi and Fujian provinces on the mainland, the islands of Taiwan and Hainan, and the South China Sea islands. Roughly conforming to the Tropic of Cancer, the northern boundary of this region begins north of Guangxi's Bose, moves along the northern bank of the Youjiang River to north of Nanning, then goes south of Wuzhou along the northern bank of the Xijiang River to north of Guangzhou and Shantou. Owing to the influence of the ocean, the line after Shantou turns northward to Xiamen along the coast of Fujian and the coastal area south of Fuzhou. The boundary between the South China and Central China regions is also the line separating China's tropical and subtropical zones. The specific boundary is mainly determined by natural vegetation and the growth and distribution of the tropical crops. Therefore all the South China Region, except areas high in mountains, belongs to the tropical zone.

1. Tropical Natural Landscape

Largely situated south of the Tropic of Cancer, the South China Region faces the ocean on the east and south. This region is under 1,000 m. above sea level in most areas, and abounds in heat and water resources. Its landscape is mainly tropical.

Although this region is on the northern margin of the global tropical zone, the tropical landscape in this region is not so typical as that in Malaysia, Indonesia and other areas, the South China Region is occasionally invaded by cold waves since the winter monsoons in China are extremely strong. At such times the lowest temperatures in the mainland section may plummet below 0°C. Frost may also appear in the northern part of Hainan Island. Therefore, compared with the other tropical regions in the world, the South China Region has a natural landscape that differs somewhat from other tropical landscapes.

(1) Humid and Hot Tropical Climate

This region has the richest heat and water resources in China. The cumulative temperatures are 7,000° to 9,500°C., the annual mean temperature is 20° to 26°C., and there are more than 150 days when the average temperature stands above 25°C. The South China Region has no winter in its true sense, and summer here lasts for more than six months. Southern Taiwan has a long summer of nine months (from March to November), and it is summer all year round in the southern part of Hainan Island and on the South China Sea islands. The annual range of temperature is not large — no more than 10°C. for Hainan Island, 10° to 12°C. for Taiwan, and about 13° to 17°C. for the mainland section. The diurnal range is generally smaller than it is in other parts of the country, about 6°C. on the average.

Winter temperatures are rather low because of the southward invasion of cold air. The coldest monthly average for the mainland section may drop to about 13°C., with an extreme low at or below 0°C. In January 1955 and 1961, violent cold waves sent the mercury plummeting below 0°C. for the mainland portion of the South China Region, and a low temperature of about 0°C. appeared briefly in the northern part of Hainan Island. The South China Region has virtually no frost or snow. Frosts may occur only in areas along the track of violent cold waves. For example, still waters froze in Guangzhou in January 1955 and 1957 when the city was attacked by cold waves.

Heat in this region increases from north to south whereas low temperatures and frosts weaken and even disappear. The northern part, with a coldest monthly mean temperature of 13° to 15°C., average extreme low at 0° to 5°C. and an average 1 to 10 days of frost, belongs to the light frost zone. Leizhou to the south of Zhanjiang belongs to the little or virtually frostless zone, with a coldest monthly mean temperature of 15° to 18°C., average extreme low at 5° to 8°C. and no frost in normal years except in the event of an exceptionally violent cold wave. From the southern part of Hainan Island to the Nansha Islands is a frostless zone because in winter this part is free from the influence of cold waves; the coldest monthly mean temperature stands at above 18°C. and the extreme low exceeds 8°C.

The South China Region can be divided into a tropic zone and an equatorial zone in accordance with heat conditions and the features of the natural landscape, particularly natural vegetation and agricultural vegetation. The equatorial zone has summer all year round, with a cumulative temperature above 9,000°C. Only the Nansha Islands in this region belong to the equatorial zone. The tropic zone can be further divided into two subzones. The southern part of the tropic zone has cumulative temperatures of 8,000° to 9,000°C. and is called tropical zone. It embraces the Leizhou Peninsula, areas to the south of this and also southern Taiwan. The northern part of the tropic zone has cumulative temperatures of 7,000° to 8,000°C. and is called quasi-tropical zone. It embraces the areas of Guangdong and Guangxi, Fujian's coast and all but the southern part of Taiwan.

A delineation of the quasi-tropical zone shows considerable differences between its natural landscape and that of the subtropical zone. The northern boundary of the quasi-tropical zone is climatically the northern boundary of the snowless line and the virtually frostless line. The vegetation is evergreen broadleaf forest of the monsoon rain forest type, which has many of the features of tropical forests. Many tropical animals, such as the gibbon, palm civet, hornbill and peacock, are distributed in the quasi-tropical zone, but they will not be found in the subtropical zone. A number of tropical insects are found in Taiwan, southern Guangdong, southern Guangxi and southern Fujian as well as on Hainan Island, but are not in Jiangxi and Hunan. These include the bollworm and the cotton stainer. The quasi-tropical zone has a variety of tropical fruit trees; and equatorial crops, such as rubber plants, grow well in small-scale environments of the quasi-tropical zone, but they cannot grow in the subtropical zone. Conversely, some commercial trees of the subtropical zone, such as tung-oil and tea-oil trees, are rarely planted in the quasi-tropical zone.

From this one can see that the quasi-tropical zone and the tropics are largely similar, and that there are only quantitative differences between the two. But the quasi-tropical zone has notable qualitative differences from the subtropical zone because cold waves in winter exert such a great influence on the growth of the tropical plants. However, exceptionally low temperatures occur only once in several or a dozen years and only have a brief duration. Thus they are not decisive to the development of the natural landscape. Within the quasi-tropical zone the factor that plays the most decisive role is the constant high temperature and absence of winter, which, combined with the water conditions, makes tropical organisms grow and develop continually. Full-sized tropical trees generally suffer little from the cold, and they can grow again after the cold waves disperse. Tropical insects can also survive short periods of low temperature. Therefore we delineate the quasi-tropical zone as a subzone of the tropics although its conditions are not entirely like those of the tropics.

The northern boundary of the quasi-tropical zone in Guangdong and Guangxi is rather tortuous because of the role of the Nanling Mountains, which act as a temperature barrier. These mountains lie between Guangdong and Guangxi on the one side and Hunan and Jiangxi on the other. They are an important dividing line for China climatically. But they are rather broken, and there are a number of low breaches that since ancient times have been passages for north-south communication. Chief among these are the Meiling pass between Jiangxi and Guangdong, the Zheling pass linking Hunan and Guangdong, and the Xingan pass connecting Hunan and Guangxi. These breaches are just 250 m. above sea level at their lowest point, and so they serve as a passage for cold waves in their southward march. Places near these passes have lower temperatures in winter and so the boundary for the quasi-tropical zone makes a series of southward turns near them.

Generally the South China Region has an annual precipitation rate of 1,500-2,000 mm., but the windward mountain slopes get more precipitation. For instance, the southeastern slopes of Daiyun Mountain, Lianhua Mountain, Yunkai Mountains, Shiwan Mountains, Wuzhi Mountain and the mountains in Taiwan each receive more than 2,500 mm. of rainfall a year. Conversely, the leeward areas, such as the western part of Hainan Island, get less than 1,000 mm. Also the mountains of the Taiwan Straits produce a rain-shadow zone on the leeward side where the yearly precipitation is only 750 to 1,000 mm. As for the seasonal distribution of precipitation, it is evenly spaced throughout the year on the South China Sea islands, and winter rains are greatest for Jilong and Taibei. The other areas get their greatest amount of rainfall in the summer, roughly 40 per cent of the annual total.

The South China Region is most frequently visited by typhoons in China. Statistics gathered between 1949 to 1969 show that the number of typhoons that landed on Guangdong, Fujian and Taiwan accounted for 88 per cent of the total reaching China. Guangdong got the most landings, about 45 per cent of the national total.

(2) Abundant Runoff and Long Flood Period

The Zhujiang River basin has an annual precipitation of about 1,500 to 2,000 mm., almost double that reaching the Changjiang River basin. Thus it ranks first in per unit water output, with an annual average runoff modulus of 25.9 sec. li./km^2. In area, the Zhujiang River basin is less than a quarter of the size of the Changjiang River basin, or three-fifths the size of the Huanghe River basin, but its average runoff over the years comes to 303.7 billion cu. m., about one-third that of the Changjiang and seven times that of the Huanghe. It is second only to the Changjiang in volume of water. Because of the heavy rainfall and big river flow, the mineral content of the river water is quite small, less than 50 mg./li., and its hardness is below 1.0 mg. equivalent/li.

Because the rainy season in this region is quite long, the flood period generally lasts about six months. The river water begins to rise after April each year and does not subside until October. This flood period for the Zhujiang River can be divided into three parts: (a) The spring flood period, between the lunar date of Pure Brightness (about April 5) and the beginning of summer, is quite short and the water level is not very high. (b) The summer flood period, between the beginning of summer and the Autumnal Equinox, has two flood peaks, the first at about the fifth day of the fifth lunar month and the second around the beginning of the seventh lunar month. The summer flood period is quite long and the water level is high, posing a threat to the dykes. (c) The autumn flood period, between the Autumnal Equinox and the lunar date of Frost's Descent (late September), is very brief, but it often comes close on the heels of the summer flood period so that the two combine to form a long stretch of high water.

(3) Tropical Vegetation and Soil

The natural vegetation in this region — tropical rain forest and monsoon rain forest — is characterized by multiple layers (generally 5 to 7) and a great variety of plants (a wooded area may contain over 100 different families and over 300 different species). In the tropical rain forests on Hainan Island grow typical rain forest plants, such as *Vatica astrotricha* and *Hopea hainanensis* of the Dipterocarpaceae and *Tarrietia parvifolia* of the Sterculiaceae, and tropical needle-leaf plants, such as the merkus pine (*Pinus merkusii*). The natural vegetation in the quasi-tropical zone — evergreen broadleaf forest of the tropical monsoon rain forest type — contains a great deal of subtropical components, but more than 60 per cent of the dominant tree species are of tropical families and genera. For instance, the mainland in Guangdong has 1,494 genera of seed plants, of which 84.06 per cent can be found both there and in Viet Nam, 70.21 per cent in the Philippines, and 63.98 per cent in Malaysia. There is a wide distribution in this region of plants of tropical families and genera, such as Myrtaceae, Anonaceae, Euphorbiaceae, Moraceae, Sapindaceae, Guttiferae, Meliaceae, Burseraceae, Sterculiaceae and Tiliaceae. Buttress, epiphytes, ligneous lianas, cauliflory and ligneous ferns can also be found. Besides, there are mangroves in the coastal areas, woods of *Burretiodendron hsienmu* in the limestone regions, and tropical savannas composed of *Eriachne pallescens* and *Eremochloa ciliaris*.

The types of plants change from north to south due to variations in temperature. Mangroves, for example, are found as far north as Changle in Fujian Province, but from Hainan Island northward, these trees occupy an increasingly narrower area along the coast. They also become increasingly shorter and fewer in variety. The highest mangroves on Hainan Island may stand 8 to 10 m. in height, and the plants that form a mangrove community include 18 species (Malaysia has 40), of which six belong to the Rhizophoraceae family. The mangroves on the Leizhou Peninsula are no taller than 6 m., and there are no more than 10 species here, four of which belong to the Rhizophoraceae family. The mangroves in Yangjiang, Chixi, Dapeng Bay and Haifeng belong to only 8 species,

2 of which are of the Rhizophoraceae family. The mangroves along the Xiamen coast are less than 2 m. tall and of 4 species. The mangroves in Zhangle, Jilong and Danshui represent only one species, *Kandelia candel.*

The soil in the tropical zone is laterite and that of the quasi-tropical zone is lateritic soil, also called "lateritic red earth". Thanks to the damp and hot climate in this region, the soil undergoes strong desilicification and allitic weathering. The silicates decompose intensively, silica and bases are leached away, and iron-alumina oxide accumulates notably. In other words, the elements of Ca, Na, Mg, K and Si are removed in some quantity while Al and Fe are concentrated. Therefore, the clay particles in the soil have a low siallitic ratio: 1.5 to 1.8 for laterite and 1.7 to 2.0 for lateritic soil. Owing to the strong desilicification, the SiO_2 content in the percolating water of the tropical soil is far greater than it is in subtropical areas (Table 13).

Table 13. SiO_2 Content in Percolating Water of the Tropical, Quasi-tropical and Subtropical Zones

Area	Type of soil	SiO_2 content (mg. equivalent/li.)
Tropical zone (Hainan Island)	laterite	1.173
Quasi-tropical zone (near Guangzhou)	lateritic soil	0.818
Southern subtropical zone (Liujiazhan, Jiangxi Province)	red earth	0.437

The clay minerals in the soil consist chiefly of kaolinite, gibbsite and iron oxide, which reflects the intensive weathering under tropical conditions. The northern boundary of the soil region that has kaolinite as the chief clay mineral basically tallies with the boundary of the quasi-tropical zone in South

China (Fig. 24), which shows that the quasi-tropical zone comes under the category of the tropics.

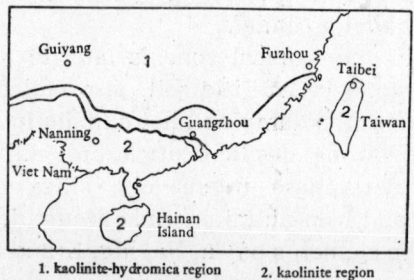

1. kaolinite-hydromica region   2. kaolinite region

Fig. 24   Clay Minerals in the Soil of the South China Region

Plants grow all year round in the South China Region thanks to its damp and hot climate, so that there is a strong exchange of matter between plants and soil. This exchange mainly depends on the quantity, quality and decomposition of the litters on the forest floor. The amount of duff on the forest floor is roughly 2.5 to 3 times that found on a temperate or sub-tropical forest floor (Table 14). The duff contains large quantities of nitrogen and ash-content elements. In tropical areas there is stronger microbiological activity, so that the duff decomposes at a faster speed. On a tropical monsoon rain forest floor, as much as 32 kg. of nitrogen, phosphorus, potassium, calcium, magnesium and other nutrient elements is returned to the soil in the form of duff every year. Therefore, despite strong leaching and allitic weathering, the intensive exchange of matter between plants and soil and the continuous supply in large quantities of fallen matter to the forest floor gives tropical forests a relatively thick layer of humus (generally 15 to 25 cm.) containing 8 to 10 per cent in organic matter. So, if properly reclaimed and utilized, the soils in the South China Region can maintain a considerably high level of organic matter and other nutrients, such as nitrogen, phosphorus and potassium.

Table 14. Amount of Duff on Forest Floor in China's Different Zones (Annual Amount: kg/ha)

Zone	Vegetation	Location	Total amount of duff
Tropical	Rain forest	Xishuangbanna	11,550
Tropical	Secondary forest	Hainan Island	10,200
Subtropical (southern)	Forest of white oak, Chinese sweet gum, and other woods	Huitong, Hunan	4,530
Temperate	Forest of spruce, fir, and Korean pine	Lesser Hinggan Mountains	4,080

(4) Tropical Animals and Corals

Fruit trees thrive in this region, providing favourable conditions for a rich variety of animals, especially those species that live in trees and on fruit. Prominent among the mammals are the gibbon, leaf monkey, rhesus monkey and red-faced monkey. Snakes comprise 120 to 130 species, far more than in any other region of the country. The abundance of snakes leads to many kinds of snake-eating birds on Hainan Island. The variety of animals on Hainan Island is somewhat different from that on the mainland. For instance, the South China Tiger, often seen in this region on the mainland, cannot be found on Hainan.

Coral is marine life peculiar to this region. It grows in warm and shallow seas, and the condition for its survival is an annual mean temperature of no less than 20°C. Coral will die if the temperature drops below 13°C. The corals of China are distributed in the South China Sea islands, on Hainan and Taiwan islands and along the coast of the mainland. They are found up to latitude 25° N. on the east coast of Taiwan because the water temperature there is under the influence of the warm current (Kuroshio) all year round. The mainland coast is affected by cold waves in winter and so corals in Penghu-Xiamen area often die from cold. But sea water in mainland bays sheltered by mountains remains warm, and so these bays, such as Daya Bay and Dapeng Bay, often have a concentration of corals.

(5) Tropical Agricultural Vegetation

The agricultural vegetation in the South China Region is tropical.   The crops (fruit trees included) can roughly be divided into two types: (a) equatorial crops that require a high order of heat and no frost, such as rubber, cocoa, pepper, coconut, oil palm and betelnut; and (b) tropical crops that are a little resistant to cold and can grow in areas occasioned by light frost, such as pineapple, mango, banana, papaya, coffee and anise. Equatorial crops can be grown everywhere in the tropical zone; and tropical crops, everywhere in the quasi-tropical zone.   Equatorial crops can also grow in the quasi-tropical zone in places with the proper microrelief environment. But the overwhelming majority of tropical crops are distributed in areas south of the northern boundary of the quasi-tropical zone. Coconut palms, for example, can grow normally and bear rich fruit on the Leizhou Peninsula and on Hainan Island, but in the Guangzhou-Nanning area coconut palms will bear no fruit. This reflects the difference in the amount of heat received in the tropical and quasi-tropical zones. Conversely, areas reaping good harvests of tropical crops are all located in the quasi-tropical zone. For instance, the area around Guangzhou obtains good harvests of pineapples, papayas, bananas and mangos. Anise and false ginseng are specialities of the quasi-tropical mountains because they prefer a habitat of cool summers, warm winters and little frost.   A number of subtropical trees, such as China firs and tea-oil trees, either grow poorly or mutate in the quasi-tropical zone. For example, the China firs that grow well in northern Guangxi (subtropical), grow very slowly and with yellowish leaves in Nanning and in the Liuwan Mountains (quasi-tropical).

With its high temperature and no frost all year round, the tropical zone can grow three crops of paddy rice a year, and no separate plots are necessary to nurse the paddy seedlings. The farms here can also produce three crops of rice, winter peanuts and winter sugarcane. But winter wheat does not do well because of the high winter temperatures. The quasi-tropical zone is where heat-loving crops, such as sweet potatoes, maize and sugarcane, can winter and grow. The farms in this zone grow two crops a year of rice, winter sweet potatoes, winter maize and winter sugarcane, none of which can winter or grow in the subtropical zone. There are also places in the quasi-tropical zone that grow three crops of rice a year.

2. Regional Differentiation of the Natural Landscape

Topographically the South China Region is mostly composed of low mountains and hills alternating with broad valleys and intermontane basins. The only exception are the Cenozoic folded mountains in central Taiwan, which have many peaks over 3,000 m. above sea level. Mid-mountains over 1,000 m. above sea level are confined to the peaks of the larger ranges, and fill only small areas. On the other hand, the plains in this region are not large either. The large coastal ones are chiefly the Zhujiang River Delta and the western plain of Taiwan. The larger inland plains include mainly the alluvial plain of the Yujiang River in Guangxi.

As the terrain of this region is rather low, there is generally no universal vertical differentiation in the natural landscape, and the gradual changes in latitudinal zonality are mainly determined by solar radiation and the influence of cold waves in winter. As the amount of heat increases from north to south, the tropical landscape becomes increasingly distinct.

In the course of the north-south zonal changes, winter temperatures have the most profound effects on the growth of the winter-sown crops, tropical crops and natural vegetation. But since the annual accumulated temperatures are quite high in most parts of this region, minor fluctuations in temperature do not suffice to bring about marked differences in crop growth. Therefore, the north-south differences in the natural landscape of the South China Region are chiefly caused by latitudinal variations in winter temperature. Judging by the winter temperatures and the related north-south differentiation in winter-sown crops, tropical crops and natural vegetation, the South China Region can be divided into three subregions, namely, the Guangdong-Guangxi-Southern Fujian-Taiwan Subregion, the Leizhou-Hainan Subregion and the South China Sea Island Subregion. These roughly correspond to the evergreen broadleaf forest of the quasi-tropical monsoon rain forest type with lateritic red earth zone, the tropical monsoon rain forest with laterite zone, and the equatorial rain forest with tropical phosphorite zone.

Within these three subregions, the heat conditions are basically the same, but the humidity and wind forces may vary. Such differences are closely related to distance from the sea and other topographical conditions, and they lead to variations in the natural landscape. Therefore, each subregion may be classified into several areas according to the topographical factors.

IV$_A$ Guangdong-Guangxi-Southern Fujian-Taiwan Sub-region

IV$_{A1}$ Taiwan-Penghu Area

IV$_{A2}$ Fujian-Guangdong Coastal Hill and Plain Area

IV$_{A3}$ Southern Guangxi Basin Area

IV$_B$ Leizhou-Hainan Subregion

IV$_{B1}$ Leizhou Peninsula Area

IV$_{B2}$ Hainan Island Area

IV$_c$ South China Sea Island Subregion

The boundaries of the three subregions do not tally exactly with the boundaries of the physical zones. The equatorial rain forest zone is confined to below latitude 12° N., but the South China Sea islands are all coral reefs and the vegetation and soil on these islands is roughly the same — coral reef vegetation and tropical phosphorite. The climate varies, but not much. Therefore, their natural landscapes are basically identical and we group them into one subregion. At the same time, the plain in southern Taiwan belongs to the tropics, but it is obviously inappropriate to separate it from the rest of Taiwan. Because most parts of Taiwan belong to the quasi-tropical zone, we place Taiwan together with Guangdong, Guangxi and southern Fujian under one subregion.

(1) Guangdong-Guangxi-Southern Fujian-Taiwan Subregion

This subregion includes the southeastern part of Fujian, the southern parts of Guangdong and Guangxi, Taiwan and nearby islets. It has the natural landscape and agricultural production characteristics of an area between the tropical and subtropical zones, but the landscape is similar to that of the tropics.

1) Taiwan-Penghu Area

This includes Taiwan and the nearby islets (the Penghu Islands, Huoshao Island, Hongtouyu Islet, etc.). Taiwan Island appears like a spindle, stretching from north-northeast to south-southwest. It is about 380 km. from north to south and some 145 km. from west to east at its widest point. With an area of 36,000 sq. km., it is China's largest island. The Pacific lies to its east, and it faces the mainland across the Taiwan Straits in the west, the narrowest part of the straits being less than 150 km.

The Taiwan mountain chain forms a major part of Taiwan Island, accounting for about two-thirds of its area. All the Taiwan mountains run in a north-northeast to south-southwest direction. They include four mountain systems from east to west: the Taidong Mountains, the Central Mountains, the Yushan Mountains and the Ali Mountains. Between them are longitudinal faults. On the grand rift belt between the Yushan Mountains and the Ali Mountains are Riyuetan (Sun and Moon Pool), Puli and other rift basins. Riyuetan is a famous scenic spot. The Central Mountains are the watershed of the island, many of their peaks towering more than 3,000 m. above sea level, while the Yushan Mountains are the central axis of the Taiwan mountain chain. Their main peak, Yushan, rises 3,950 m. above sea level. Rivers originating in these mountains radiate into the sea. The longest of these is the Zhuoshui River, 170 km. long. Owing to the relative heights of these peaks and the abundant water flow, the mountains provide many rapids and waterfalls with rich hydraulic resources. In the eastern part of the island is the Taidong longitudinal valley sandwiched between the Central Mountains and the Taidong Mountains. It is a narrow graben belt along a north-northeast rift line starting at Hualian in the north and ending at Taidong in the south. In size, it is 150 km. long and less than 5 km. wide. On the western part of the island is a relatively broad coastal plain, which is some 40 to 50 km. in width at its broadest point in the vicinity of Jiayi and Tainan. This is a delta plain and a most important farming area on Taiwan. As Taiwan experienced strong neotectonic movements in the past, it abounds in volcanoes and hot springs. Earthquakes are also frequent there. For instance, the Quaternary volcano group at Datun, near Taibei, consists of 16 volcanoes, the highest being 1,120 m. above sea level. The Xiaoguanyin Crater in this group measures over 1,000 m. in diameter and 300 m. in depth. There are 57 volcanoes between Tainan and Gaoxiong, 32 of which are active mud volcanoes that spew mud water and natural gas intermittently or continuously. There are also over 100 hot springs on Taiwan, all distributed along fault lines.

The climate of Taiwan is a maritime one. Influenced by the Kuroshio winds all year round, the annual range of

temperature is rather small, generally about 10° to 12°C.
February has the lowest monthly temperature in the year,
and the annual average temperature is higher than it is on
mainland coastal areas of the same latitude. The plains of
Taiwan have no winter, and summer lasts about 200 days
(270 days at Hengchun). The coldest monthly mean temperature is above 15°C. Taibei has an average of 15.2°C. in January,
similar to that of Hong Kong and higher than that of Zhangzhou in Fujian. In times of violent cold waves in winter, the
western and northern parts are affected to a certain extent.
Take the violent cold wave of February 13, 1901, for example.
The extreme minimum in Taibei and Taizhong came to -0.2°C.
and -1.0°C. But such cold wave invasions seldom occur.

Monsoons have an important effect on Taiwan's climate.
According to the alternation of monsoons, Taiwan has four
seasons: (a) the northeast monsoon period (from late October
to mid-March), rainy for the northeast and clear for the
southwest; (b) the monsoon change period (from mid-March
to early May), generally becoming clear for the northeast; (c)
the summer monsoon period (from early May to mid-
September), rainy throughout the island; and (d) the monsoon
change period (from mid-September to late October), the
weather being fine.

The distribution of rainfall in Taiwan is closely related
to the terrain. The northeast corner is windswept throughout
the year and has an annual precipitation of more than 3,000
mm., the same as that for the Central Mountains. Some
windward slopes may have as much as 5,000 mm., and the
rest generally have about 2,000 mm. The amount of rainfall
is less on the west coast, only about 1,500 mm. The Taiwan
Straits, situated in a rain-shadow belt and with a low and
level island surface, have about 1,000 mm. of rainfall a year.
But the evaporation there exceeds 1,600 mm., so that the
climate is quite dry. In terms of the seasonal distribution of
precipitation, the rainfall on Taiwan may be divided into two
types. The northeast is rainy all year round, with the

maximum precipitation in winter because the northeast monsoons bring water vapour from the ocean that becomes rain over the mountainous island. Conversely, the southern and western parts of Taiwan have their maximum precipitation in summer. Winter there tends to be dry, just the opposite from the northern part.

The natural vegetation of Taiwan is mainly evergreen broadleaf forests of the quasi-tropical rain forest type. These are distributed on the hills and low mountains less than 500 m. above sea level. The plants of the upper tree layer are mainly castanopsis of Fagaceae and camphor of Lauraceae. Taiwan used to be famous for the abundance of its natural camphor. But these are now mixed with *Ficus retusa*, *Podocarpus nakaii* and other tropical species. Plants in the middle and lower layers are chiefly *Helicia formosana*, *Tirpinia formosana* and other tropical varieties. The brush layer is also mostly of tropical species, such as *Psychotria rubra*, *Psidium guajava* and *Rauwolfia verticillata*. On the forest ground are many *Cyathea podophylla*, *Musa formosana* and *Alocasia odora*, similar to the plants found in tropical rain forests. Because the eastern slopes of Taiwan have more rainfall than the western slopes, tropical rain forests are only distributed in the Gaoxiong-Hengchun-Taidong area at the southeastern tip of the island. The special feature of the tropical rain forests here is that, without Dipterocarpaceae, the upper tree layer consists of *Myristica simiarum*, *Pterospermum niveum* (Sterculiaceae), *Sideroxylon duclitan* (Sapotaceae) and *Artocarpus lanceodata* (Moraceae).

In the mountains, the vertical distribution of the vegetation is roughly as follows:

500-2,000 m. above sea level — evergreen broadleaf forests and subtropical needleleaf forests. The upper-layer trees in the evergreen broadleaf forests are mostly camphor wood, as well as Nanmu, *Schima superba*, and castanopsis. On damp slopes in the south, there are clusters of tree ferns, huge ligneous vines and epiphytes in the forests.

2,000-3,000 m. above sea level — mixed deciduous broad-leaf, evergreen broadleaf and needleleaf forests. The deciduous broadleaf trees include beech and kawakawa Acer; the evergreen broadleaf trees include *Cyclobalanopsis glauca*; and the evergreen needleleaf trees include *Tsuga formosana, Chamaecyparis formosensis, Taiwania cryptomeria* and *Chamaecyparis taiwanensis,* some of which are valuable species peculiar to Taiwan. These trees grow to 50-70 m. in height, their trunks measure 7 m. in diameter and some are 1,000 to 3,000 years old. It is a pity that not many of them remain because of devastation over many years.

3,000-3,600 m. above sea level — subalpine needleleaf forests. The needleleaf trees consist mainly of Taiwan fir and Taiwan spruce, accompanied higher up by *Juniperus squamata* and *J. formosana.* On the forest ground are brushwoods made up of honeysuckle and rhodidendron.

3,600-3,950 m. above sea level — subalpine shrubbery with evergreen brushes and subalpine meadows. The shrub-bery is mainly azalea shrubs and meadows with *Festuca ovina* and *Parnassia foliosa.*

The soil on the hills and low mountains is primarily lateritic red earth. The lateritic red earth in Taizhong has a siallitic ratio of 1.91, the same as that of the quasi-tropical areas in Guangdong and Fujian. The soil on mountains is yellow earth, mountain yellowish brown earth, mountain brown earth and mountain meadow soil. Owing to the high temperature and abundant rainfall, these mountain forest soils are very fertile, yielding a high timber output per area unit.

Both Taiwan and Hainan are tropical treasure islands. The low mountains and hills can grow rubber, teak, mahogany and *mesua ferrea,* as well as many kinds of tropical fruit trees. Nothern Taiwan is one of China's most famous banana producers. Cane sugar and pineapples are important export crops for Taiwan.

The island is rich in forest resources. The Ali Mountains are one of China's most famous timber bases. *Chamaecyparis formosensis, chamaecyparis taiwanensis, Taiwania cryptomeria, Tsuga formosana* and *Pinns formosana* are known as the "five woods of Ali Mountains" and are noted for their fine timber.

    2) Fujian-Guangdong Coastal Hill and Plain Area

This area is roughly divided by the Yunkai Mountains from the Southern Guangxi Basin Area. East of the Yunkai Mountains, low mountains and hills intermingle with basins and plains. The mountains are chiefly composed of granite that runs in a northeast direction. The noted peaks of Mount Lianhua and Mount Luofu are just about 1,000 m. above sea level. Several rivers that flow into the sea form alluvial plains or deltas in their lower reaches. The biggest of these are the Zhujiang River Delta, Hanjiang River Delta (Chaoshan Plain), and the Zhangzhou Plain on the lower reaches of the Longjiang River. There are many offshore islands and islets, the biggest of these being Pingtan, Jinmen and Tongshan.

Climatically, this area has sufficient heat and water in normal years. In the event of an extreme cold wave, the temperature in many places may plummet below 0°C., but the occasions are few (Guangzhou may experience 0°C. once in a decade) and for a short duration. There is no snowfall except in the mountains. In Guangzhou, chrysanthemum and osmanthus flowers can blossom in the open even in winter. Phenologically there is no contrast in seasons. Therefore, low winter temperatures are only a temporary and occasional factor and do not have a decisive effect on the development of the natural landscape. Areas with the right small-scale topographical conditions suffer little from cold. For instance, Xinyi, Maomin and Huazhou in western Guangdong are encircled by the Yunkai Mountains to the north, east and west. These mountains serve as a natural defence against cold currents. So whenever a strong cold wave marches southward, the lowest temperature here remains higher than it does on the southern Leizhou Peninsula, which lies farther to the south latitudinally yet is more open topographically. Therefore, rubber and other equatorial crops can still grow and yield here during the advance of a cold wave. Guangzhou, however, is affected by low temperatures in winter. Some tropical plants, such as bananas and padauk wood, can grow in winter but with reduced speed. Some of the tropical plants stop growth in winter altogether, but resume growth the following year. Such plants include the silk-cotton tree, teak, papaya, pineapple, lemongrass and sisal plant. Guangzhou is called "the Cotton City" because of its abundance of silk-cotton trees. The district near Qixingyan (Seven Star Cave) in Zhaoqing City displays a beautiful scenery of karst pinnacles against a background of mango trees. The fields in the Zhujiang River Delta are grown with Chinese fan palms, a tropical plant and a famous specialty. Yangchun in western Guangxi produces *Amomum villosum*, a medicinal herb peculiar to tropical mountains. Besides, Xinhui and Chaozhou produce fine quality tangerines and oranges, showing that southern subtropical fruit trees have invaded this quasi-tropical zone.

The Zhujiang River Delta[1] includes the Xijiang-Beijiang River Delta and the Dongjiang River Delta. It has a total area of about 11,000 sq. km. Land here is fertile. It is Guangdong's principal marketable grain producer and an important industrial crop grower. As the Xijiang and Beijiang rivers flow largely from northwest to southeast, the delta also runs in a northwest-southeast direction. The delta is crisscrossed with small rivers, forming China's famous "network of rivers". These empty into the sea at eight outfalls, the most important of which are Muodao Gate and the Humen Gate. The Zhujiang River system has an average sediment discharge of over 80 million tons a year, so that the delta near the estuary is growing rapidly out into the sea at a maximum speed of 100 m. a year. The newly silted land is called a "sandy field".

The soil of this sandy field area of the Zhujiang River

---

[1] The name "Zhujiang River" originally denoted the section of river that flowed through Guangzhou, but it has now become the name of the river system formed by the Xijiang, Beijiang and Dongjiang rivers.

estuary is mainly strong-acid saline paddy soil, also called salt acid field. It develops from mangrove bog soil. The mangrove remains in the soil decompose under anaerobic conditions, producing an abundance of sulphides. Thus the salt-acid fields have a high sulphur content, reaching 2.3 per cent at the most. Drained, the soil has better aeration and the sulphides are oxidized into sulfuric acid (H_2SO_4). This leaves a strong acid reaction in the soil which has a pH value of only 2.5 to 3.5. This kind of soil is widely distributed in the estuary areas of the big rivers in the South China Region, such as the Qinjiang River in Guangxi, the Hanjiang River in Guangdong, and the river mouths in Taiwan and southern Fujian. It is a special soil that develops after coastal mangrove bogs in the tropics are reclaimed. Although this paddy soil is a man-made farming soil, it still retains zonal characteristics. In other words, it reflects the characteristics of the local physical geography.

The land in the Zhujiang River Delta is most intensively utilized. The local people make full use of the natural conditions to create a number of unique modes of farming. The "mulberry wood and fish pond" farm is an example. Here a pond to breed fish was dug in a low-lying field, and the mud from the excavation used as a base for growing mulberry trees. Now silkworm droppings can be used to feed the fish, and the pond mud can be used to fertilize the cropland mulberry trees. This constitutes a singular cycle of matter and form of utilization in which the land is utilized to the full according to the local conditions.

3) Southern Guangxi Basin Area

Carbonate rocks are extensively distributed in Guangxi, accounting for approximately 40 per cent of the total area of the Guangxi Zhuang Autonomous Region (Fig 25). At the same time, the natural vegetation on limestone hills is entirely different from that on sandstone, shale and granite hills and low mountains. The former is usually Hsienmu (*Burretiodendron hsienmu*) wood whereas the latter is usually olive wood.

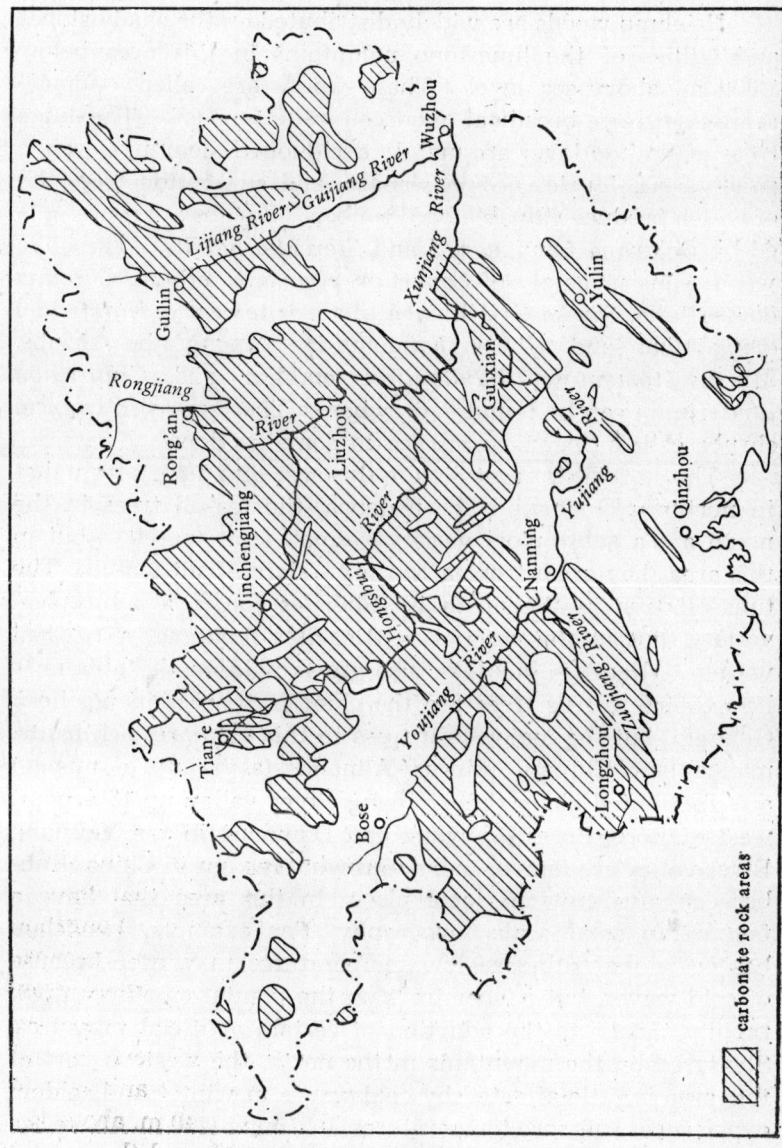

Fig. 25 Distribution of Carbonate Rocks in Guangxi

Hsienmu woods are widely distributed on the shady slopes and gullies of the limestone mountains in this area below 1,000 m. above sea level. These woods are called "tropical semi-evergreen broadleaf monsoon rain forests". The huge trees of the top layer are mainly deciduous Hsienmu, *Garcinia paucinervis*, *Muricococcum sinense*, and silk-cotton trees, all of which produce valuable hard timber. Shrubs are represented by *Delavaya yunnanensis* and *Sterculia nobilis*. The olive woods consist mainly of *Canarium pimela*, *C. album*, *Garcinia oblongifolia*, *Saraca Griffithiana*, *Artiaris toxicaria*, *Horsfieldia amygdalina* and *Hopea hainanensis*. Among the shrubs, *Myrtus tomentosa*, *Phyllanthus emblica* and *Cratoxylon ligustrinum* can be found everywhere. There are also tropical shrubs called *Dodonaea viscosa* in some sections.

The cultivated vegetation in this area also differs from that in northern Guangxi. For instance, the tea-oil trees in the north are a subtropical variety — small-fruit tea-oil — but in this area they are a tropical variety — large-fruit tea-oil. The tung-oil tree in the north is *Aleurites fordii*, a subtropical variety, but in this area it is *Aleurites montana*, a tropical variety. *Aleurites montana* also grows wild on the hills near Pingxiang. Citrus trees are the chief fruit trees in northern Guangxi, but the major fruit trees in this area are jack fruits, mangos and Chinese quinces. Almonds (a variety of mango) are distributed along the Youjiang River valley up to a point west of Bose. Bose, Dianyang and Diandong in the Youjiang River valley are famous mango-growing regions in China. Rubber can also grow in some places in this area that have a favourable small-scale topography. For example, Longzhou has occasional sub-zero low temperatures in winter because of cold waves, but rubber trees on the plantations there grow rapidly thanks to the adoption of certain artificial measures. Sheltered by the mountains in the north, the western part of this area is little affected by cold waves in winter and seldom experiences sub-zero temperatures. In Jingxi (740 m. above sea level) the accumulated temperature is 7,000°C. and the annual lows average 1.4°C. So, around Debao, coffee can grow in the mountains 1,100 m. above sea level.

The soil in the limestone area is mainly brown limestone soil. Owing to the high temperature, plentiful rain and the alternation of dry and damp weather, calcium carbonate is leached away in large quantities. This deprives the topsoil of its normal lime reaction and leaves it with a pH value of 6.0 to 7.5. There is also desilification and allitic weathering to a certain degree, and the siallitic ratio of the clay particles is about 1.8.

To sum up, rock mountains and earth mountains are not only two different geomorphic types, but they are also two different types of landscapes. This shows that lithology is an essential factor in the formation of the natural landscape.

(2) Leizhou-Hainan Subregion

This subregion includes the Leizhou Peninsula and Hainan Island, which is a tropical monsoon rain forest with laterite belt. It is rich in heat resources, the coldest monthly average temperature being 16° to 20°C. Plants can grow all year round, and coconuts and oil palms can grow normally. This subregion is China's most important base for tropical crops. Assured of an abundant water supply, three crops of paddy rice can be reaped here each year.

1) Leizhou Peninsula Area

The topography of the Leizhou Peninsula is simple, chiefly platforms and hills less than 100 to 200 m. above sea level, composed of sand sediments and basalt. On the basalt platforms are found isolated volcanic cones. For instance, Huguanyan (160 m. above sea level) near Zhanjiang City is a Quaternary volcanic cone. On its summit is an intact crater lake with an area of 3.6 sq. km. and containing water over 20 m. in depth.

The characteristics of the climate on the Leizhou Peninsula are scanty rain, strong winds and few foggy days. Zhanjiang, for instance, has only about 1,300 mm. of precipitation a year, the annual average wind velocity reaches 4 m./sec., and there are only 33 foggy days in the year. So it presents an arid scene because of strong evaporation. The natural forests have been mostly destroyed, and the present vegetation is mainly of the savanna type, formed by *Aristida chinensis*, *Eremochloa ciliaris, Imperata cylindrica, Ischaemum crassipes* and *Dodonaea viscosa.* The peninsula is also sparsely dotted with small trees, such as *Phoenix Hanceana* and *Aporosa chinensis.* The laterite, developed on shallow sea sediments, contains 60 to 70 per cent sand. These soils are called silica laterite. Their content of organic matter is low (less than 1 per cent); their phosphorus content is also low. The soil is loose and easy to plough, but it is weak in its ability to conserve water and its fertility. Rain water is easily lost through seepage, and drought poses a serious threat. If not properly reclaimed, the soil is soon seriously eroded. Shelter belts have been planted in recent years over large areas, and a canal, the Leizhou Youth Canal, has been dug. The canal runs from north to south across the peninsula for more than 170 km. As a result, there has been a large increase in the harvesting of grain, rubber and other tropical crops.

2) Hainan Island Area

Hainan Island, with a size of 32,200 sq. km., is China's second largest island. To the north it faces the Leizhou Peninsula from which it is separated by Qiongzhou Strait, some 15 to 30 km. wide. In the central part stands Wuzhi Mountain, whose peak rises 1,867 m. above sea level. This is composed mainly of granite and looks like a dome mountain. In the mountainous area are some local basins like Tongshi and Lechang, about 200 m. above sea level. The rivers on the island all flow from the mountainous area to form a radiation drainage system. The Nantu River flows northward into the sea via Haikou City. The Changhua River flows westward and empties into the sea in Changjiang County. The Wanquan River flows eastward to the sea near Qionghai. These rivers are short and small. The northern part of the island is a broad platform formed by shallow sea sediments and basalt, mostly less than 50 m. above sea level. On this platform are some modern cones, such as Mount Gaoshan in Lingao and Mount Leihu in Qiong-shan. The terrain is similar to that of the Leizhou Peninsula. At Danxian (Nada) and Tunchang, to the south of the basalt platform, there are granite hills. The hills shelter segments of local terrain from cold and wind, thus forming microclimatic conditions suitable for the growth of tropical crops.

Though it is a tropical island, Hainan is still influenced by continental monsoons in winter because of its short distance from the mainland. This is particularly true north of Wuzhi Mountain. When an exceptionally violent cold wave comes southward, the extreme low temperature here can drop to around 0°C. In January 1955, for example, under the succes-sive onslaught of three violent cold waves, the temperature at Dingan plummeted to -0.3°C., and that at Danxian to 0.8°C. The distribution of rainfall is closely related to the topograph-ical position. The southeastern part of the island is swept by wind all year round, and it is in the path of many typhoons and so it has more than 2,000 to 2,500 mm. of rainfall a year. The western part of the island is on the leeward side and re-ceives an annual rainfall of less than 1,000 m. The amount of evaporation here by far exceeds the amount of precipitation, making this the driest place on the island. Yinggehai, on the southwestern section of the island, is a noted salt field in South China. This difference in rainfall distribution is the most im-portant factor determining the various landscapes of Hainan Island.

The natural plants in the southeastern part of Hainan Island are those of tropical rain forests. *Vatica astrotricha* of the Dipterocarpaceae family and *Tarrietia parvifolia* of the Sterculiaceae family are most outstanding among the upper arborous layer. These trees have massive trunks, greyish white and glossy bark, and huge buttress like roots that rise as high as four metres above the ground. Under the arborous layer there are plenty of palmaceous plants, including gomuti palms whose leaves stretch up to five metres each. There are also quite a number of ligneous vines, which are found in all tropical rain forests.

The western part of Hainan is located in a rain-shadow belt, and for five to six months in the year this part gets a monthly rainfall of less than 50 mm. The natural vegetation here consists of deciduous, semi-deciduous and evergreen arbors, such as deciduous *Kleinhovia hospita* (Sterculiaceae) and *Spondias pinnata* (Anacardiaceae), semi-deciduous *Tilia hainanensis* (Tiliaceae), and evergreen *Diospyros potingensis* (Ebenaceae) and *Meyna hainanensis* (Rubiaceae). The shrub layer contains many drought-enduring, thorny bushes, reflecting the rather arid climate. In sections seriously denuded of trees, the vegetation is that of a savanna replete with thorny bushes.

In the limestone area, the climate is arid and the arbors are not tall, only 4 to 8 m. high. They form tropical shrub coppices because they are mixed with thorny lianoid shrubs and drought-enduring fleshy plants. The main tree species on the limestone low mountains in Yaxian and thereabouts are *Ficus microcarpa*, *Pterospermum heterophyllum* and *Terminalia hainanensis*.

The coastal areas in western and southwestern Hainan receive only 800 to 1,000 mm. of rainfall per year, while the amount of evaporation is twice as much and even ten times as much in the dry season. The natural vegetation is that of a savanna, with plant communities formed chiefly by xerophytic grasses scattered with deciduous trees, such as *Albizzia procera* and silk-cotton trees.

The soil in southeastern Hainan is yellow laterite. It has a high water content and is yellowish brown or yellow in colour. It is suitable for the growth of rubber trees, cocoa plants, oil palms and many other kinds of tropical crops. In the southwest, with its arid and hot climate, the soil is savanna soil (arid red soil). Here, plants above ground grow luxuriantly in the rainy season; and, in the dry season, organic

matter decomposes slowly. This facilitates the accumulation
of coarse organic matter. Thus the topsoil often contains
3 to 4 per cent organic matter. The arid climate weakens
the soil-forming process, reducing the weathering of the
minerals and making the desilicification and allitic weathering
less obvious. The siallitic ratio of the clay particles of the
savanna soil at Yaxian is as high as 2.6 to 3.3. Owing to little
leaching, coupled with the evaporation in the dry season, salts
accumulate in the top layer of the soil where the base saturation may be as high as 70 to 90 per cent and the pH value
6.0 to 6.5.

Wuzhi Mountain rises over 1,800 m. above sea level. It
has a marked vertical spectrum in its vegetation. The eastern
slopes receive plenty of rainfall. From 700 to 1,000 m. above
sea level is a mountain rain forest in yellow earth zone. The
arbors in the upper layer of this mountain rain forest are
Vatica astrotricha, Hopea hainanensis and *Tarrietia parvifolia.*
The forest contains a considerable variety of lauraceous and
palmaceous trees, as well as a rich growth of epiphytes and
lianas, so that it almost resembles a tropical rain forest scene.

From 1,000 to 1,600 m. above sea level is a mountain
evergreen broadleaf forest, which also has some features of
a tropical rain forest. The main trees here are various species
of castanopsis, Lithocarpus, Lauraceae and Theaceae, mixed
with many tropical varieties such as Pentaphylacaceae and
Araliaceae, and also *Dacrydium pierrei* and *Podocarpus im-
bricata* of the tropical Podocarpaceae family. The soil is mountain yellowish brown earth. Over 1,600 m. above sea level are
mountain mossy elfin forests and shrubbery.

Hainan Island, with its favourable climatic conditions,
produces an abundance of rubber, oil palms, coconuts, cocoa,
pepper and coffee. Owing to the dry climate, the western part
is only suitable for the growth of drought-enduring tropical
crops, such as sisals and century plants.

(3) South China Sea Island Subregion

The South China Sea islands embrace four island groups — Dongsha, Xisha, Zhongsha and Nansha — as well as Huangyan Island, all of which are either coral reefs or coral islands. Although the general practice among geographers is to separate the equatorial from the tropical zone to the south of the Zhongsha Islands, we group these coral-reef islands into one subregion because their climatic conditions are basically the same and their landscapes and utilization are identical.

The South China Sea islands include more than 200 islands, cays, reefs, shoals and banks. According to their height relative to the surface of the sea, they can be divided into submerged banks, submerged shoals, reefs, sand cays and islands. The overwhelming majority are submerged shoals, banks and reefs. There are not many surfaced islands. One is Yongxing Island, the largest of the Xisha Islands, which is only 1.85 sq. km. in area and is the administrative centre of the Xisha, Zhongsha and Nansha island groups. The tallest island, Shidao, stands only 15 m. above sea level, and it is only recently that these coral reefs and islands have emerged from the sea. For instance, the coral limestone on Shidao Island is only about 14,000 years old.

The coral islands are mostly atolls. Because the winds over the South China Sea are generally northeasterly and southwesterly winds, the atolls are mostly oval in shape with their long axis running in a northeast-southwest direction. For example, the Zhenghe Atoll and the Jiuzhang Atoll of the Nansha island group both stretch in a northeast-southwest direction. The Xisha Islands consist of seven northern islands and eight southern islands. The southern ones are the Yongle Islands that form the Yongle Atoll, which surrounds a vast lagoon. The Zhongsha Islands are composed of more than 20 submerged shoals and banks arranged in an oval shape, the long axis of which also runs in a northeast direction. The Nansha Islands embrace more than 100 islands, cays, reefs, shoals and banks. Over ten of them are bigger islands. The biggest one is Taiping Island, which stands 4 m. above sea level on the average and covers an area of 0.43 sq. km.

  The climate here has all the features of a tropical island monsoon climate. The annual range of temperature is quite small, a mere 4° to 6°C., and the annual average precipitation is about 1,500 mm. The seasonal alternation of wind direction is highly noticeable: southwesterly winds prevail from April to September and northeasterly winds are predominant from October to March. As these islands are particular close to the source of typhoons, the wind velocity is quite impressive throughout the year. The annual average wind velocity is 5.4 m./sec. for the Xisha Islands and 6.4 m./sec. for the Dongsha Islands. The monthly wind velocity is at its maximum from October to February. In this period typhoons are predominant at the beginning, and then the northeast monsoon coincides with the northeast trade winds to amplify the wind force.

  The soil here is rich in calcium because these coral islands have not emerged from the sea for very long. The islands are washed by the waves and swept by fast winds all year round, and the vegetation is fleshy evergreen broadleaf shrubbery and coppice, a type of vegetation peculiar to tropical coral reefs. The plant species are scanty, trees low (because of the strong winds), and they have the features of xerophytes and holophytes. Inside the coastal coral beaches is evergreen shrubbery, 2 to 5 m. high, mostly fleshy, juicy brushes, such as *Scaevola sericea, Messerschimidia argentea* and *Guettarda speciosa.*

  The South China Sea Islands provide an ideal haven for sea birds. As the sea abounds in fish, these birds are legion. The birds are mainly white-bellied brown boobies. The Xisha Islands are known locally as the "Kingdom of Birds", and the bird droppings are piled up on the island surface to about one metre in thickness. Under the high temperatures and wet conditions, guano decomposes rapidly, releasing large quantities of phosphate, which, once leached, combines with the calcium to form guano-phosphorite — an excellent natural fertilizer.

Under the above-mentioned climatic, vegetative and parent material conditions, the soil is mainly phosphorite, rich in phosphorus and calcium. The top layer contains 30 per cent P_2O_5 and about 40 per cent CaO. The soil on the outside of the sand banks is mostly coastal saline soil because the soil here is constantly washed by the tides, whereas phosphorite is mainly distributed on the upper part and inner side of the sand banks. The phosphorite is very coarse, mostly belonging to the category of sandy soils. Its grains are composed of the skeletons of coral sea shells and other marine life. This soil is young, and so it is only slightly developed and the minerals are only slightly weathered. The clay composition is chiefly mica and hydromica, which is quite different from that of conventional soils in the tropics. The most salient feature of phosphorite is its high phosphorus content, which exerts a significant influence on the chemical composition of plants and on ground water. The plants of these islands contain more than one per cent phosphorus, 5 to 10 times as much as found in other plants of the tropics. The ground water may contain as much as 4.9 mg. of P_2O_5 per litre.

Shelterbelts of beefwood and other trees have recently been planted on some of the Xisha Islands. Tropical crops, such as coconuts, papayas, bananas and pineapples, as well as vegetables are now growing there. Some of the Nansha Islands (Zhongye Island and Nanwei Island) also have coconut trees and other cultivated crops, and these have become bases for fishermen operating in the South China Sea.

3. Utilization and Transformation of the Natural Environment

With its high temperature, abundant rain, rich heat resources and vast expanses of plains and hills, the South China

Region is an ideal environment for the development of tropical industrial crops. Because the region lies on the northern margins of the tropics, its heat resources are not as rich as are those of the tropics proper. But it is possible to take artificial measures to transform the habits of tropical crops. Practice proves that tropical crops subjected to low temperature sometimes grow better and are more productive than they are in their natural environment. There are, of course, some unfavourable climatic factors in the South China Region for the development of tropical crops, such as occasional low temperatures in winter, seasonal dry spells and strong winds. But these can all be prevented or alleviated by artificial means.

(1) Effect of Winter Low Temperature on Crops

The invasion of cold waves and the intense radiation cooling in the wake of a cold front often leads to low temperatures in winter. This affects the growth of tropical crops. Take the cold wave in February 1957, for example, which lasted for about 20 days in Guangdong. This caused losses in the banana crop in the Zhujiang River Delta — China's principal banana growing area.

The invasion route for cold waves is closely related to the topography. The Hunan-Guangxi Passage in the Nanling Mountains is over two kilometres wide, and more often than not the main current of a cold wave flows through this to eastern Guangxi via Guilin. Because there are no high mountains between Guilin and western Guangdong to obstruct it, a cold wave can drive its way southward into the Leizhou Peninsula and even to Hainan Island. Under the onslaught of one such cold wave in January 1955, the extreme low temperature in Suixi dropped to -2.5°C., and at Danxian on the northern plain of Hainan Island to a record low of 0.8°C. However, because the Qidianling Pass on the Beijing-Guangzhou Railway is rather narrow, the cold wave swept past this, pushed southward along the Lechang Gorge in the Pingshi area and along the Beijiang River to affect Yingde, Guangzhou and other areas, but its force was rather weak. The extreme low for Guangzhou was only -0.3°C. The invasion routes of the cold waves are always frost areas in South China. Therefore, consideration must be given to the scope of the areas affected by cold waves and the local topographical conditions when it comes to developing tropical crops.

(2) Seasonal Dry Spell

The high temperature period in South China coincides with the rainy season, and the low temperature period tallies with the rainless season. For about six months (April to September for the mainland, March to October for Hainan Island) the monthly average temperature is above 20°C. and the monthly amount of rainfall exceeds 100 mm. This is a period in which water and heat work in perfect cooperation. On the other hand, most areas also have four to five months in which the monthly rainfall is less than 50 mm. The Leizhou Peninsula has five to six such months. Therefore, seasonal deficiency in water plays a certain inhibiting role on some tropical crops. Some tropical crops only require sufficient water in the soil, others demand a high amount of atmospheric humidity as well. In the case of the former, it is possible to provide artificial irrigation to make up for its lack in the natural environment.

(3) Hazards of Strong Winds

The South China coasts are swept by strong winds with an average annual velocity of over three metres per second. These winds are of two types: land and sea breezes and typhoons. The period for possible typhoons is longer here than on any other coastal area of China. It ranges from May to November, seven months in all. The land and sea breezes are constant in direction and of mighty force, often bringing considerable damage to the tropical crops. The farms along the South China coast have all in recent years been planted with shelterbelts. This has alleviated the hazards otherwise caused by windstorms or droughts.

The region has vast expanses of savanna dominated by tropical short grass. These are not the product of the climatic conditions, but mostly of human activity over a long period time. With the destruction of natural vegetation and increasingly serious soil erosion, the character of the soil has also changed gradually, thus greatly reducing its fertility. For instance, under the cover of natural forests, the lateritic red earth contains 2 to 5 per cent organic matter and laterite 8 to 10 per cent. But after forests have been destroyed and replaced by grasslands, the water and heat conditions change. The result is intense mineralization and leaching away of the organic matter, and humus content in the soil rapidly drops to 1-2 per cent. Therefore proper protection of the natural vegetation and rational use and planning of the land already reclaimed should play an important role in preserving and raising the fertility of the soil in the future. Under the leadership of the government, the people in this region have made energetic efforts to plant vast tracts of forests so as to stabilize the sands of the coastal zone as well as to protect the farm lands and conserve water and soil. In Hainan, Zhanjiang and Hepu prefectures, for example, it has been decided that 15 to 30 per cent of the land area will be covered by shelterbelts in order to protect the croplands.

Chapter XI

THE SOUTHWEST CHINA REGION

Lying to the southeast of the Qinghai-Tibetan Plateau and west of the Guizhou Plateau, the Southwest China Region embraces almost all of Yunnan Province and the southwestern corner of Sichuan Province. Its northern boundary starts at about latitude 28° N., somewhere north of Xichang, and passes through Jiulong and Muli up to the vicinity of Zhongdian. Its eastern boundary begins at Daliang Mountain, turns south past Leibo, Zhaotong, Huize, Xuanwei, and then follows the western portion of the Beipan River up to the vicinity of Funing. It follows the national boundary in the west and in the south.

Judging by atmospheric circulation, the climate in the Southwest China Region can be divided into two types. One is the western tropical monsoon type and the other the eastern tropical monsoon type. The area for the latter is rather small. For most of the region, the summer half-year is controlled by the southwest monsoon and the winter half-year is under the influence of the tropical continental air mass. The region is therefore basically free from the influence of cold waves. The circulation situation is the same as that over India and Burma. The region, moreover, is directly linked in the west with northern Burma. Although it is topographically a mountainy plateau about 2,000 m. above sea level, its basic zone is still tropical, and so the region is called a tropical mountainy plateau. In the winter half-year, the tropical continental air mass meets with the cold air mass from the north over the borders of Yunnan and Guizhou, forming the famous Kunming quasistationary front. To the east of this Kunming quasi-stationary front is the Guizhou Plateau of the Central China Region where

314

overcast and rainy weather lingers on in winter and "the sky is not clear for three days on end". This is a masson pine with yellow earth area. To the west of this Kunming quasi-stationary front is the Yunnan Plateau of the Southwest China Region where the weather is warm and clear in winter. This is a Yunnan pine with red earth area. The small area of this region with the eastern tropical monsoon climate covers the section east of Ailao Mountain in southeastern Yunnan. It is under the influence of the southeast monsoon in summer and the polar continental air mass in winter, so that it is visited by cold waves. The weather here is similar to that of the South China Region. Because the area is quite small and the cold waves are vastly weakened at this point by the plateau and mountains in the north, it is designated as belonging in the Southwest Region.

1. Tropical Mountainy Plateau Landscape

The geomorphic structure of the mountainy plateau in the Southwest Region includes vast expanses of planation surface, towering mountains, low basins and incised valleys. West of the Yuanjiang and Yalong rivers, the mountains and rivers run from north to south, with high mountains and deep valleys paralleling one another. This is called the Hengduan Mountain area. These parallel mountains lie approximately north of latitude 26° N., and from west to east are Gaoligong Mountain, Nushan Mountain and Daxue Mountain. Between these mountains flow several big rivers, the Nujiang, Lancang, Jinsha and Yalong. Here the geological structure is complicated by close folding and clusters of faults, probably resulting from a violent thrust northeastward by the Indian Plate. A number of big rivers have developed along fractures to form deep downcutting valleys. North of latitude 26° N., the interfluvial peneplains have been totally destroyed, and there is a sharp difference in elevation between the mountains and the valleys. The valley bottoms are generally 1,500 to 2,000 m. above sea level, while the mountains often reach as much as 4,000 m. above sea level and more. Owing to the influence of the fracture zone, the Jinsha River makes a zigzag turn below Shigu. So does the Yalong River in the vicinity of Wali. At Hutiaojian Gorge on the Jinsha, below Shigu, the river level is less than 1,800 m. above sea level. But Yulong and Zhongdianxueshan mountains on the banks of this river rise more than 5,000 m. above sea level, a difference of some 3,000 m. The river is a mere 30 m. wide at its narrowest point and the water roars past in a torrent that can be heard several miles away. The famous Changjiang Gorges between Sichuan and Hubei pale before this tremendous canyon.

Vast areas of planation surface stand to the south of latitude 26° N., producing the "Yunnan Plateau surface". Here the mountains gradually decrease in height, with isolated peaks exceeding 3,000 m. Thanks to tectonic action, the mountains branch out like a broom and are designated as the broom mountain system in southern Yunnan. From west to east they are Xueshan, Bangma, Wuliang and Ailao mountains, interspersed by the Nujiang, Lancang, Babian and Yuanjiang rivers, with relative hights of less than 1,500 m. East of Ailao Mountain and Yuanjiang valley is the Yunnan Plateau 2,200 to 2,400 m. above sea level. Karst landforms are well developed here in the southeastern section of the plateau, a typical karst plateau, of which the "stone forest" at Lunan is widely known.

On the mountainy plateau of the Southwest Region are also distributed many low but broad basins, locally known as "level land". These include Yingjiang, Mangshi, Yunjinghong and Mengla, all less than 1,000 m. above sea level, and Wenshan, Kunming, Baoshan, Lijiang and Xichang, between 1,300 and 2,000 m. above sea level. The level lands are populated, farming centres. (Fig. 26)

The topography of the mountainy plateau sets forth the unique landscape of the Southwest Region. The complex topographical structure, the wide differences in elevation and

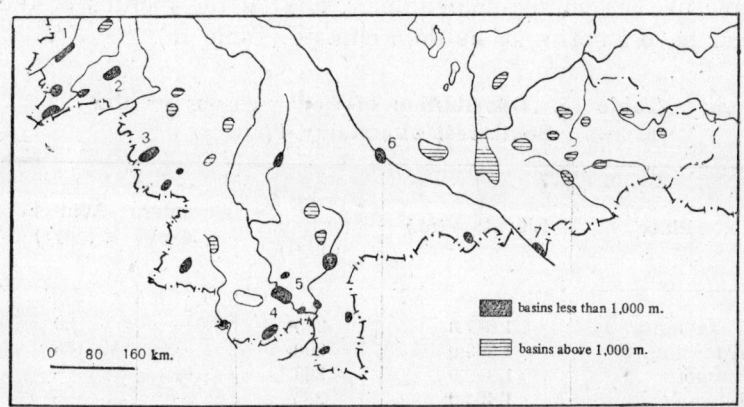

Basins: 1. Yingjiang 2. Mangshi 3. Mengding 4. Dame..glong 5. Yunjinghong
6. Yuanjiang 7. Hekou

Fig. 26 Distribution and Elevation of Basins in Southern Yunnan

the north-south mountain ranges and rivers are the main factors distinguishing the landscape of the Southwest Region.

(1) Spring All Year Round

The climate is characterized by warm winters, cool summers and spring-like weather for all four seasons, because the temperature in winter is rather high under the control of the tropical continental air mass, while the weather in summer is cool thanks to the high altitude. This is the common feature of the world's tropical mountainy plateaus (1,000 to 2,000 m. above sea level). The Shan States Plateau in Burma, the Central-Plateau of Africa and the Mexican Plateau all bear this feature. Basins at an elevation of 1,500 to 2,000 m. in central Yunnan, such as Kunming, generally have no summer, with spring and autumn extending for as long as nine to ten months and winter lasting only about two months. But the January mean temperature is over 9°C. Besides, winter has many fine days with dry air and sufficient sunshine so there is no feeling of cold. Basins about 1,300 m. above sea level, such as Simao, have neither winter nor summer, and all the months of the year have a spring or autumn climate (Table 15).

Table 15. Distribution of Four Seasons on the Southwest Mountainy Plateau

Place	Elevation (m.)	Spring & autumn (days)	Summer (days)	Winter (days)
Tengchong	1,647.8	285	—	80
Kunming	1,893.0	300	—	65
Simao	1,319.0	365	—	—
Lincang	1,464.0	365	—	—

The annual range of temperature on the southwest mountainy plateau is generally small and the diurnal range is large, reflecting the characteristics of tropical mountains. At Kunming, for example, the annual range of temperature is a mere 11°C., but the January mean diurnal range amounts to 14°C. The diurnal temperature variation in January tops 20°C. at Yingjiang. Subtropical plains of the same latitude in eastern China experience a larger annual range of temperature and a smaller diurnal range. That's why Baoshan, Kunming and other places on the plateau in central Yunnan have a climate so vastly different from that of Hengyang in the Central China Region (Table 16), although their accumulated temperatures and annual average temperatures are quite similar. Phenologically, osmanthus and chrysanthemum flowers can bloom in all four seasons in Kunming, something that cannot happen in the Central China Region.

Let's compare Xichang with Chongqing and Luzhou (217 and 305 m. above sea level) in the Sichuan Basin, places noted for their warm winters. Although Xichang is 1,200 to 1,300 m. higher than the latter in altitude, its January average temperature is about 2°C. higher. This suffices to show that the winter

Table 16. Thermal Conditions in the Southwest Region and Central China Region

Region	Place	Latitude	Elevation (m.)	Coldest month (°C.)	Hottest month (°C.)	Annual range (°C.)
Tropical Mountainy Plateau	Kun-ming	25°01′	1,893	9.5	20.9	11.4
	Xi-chang	27°53′	1,597	10.6	22.8	12.2
Subtropical Plain	Heng-yang	26°56′	64	5.1	29.1	24.0
	Luzhou	28°53′	305	9.0	28.0	19.0

warmth in Xichang is definitely not due to its topography alone, but is also the result of its belonging to a tropical mountainy plateau.

The climate of the southwest mountainy plateau — warm winter, cool summer and spring-like weather in all four seasons — enables some plants that are not resistant to cold to grow at places of high elevation. For example, anise grows well at Taihua Temple in the Western Hill of Kunming, which is over 2,250 m. above sea level. But this plant would die from cold at the same altitude in the subtropical zone of eastern China. Paddy rice can also grow at elevations of 2,400 to 2,700 m. in Yunnan, the highest point that rice can be grown in China. The year-round influence of warm air currents and the large diurnal temperature range facilitate the development of tropical crops. Therefore, the altitude (as much as 900 m.) for growing tropical crops in the Southwest Region is much higher than it is in the South China Region. But the disadvantages are cool summers and insufficient intensity of temperature. Kunming and elsewhere on the plateau in central Yunnan have only one or two hottest months with an average temperature of

20°C. Studies show that places having seven or eight months with a monthly average temperature above 10°C. and a total average exceeding 20°C. are suitable for growing two crops of rice. Kunming has ten months with a monthly average temperature above 10°C., but the total average for these months is only 16.7°C. So its heat resources are not great enough for two crops of rice; and cotton, peanuts and other warmth-loving crops can be scarcely cultivated.

(2) Well-Marked Alternation of Dry and Wet Seasons

Although climatically the region doesn't have marked contrasts in seasons, it does have notable differences in dry and wet weather. Generally, it is dry from November to April and wet from May to October. Rainfall in the dry period accounts for about 10 to 20 per cent of the annual precipitation. Rainfall during the dry period at Kunming is only 11 per cent of that in the wet period. For Xichang and other places it is less than 5 per cent. Because of the large amount of moisture, high humidity, many rainy days and less sunshine in the wet period (sunshine in the dry period is generally 20 to 30 per cent more than in the wet season), the daytime temperature is not high, nocturnal radiation cooling is not sharp and the temperature drops slowly. Thus the differences in temperature between day and night are small. During the dry period, however, the humidity is low and there is much sunshine, daytime temperature in winter is high and radiation cooling at night is rather strong, resulting in a bigger diurnal temperature range. Take Kunming, for example. Its diurnal temperature variation averages 14°C. in January, and only 8.8°C. in July.

The climate of the Southwest Region (especially in winter) differs vastly from that of the Central China Region. In winter, the climate of the former is dry and warm, and there is sufficient sunshine, whereas the latter region is cold and rather damp. In the Sichuan Basin to the east of Daliang Mountain, for example, it is cloudy and foggy throughout the winter, while the area west of the mountain often enjoys clear days and sunshine (over 2,300 hours of sunshine at Xichang and 1,300 hours at Luzhou). The area west of the quasi-stationary front has warm and clear weather (Table 17) and much sunshine. Kunming, for instance, has an average of over 9°C. in January and 2,522 hours of sunshine a year. But Shuicheng at a similar altitude (1,811 m. above sea level), east of the quasi-stationary front, has a January average temperature of only 2°C. and its winter has an unbroken spell of clouds, rain and snow. Shuicheng has as many as 235 cloudy and rainy days in a year, and only 1,505 hours of sunshine.

Table 17. Comparison of the Half-Year Distribution of
Rainy Days at Yunnan and Guizhou

Place	Elevation (m.)	Percentage of rainy days from May to October	Percentage of rainy days from November to April
Qujing	1,898	77	23
Kunming	1,893	79	21
Shuicheng	1,811	55	45
Guiyang	1,070	55	45

(3) Vegetation and Soils

The topography of the Southwest Region is varied, ranging from valleys and basins less than 1,000 m. above sea level to high mountains over 3,000 m. and even more than 5,000 m. above sea level. Particularly in the Hengduan Mountain area of the western part of the region, the climate differs vastly from one place to another owing to differences in altitude. In fact there is a saying about this region, "The sky is not the same at a distance of ten *li*." The mountains and rivers mainly run in a north-south direction, favouring the penetration of humid and warm air currents from the south. River valleys provide an invasion route for Malayan flora and fauna and also provide a complex environment for the settlement and evolution of plants and for the development of soils. Yunnan Province alone boasts about 12,000 species of plants, nearly half that for the total country.

Roughly, the vegetation and soils in basins and valleys less than 1,000 m. above sea level bear the marks of the tropics. The vegetation belongs to the tropical monsoon rain forest type, and laterite is well developed. Areas of 1,000 to 2,500 m. above sea level have the features of a subtropical zone, with subtropical dry evergreen broadleaf forests and mountainy plateau red earth. Because the Yunnan Plateau is hardly accessible to cold waves, subtropical evergreen broadleaf forests may spread to an elevation of 2,800 to 2,900 m. above sea level, whereas they can be located only in places below 1,500 m. on the Guizhou Plateau at the same latitude. The subtropical evergreen broadleaf forests here differ from those of the subtropical zone of the eastern China, with rather simple species of the chinquapin and castanopsis genera, composed mainly of drought-enduring *Cyclobalanpsis glaucoides*, *Castanopsis delavayi* and *Pasania spicata*. Lianas and epiphytes are rarely seen in the forest and there are none or few of the hydrophilous ferns, such as *Woodwardia japonica*. The mixed forests of coniferous and broadleaf trees at elevations of 2,600 to 2,900 m. above sea level also differ from those in the subtropical zone in eastern China. They have drought-enduring yellow oaks (*Cyclobalanopsis delavayi*) with thick-skinned evergreen broad leaves, but no hydrophilous beeches. Besides, Yunnan pines are the representative plants for the Southwest Region. This is a strongly heliophilous species, loving warmth and enduring drought, so it is widely distributed in the acid soil areas of the Yunnan Plateau. These vegetative characteristics are closely related to the climate of the tropical mountainy plateau, which is warm and dry in winter.

The soil of the southwest mountainy plateau is chiefly

red earth, while that of the nearby Guizhou Plateau is mainly yellow earth. This significant difference also notably reflects the bioclimatical characteristics of the tropical mountainy plateau. The red earth of this region is called mountainy plateau red earth to distinguish it from the red earth on the plains south of the Changjiang River. It is found up to over 2,000 m. above sea level on the Yunnan Plateau. Central China experiences high temperatures and plenty of rain in summer, there is intense leaching and allitic weathering of the soil, and so the soil has a higher content of active aluminium and acidity (belonging to the strong acid type) and the humus is strongly decomposed. Under the singular climatic conditions of the tropical mountainy plateau, the soil in central Yunnan undergoes weaker allitic weathering, leaching and decomposition of humus. For instance, the total amount of exchangeable salts (mg. equivalent/100 g. of soil) of the dark red earth on the floor of an evergreen oak forest in Kunming is often greater than that of the dark red earth in the Central China Region.

During much of the Tertiary Period, the Southwest Region was a tropical lowland. Towards the end of this period, in the Pliocene Epoch, the land was uplifted over a wide area and dissected by rivers. On the present mountains and eroded surfaces at higher elevations are preserved many Tertiary tropical plants and old residuum. At places over 2,000 m. above sea level, as on Jinpinglao and Pingbiandawei mountains in southern Yunnan, Tertiary paleotropic remnant plants can be found. These include *Brassiopsis hispida*, *Manglietia fordiana*, *Rehderodendron macrocarpum* and *Diplopanax stachyanthus*. Old residuum and lateritic soils of the Tertiary Period have been discovered at an elevation of 2,000 m. above sea level near Kunming. The siallitic ratio in these soils is even less than 1.0. They are not in keeping with the present bioclimatic conditions and must have developed during the wet and hot climate of geological times. Remnants of paleotropical karst pinnacles can be found at many spots on the plateau in eastern Yunnan. The well-known "stone forest" at Lunan is one kind of karst landform that developed in the wet and hot climate. Its lower part is usually found covered by Tertiary stratigraphy. This shows that it is a Tertiary landform preserved at its present elevation by the subsequent uplift of the earth's surface.

In the course of the uplifting process and cooling of the climate, the paleotropical plants changed gradually to adapt themselves to the ecological environment. But many plants of paleotropical Malayan flora were preserved, such as the Dipterocarpus, Garcinia, Hopea and Dalbergia genera, as well as *Cycas peotinata*, *Cephalotaxus harringtonia* and other paleophytes. A number of species were preserved, and they developed under suitable conditions, sometimes achieving the ability to grow at considerable heights. For instance, in Yingjiang, Mangshi and other basins in the southwestern part of the region the upper limit for the distribution of tropical tree species is quite high. *Ficus altissima* and *Musa wilsonii* can grow here at an elevation of 1,300 m. above sea level. But because it is cool in summer in the basins, northern subtropical species, such as deciduous oaks, *Betula cylindrostachya* and *Schima wallichii*, can spread along the mountains down to the basins forming a type of vegetation in which southern species mingle with northern species.

The vegetation and soil spectrum in the Southwest Region is complex, but may be largely grouped into two types, namely, the tropical mountain vertical spectrum with mountain yellow brown earth and mossy forest and the subtropical mountain vertical spectrum with mountain bleached podzolic and meadow soils and fir and larch forests. The southern sections of Gaoligong, Wuliang, Jinpinglao and Pingbiandawei mountains are of the former type, while Diancang Mountain, Yulong Mountain and the southern tip of Shaluli Mountain are of the latter type. Examples are as follows:

   (1) Jinpinglao Mountain

       elevation 300 to 800 m. — tropical rain forest with mountain laterite

800 to 2,000 m. — evergreen broadleaf forest with mountain red earth

over 2,000 m. — mountain mossy forest composed mainly of *Lithocarpus glaber* with mountain yellow brown earth

(2)   southern tip of Shaluli Mountain (Muli, 28° N., 101° E.)

elevation below 1,600 m. — river valley dry grassland with red drab soil

1,600 to 2,200 m. — Yunnan pine forest and broadleaf trees with mountain red earth and yellow earth

2,200 to 3,200 m. — Yunnan pine forest with mountain brown earth

3,200 to 3,600 m. — spruce and fir forest with mountain dark brown earth

3,600 to 3,900 m. — fir forest with mountain bleached podzolic soil

3,900 to 4,000 m. — larch forest with mountain bleached podzolic soil

over 4,000 m. — alpine creeper shrubs and meadow with alpine meadow soil

As the eastern and western slopes of the north-south Hengduan Mountain vary in humidity, their vertical spectrums are also different. At elevations of 2,000 to 2,500 m. on Gaoligong Mountain, for example, the western slope faces the southwest monsoon and the vegetation is of the wet mountain evergreen oak forest with mossy forest type, mainly composed of *Cyclabalanopsis yodon* and *Pasania variolosa*. The forest has complicated layers and a multitude of epiphytic and parasitic species. But on the eastern slope at the same height, there is a subtropical pine forest composed chiefly of Yunnan pines. As for the lower elevations owing to the marked foehn effect, the vegetation is that of a savanna with mainly *Bauhinia sp.*, *Gossampinus malabaricus*, *Euphorbia royleana*, *Opuntia monacantha*, *Calotropis gigantea* and other plants.

2. Regional Differentiation of the Natural Landscape

From the above-mentioned characteristics of landscape in the Southwest Region, one can obviously see that it differs from the subtropical landscape of the Central China Region mainly because in the half-year that includes winter the weather is warm and dry providing favourable conditions for the wintering of the thermophilous plants. A number of basins at lower elevations have a particularly rich amount of heat. Yingjiang, Mangshi and other basins, for instance, lie near 24°45′ N. and 800 to 900 m. above sea level, but their active accumulated temperature reaches 7,000°C. and their coldest monthly average temperature is 12.4°C. This temperature is suitable for growing tropical crops. From here westward across the national boundary up to the valley plain of the upper Irrawaddy River in northern Burma are typical tropical monsoon rain forests. This shows that the basic zone of the Southwest Region is tropical.

This region spans eight degrees of latitude from north to south and the amount of heat received decreases from south to north. The active accumulated temperature is over 7,500°C. in Xishuangbanna, southern Yunnan, 5,500° to 6,500°C. in the Simao area, 4,500°C. near Kunming, and 4,000° to 4,500°C. or less farther north up to southwestern Sichuan. Such a progressive decrease in heat northward is, apart from the latitudinal effect, mainly due to elevation. The basins or valleys at different latitudes are rather warm and have become agricultural centres. Therefore, predominant basins and valleys can be regarded as the basic zones for the division of the Southwest Region into subregions. And the Hengduan Mountains are a special area of high mountains and deep valleys that should become a subregion. The Southwest Region is subdivided as follows:

V_A Yunnan Plateau Subregion
V_B Hengduan Mountain Subregion
V_C Southern Yunnan Intermontane Basin Subregion

(1) Yunnan Plateau Subregion

This subregion includes the central and eastern parts of Yunnan Province and the southwestern part of Sichuan Province. It lies to the east of Diancang and Ailao mountains and is a plateau with an elevation of 1,400 to 2,200 m. High in the north, the plateau gradually lowers towards the south. The valleys formed by the Nanpan, Pumei and Panlong rivers are each less than 1,000 m. above sea level.

The heat reserve in this subregion is abundant throughout the year. The active accumulated temperature is 4,000 to 6,500°C. for most areas, except in mountains over 2,500 m. above sea level. Winter temperatures tend to be high and the average temperature in the coldest month is about 8° to 10°C. in most cases. Because the mountains in the north act as a natural defence and the tropical continental air mass is strong and stable, cold waves have little chance to invade the region. Areas west of the Xuanwei-Kunming-Yuanjiang line are virtually free from cold wave attacks and never experience sharp temperature drops in winter. But cold waves may invade southeastern Yunnan from the Guizhou Plateau along the Nanpan River valley or from the Guangxi Basin along the Youjiang River valley. Extreme lows of about 0°C. may then appear. But, as the duration of such low temperatures is not long, they do not cause much damage to agricultural production.

This subregion receives about 1,000 mm. of precipitation a year, with marked contrasts between dry and wet seasons. About 80 to 90 per cent of the precipitation is concentrated in the summer half-year. Its distribution decreases from south to north. The valleys of the tributaries of the Jinsha River on its southern bank are on the leeward side and receive little precipitation. The annual amount of rainfall at Yuanmou, Chuxiong and Xiangyun, for instance, is less than 750 mm. The leeward sections of the river valleys in the south, such as Yuanjiang on the eastern slope of Ailao Mountain, receive only

735 mm. of precipitation a year and have an arid, hot savanna-type landscape.

The plateau in central Yunnan contains a well-preserved planation surface of which the section between Kunming and Xiaguan is most typical. The Mesozoic red beds are widely distributed on this planation surface. The material composing the red beds is loose and easily weathered to form gentle hills on top of the plateau. Neotectonic movements are still occurring within the plateau. The creation of up and down rifts are frequent, and many faulted depression basins and rift lakes have been formed. The basins developed in the south-north fractural belts are Dali, Kunming, Chengjiang, Kunyang, Jinning, Kaiyuan and Mengzi; and the lakes are Erhai, Dianchi, Fuxian and Yangzong. The basins developed in the east-west fractures are Shiping, Jianshui and Jijie; and the lakes are Yilong and Qilu. Fault lakes are generally deeper than other lakes. Fuxian Lake, for instance, is 150 m. at its deepest point.

The rainy season in this subregion begins in the first ten days of June and ends in late October. The annual rainfall is generally 1,000 mm. It is drier in the low basins, such as in Yongren, Chuxiong, Xiangyun and Yuanmou. The annual amount of precipitation for Yuanmou is only 538.9 mm., of which 13.1 mm. falls in the three winter months; that for Chuxiong is 782.3 mm., of which 28.5 mm. falls in winter. Most areas are covered with mixed forests of pine and oak and Yunnan pine forests with mountainy plateau red earth or drab red earth.

Agriculturally this subregion is Yunnan Province's farming centre. It is most suitable for growing paddy rice, maize, winter wheat and other grain crops, as well as tobacco, oranges, tea and other industrial crops. Two crops can be harvested here in the year. Sugarcane can also be grown in Kaiyuan, Mengzi and other basins. Insufficient precipitation and a marked dry season in this subregion make spring droughts an outstanding problem for agricultural production. So efforts are being made to improve irrigation and to tap water resources.

Karst landforms are found on the limestone plateau in eastern Yunnan. Karst pinnacles are predominant, intermingled with karst depressions, at Luoping, Shizong, Babao and Zhulin; karst basins are widely distributed in Yanshan, Pingyuanjie and Wenshan. The sharp difference of elevation between the plateau and incised valleys strengthens the percolation of the surface water which converges in large quantities to form huge underground rivers. The Liulang Cave at Qiubei on the slope of the Nanpan River valley, for example, is the outlet for an underground river. Large amounts of subterranean water gush out of this cave opening and fall into the valley below, forming a massive waterhead. A big hydro-electric power station has been built here.

On the dry surface of the karst plateau grow *Pistacia weinmannifolia, Burretiodendron hsienmu* and *Cyclobalanpsis glaucoides,* as well as evergreen oak forests composed of white oak, *Clelangi yunnanensis, Osyris wightiana* and other species. Limestone shrub grasslands also grow here composed of *Pistacia weinmanifolia, Coriaria sinica* and other shrubs and herbs, such as *Microstegium ciliatum, Carex haecaus* and *Themeda triandra.* The limestone soil is red because of the parent materials and the influence of bioclimatic conditions. In the dry season the soil is extraordinarily dry. The hydrous iron oxide it contains is always dehydrated and crystallized so that it forms hematite which has a red colour. Hence it is called red limestone soil. In China's limestone areas, the Yunnan Plateau has a greater share of red limestone soil than elsewhere, which is obviously due to the climatic conditions. This soil can often be used to grow maize, potatoes and other dry crops; tung-oil, China firs and other kinds of commercial wood, as well as valuable medicinal herbs such as false ginseng.

Carbonatite areas here often have outcrops of arenaceous rock. The exposed surfaces of these arenaceous rock outcroppings are comparatively moist and the mountainy plateau red earth or mountainy plateau yellow earth formed here is deep and loose. In this soil grow Yunnan pine forests or evergreen oak forests of *Schima wallichii, Castanea henryi* and *Lithocarpus glaber*. Such areas can also be used to plant chestnut trees, anise and other kinds of commercial trees. This landscape blending "rock mountains" and "earth mountains" is one of the principal characteristics of the physical geography of the plateau in southeastern Yunnan.

The area east of Daliang Mountain (in the Sichuan Basin) is prone to invasions of cold air from the north. The area west of Nushan Mountain has much precipitation evenly distributed throughout the four seasons. But the Xichang-Yanyuan area in between has little rain in winter and spring, and marked contrasts between the dry and wet seasons. Particularly during the half year that includes winter, since this area is little influenced by cold waves, a climatic condition of high heat and low humidity is formed. Because of this, the natural landscape is composed of dry evergreen broadleaf forests and Yunnan pine forests with red earth and drab red earth, whereas that for the area west of Nushan Mountain and east of Daliang Mountain is composed mainly of wet evergreen broadleaf forests and masson pine forests with yellow earth. The dry evergreen broadleaf forests consist chiefly of *Castanopsis delavayi, Cyclobalanpsis schottkyana* and other dry evergreen oaks.

In this subregion the Jinsha River and its tributaries cut deep and form valleys as low as 1,000 m. above sea level. As this area is a tropical mountainy plateau influenced by the foehn effect, the valley bottoms are rich in heat, with an average annual temperature of over 20°C. and an accumulated temperature of 7,000° to 6,000°C. But there is little precipitation so that a quasi-tropical savanna landscape is formed. The grasslands are mainly composed of the xerophytic tropical grasses *Heteropogon contortus* and *Cymbopogon citratus*, sparsely mixed with *Zizyphus mauritiana, Acacia farnesiana, Bauhinia racemosa* and other shrubs, and occasionally with Yunnan pines and *Engelhardtia colebrookiana*. The soils are savanna soil and drab red earth. A variety of tropical crops such as coffee, sisal plants and lac are harvested in the low valleys around Miyi and Huili in southwestern Sichuan. Rubber trees have been planted where the micro-topography is favourable and rubber is being tapped. This is the northernmost boundary for growing rubber trees in China. Three crops of paddy rice can be reaped a year on the Miyi farm. Jiaojia, however, produces an abundance of bananas and papayas.

(2) Hengduan Mountain Subregion

This roughly embraces the areas west of Ailao and Diancang mountains. Here north-south mountains of great height parallel deep valleys. Roughly north of the Baoshan-Xiaguan line, the mountains and valleys are the most closely arranged and have the greatest difference in relative elevation. There is no broad basin in the valleys nor wide plateau surface on the mountain tops. The natural landscape shows marked vertical zones. Small-scale present glaciers and firns still exist on the top of some of these high mountains. Take Yulong Mountain in Lijiang for example. In the Jinsha River valley less than 2,000 m. above sea level is a savanna composed mainly of medium and high grass communities, occasionally intermingled with xerophytes. Along the river bank grow cactus and crab cactus. The soils are drab soil and drab red earth. At a height of 2,000 to 3,100 m. above sea level are chiefly Yunnan pine forests, with low woods of yellow oaks in some places and mountain red earth. At 3,100 to 3,800 m. are fir forests, Lijiang spruce forests and Chinese larch forests, on the floors of which develop mountain brown earth and mountain dark brown earth. At 3,800 to 4,500 m. are alpine meadows, azalea shrubs and alpine cold desert communities; and the soils are alpine meadlow soil and alpine cold desert soil. At 4,500 to 5,000 m. and above are firn areas with present glaciers (Fig. 27).

West of Nushan Mountain is a humid area where the annual precipitation amounts to over 1,500 mm. evenly distributed over the seasons. But the windward and leeward sides of

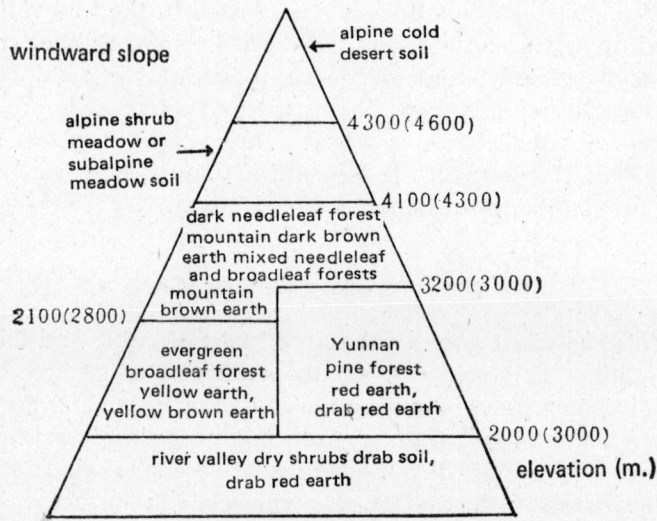

Fig. 27   Model of Mountain Vertical Spectrum in Western Sichuan and Northern Yunnan

a mountain have vastly different water conditions and natural landscapes, especially on their lower slopes. On the western slope (windward side) of Gaoligong Mountain, for example, less than 2,800 m. above sea level, is a wet evergreen broadleaf forest with yellow earth zone. On the eastern slope (leeward side), at the same elevation, is a Yunnan pine forest with red earth zone. The Nujiang canyon between Gaoligong Mountain and Piluoxue Mountain (Nushan Mountain), which is at a lower elevation (appoximately 1,800 to 2,500 m.), has a subtropical landscape.   In its valley grow wild *Hodgsonia macrocarpa*, *Manglietia forrestii*, *Magnolia rostrata* and other subtropical plants. Here southern and northern animals and plants intermix.   For example, on Piluoxue Mountain are Clark's voles and Moupin pikas, that usually inhabit the grasslands of the Qinghai-Tibetan Plateau, as well as sun bears, rhesus monkeys and Assamese macaques, natives of tropical forests.

Topographically, areas south of the Xiaguan-Baoshan line belong to the southern Yunnan broom mountain region.   The

mountains and rivers east of the Lancang River run mainly
in a northwest-southeast direction, and those west of the river,
in a northeast-southwest direction. There are sizable plateaus
between the rivers, as well as a number of broad intermontane
basins. The climate here is wetter than it is on the plateau in
central Yunnan. The annual precipitation is about 1,400 mm.
and drought in the dry season is not so pronounced as it is in
central Yunnan. The composition and community structure of
the subtropical evergreen broadleaf forests at an elevation of
about 2,000 m. above sea level here are somewhat different
from that found in central Yunnan. The forests here are mainly
composed of *Castanopsis hystrix*, Lauraceae and *Schima ka-
siana. Cyathea spinulosa* and *Musa sp.*, plants that favour shade
and moisture, are common sights among the herbs on the forest
floor, as are lianas. The difference between the western and
eastern slopes of these mountains remains quite notable. For
instance, Longling, at the southwestern tip of Gaoligong Mountain, receives 2,160 mm. of rainfall a year and is covered by
wet evergreen oak forests and yellow earth. But Lujiangba
on the eastern slope and at an elevation of 720 m. above sea
level receives only 750 mm. of precipitation a year and has a
dry savanna landscape.

Some intermontane basins (such as Simao) in the southern
part of this subregion are low in elevation, less than 1,500 m.
above sea level, and high in temperature. So Simao pine (*Pinus
szemaoensis*) forests are distributed in the acid red earth at
1,000 to 1,500 m. above sea level. Simao pine requires a higher
amount of heat than does Yunnan pine. The forests are mixed
with *Livistona saribus, Duabanga grandiflora, Wendlandia
scabra* and other arbors and shrubs. Two crops of rice may
grow each year here at elevations of 1,300-1,400 m. above sea
level. With a high relative humidity (over 70 per cent) and a
foggy dry season, the slopes of mountain red earth and mountain yellow earth are most suitable for the planting of tea trees.
"Dianhong" (Yunnan Black) and "Dianlu" (Yunnan Green) of
the Changning-Fengqing area are noted for their high quality.

(3) Southern Yunnan Intermontane Basin Subregion

This subregion begins at Funing in the east and ends at Mangshi and Yingjiang in the west. It includes both Xishuang-banna and Hekou prefectures. The mountains are not high, mostly under 1,500 m. above sea level, with only a few exceed-ing 2,000 m. The valleys of the Yuanjiang, Lancang, Nujiang and Longchuan (a tributary of the Irrawaddy) rivers are generally less than 800 m. in altitude, and drop to 300-500 m. in the lower reaches. Hekou on the lower reaches of the Yuan-jiang is only 84 m. above sea level, being the lowest point in the Southwest Region. In the valleys of these rivers and their tributaries are a number of broad basins, generally not above 1,000 m. in elevation, such as Yunjinghong and Mangshi. These basins are agricultural and tropical crop centres for this subregion.

The lowlying valley basins in southern Yunnan have rich heat resources, with accumulated temperatures above 6,500°C. and an annual precipitation of 1,500 to 2,000 mm. They have a rather typical tropical monsoon climate. In summer, areas west of Ailao Mountain are mainly controlled by the southwest monsoon and those east of the mountain are chiefly under the influence of the southeast monsoon. Cold waves from eastern China usually affect the areas east of Ailao Mountain, but areas west of the mountain are basically free from any cold wave invasion. On the occasion of violent cold waves in January 1961, for example, the lowest temperature at Hekou, east of Ailao Mountain, was 2.2°C., while Yunjinghong (533 m. above sea level), west of the mountain, received its lowest tempera-ture of 5.2°C.

The climate west of Ailao Mountain is basically similar to that of India and Burma. The year there can be divided into three seasons: (a) a rainy season that lasts from the middle or last ten days of May to the last ten days of October. Precipita-tion in this period accounts for some 90 per cent of the year's total; (b) a dry, cool season that lasts from the first ten days of November to the last ten days of March; and (c) a dry, hot season that lasts from the first ten days of April to the first ten days of May. At this time the sun projects its rays directly onto the earth's surface and the weather is clear and cloudless, so that the temperature is the highest in the year. In July and August, however, the temperature is a bit lower because not a day passes without rain. But Yunnan's tropical monsoon climate is somewhat different from that of India and Burma and it has its own characteristics. First, the elevations of some basins in southern Yunnan are rather high, generally over 500 m. above sea level, so the hottest monthly temperature (about 25°C.) and accumulated temperature are lower than those on plains of the same latitude in India and Burma. Second, the dry season is replete with heavy fog and there are many foggy days, a fact rarely seen in India, Burma or southern China. For instance, the Yunjinghong area in this subregion has 150 to 200 foggy days in the year. The heavy fog-like drizzle lasts over five hours in a day. An average of 0.1 to 0.3 mm. of precipitation is recorded every day during this period. Hence Xishuangbanna is known as the "prefecture of fog".

The heat resources vary with the elevation of the basins. Basins and valleys 800 to 1,000 m. above sea level have accumulated temperatures of 6,500° to 7,500°C. Their temperatures for the coldest month are over 11° to 12°C., the extreme low is equal to or exceeds 0°C. and they sometimes have a light frost. In such climatic conditions, the natural landscape and cultivation of tropical crops bear marked tropical features, but differ somewhat from those found in the tropics. The basins in southern Yunnan are larger in area. The Mangshi Basin (840 m. in elevation) is 22 km. long and 10 km. wide, and the Yingjiang Basin (780 to 800 m. in elevation) is 60 km. long and over 10 km. at its widest spot. Both are famous "level lands" in Yunnan. So, a subzone — a quasi-tropical zone — can be delineated within the tropical zone. Judging by the plant communities, the vegetation in this quasi-tropical area is close to that of a tropical forest and its composition includes species from tropical rain forests and monsoon rain forests, but it is

also mixed with fagaceae, theaceae and other subtropical
elements. Under the trees appear more than one layer of tropical monsoon rain forest plants including *Alpinia chinensis* and
Cyathea spinulosa. In places with better water conditions
(much fog during the dry season), such as Puwen (880 m.
above sea level), there are more tropical species and plants with
buttress-like roots and cauliflorous plants. Beneath the trees
are *Psychotria rura, Lindera glauca, Alpinia chinensis, Alocasia
odra* and other typical tropical layers. In arid places which
see little fog in the dry season, such as Mangshi and Ruili, the
plant colonies show notable seasonal phases. The upper layers
are mostly composed of tropical deciduous tree species, such
as *Chukrassia tabularis, Toona surenii, Albizzia chinensis* and
Morus laevigata. But there are not many plants with buttress-
like roots, cauliflorous plants or tropical layers on the forest
floor.

The animals in this quasi-tropical area also bear the im-
print of the tropics. In Xishuangbanna, for instance, are found
Indian bisons, Asiatic elephants, great pied hornbills, peacocks
and other tropical animals. Here, the northern boundary of the
quasi-tropical zone is a marked dividing line for the zooge-
ography: the slow loris, curl-tailed binturong, palm civet and
other tropical animals are found only south of this line. Simi-
larly, little green herons, bushcats, green-legged hill partridges,
chestnut-headed bee-eaters, bamboo-peckers and other tropical
birds are also found only south of the line.

Agriculturally, the winter temperature in Mangshi, Yingjiang and other quasi-tropical areas is quite low and rather
dry. Thus the rest period for the tropical crops is rather long,
and equatorial crops such as rubber can easily suffer from the
cold. But rubber trees may still grow and yield if they are
planted under favourable microrelief conditions and supple-
mented by artificial means. For example, the rubber trees
planted in Yingjiang in 1904 were still growing sturdily in the
1960s and were yielding normally. Coffee also grows well here.
The local variety is known for its good quality. Three crops can

be reaped in the year. Winter sweet potatoes and winter maize can also grow, but cold crops such as winter wheat and rape cannot grow satisfactorily here.

River valley basins less than 700 to 800 m. above sea level (Yunjinghong and Mengla) have accumulated temperatures of over 7,500°C., their coldest monthly average is 15°C. or more, they have no frost all year round, and their extreme low temperature is generally more than 3° to 5°C. Thus these basins belong to the tropical zone. The vegetation on their gentle hill slopes is chiefly that of tropical monsoon rain forests. The tree leaves begin to fall with the advent of the dry season, and new leaves come with the arrival of the rainy season. So the tree canopy changes from sparseness in the dry season to lushness in the wet season, which is markedly different from the year-round evergreen closure of tropical rain forests. The upper arbor layer is chiefly composed of *Lagerstroemia indica*, *Gironniera subaequalis* and *Chukrasia tabularis*, as well as evergreen *Artiaris toxicaria*. In small, damp places on the valley bottoms are local tropical rain forests with *Pometia tomentosa*, *Terminalia myriocarpa*, *Erythrina stricta* and other arbors. Under these forests, the surface layer of laterite has a high content of organic matter and nutrients composed of some 10 per cent organic matter and 0.35 per cent nitrogen. If the land is properly reclaimed, the organic matter and nutrients can be maintained at a considerable level. However, great amounts of hard rain often causes serious soil erosion after the forests are destroyed. The amount of soil washed away from the barren or grassy slopes at Xiaomenglun has been more than 340 times that washed away from wooded land. Thus, in opening up the area, it has been necessary to build terraces so as to conserve water and soil. These tropical basins, with a favourable climate and free from winter colds, are suitable for growing equatorial crops such as rubber, oil palms, coconuts, cocoa and pepper. At present, Xishuangbanna is one of China's major growing areas for tropical crops. But the places with extensive limestone are unsuitable for growing rubber trees because the soil there has a high pH value and is neutral or slightly alkaline.

Areas at an elevation of over 1,000 m. above sea level belong to a subtropical climate. Thanks to the influence of radiation cooling in winter, the temperatures close to the ground are often higher as the altitude of the mountains increase, so that temperature inversions appear in mountains having a wide range of altitudes. For instance, the lowest temperature at Menghai, 1,149 m. above sea level and located in a broad basin, may drop to subzero Centigrade temperatures, whereas the lowest extreme is over 3°C. for the slopes of Nannuo Mountain to its south (1,402 m. above sea level), and the temperature in the coldest month and the accumulated temperature there are also higher than they are at Menghai. Elevations of 1,400 to 1,500 m. on Nannuo Mountain contain mountain rain forests whose arbor layers include *Castanopisis longispicata, Cryptocarya sp., Vitex quinata* and other tropical trees, and the mountain yellow earth on the forest floor is quite fertile and has a thick layer of organic matter. Here is the home of "Puer Tea", and it is probably also the place for the origin of China's tea shrubs. A huge tea tree on Nannuo Mountain stands about 40 m. high and is estimated to be over 1,000 years old. All the tea shrubs planted here recently have grown into small trees. This is obviously due to the warm and damp microclimate of the mountain.

Valleys east of Ailao Mountain are generally rather narrow, low in elevation and without broad basins. In summer this area is controlled by the southeast monsoon and influenced by typhoons, and so it has quite a bit of precipitation, about 1,500 mm. a year in general. Hekou, for example, receives as much as 1,800 mm. of rain a year. This lowlying area has abundant heat with an accumulated temperature of 8,220°C. A number of valleys of the tributaries of the Honghe River in southeastern Yunnan, 200 to 300 m. above sea level at the lowest point, have an annual average temperature of 21 to 23°C., close to that of Hekou. Under such warm and wet conditions, tropical rain forests can be found in places less than 500 m. above sea level, places in which the upper layer trees include *Dipterocarpus yunnanensis* and *Hopea mollissima* of Dipterocarpaceae, *Tetrameles nudiflora* of Datiscaceae, *Crypteronia paniculata* of Crypteroniaceae, and other typical tropical plants in Southeast Asia. The soil has a high water content, its clay particles containing 20 per cent less hematite than red laterite, so that the soil is yellowish brown or yellow in colour, a soil called yellow laterite.

Areas east of Ailao Mountain are affected by cold waves in winter. Owing to the sheltering of the mountains, the cold waves at this point are weak in force. But in times of cold waves, the temperature may drop by cold advection to a rather low value and for quite a long duration. Tropical crops, therefore, still suffer from the cold. So the wintering conditions here are not as good as they are in the areas west of Ailao Mountain. For example, seedlings of some equatorial crops (such as cocoa and pepper) in Hekou were destroyed when the area was visited by violent cold waves. But, on the whole, rubber and other tropical crops in valleys less than 500 m. above sea level suffer little from cold; they can grow properly and yield normally. At elevations above 500 to 600 m., the absolute low temperature may drop below 0°C., and at elevations above 700 m. are found *Quercus acutissima, Cyclobalanopsis glauca* and other oaks. Therefore, in regard to areas east of Ailao Mountain, we classify elevations below 500 m. as tropical, and 500 to 700 m. as quasi-tropical. The elevation of the tropical zone is about 300 to 400 m. lower than it is west of Ailao Mountain.

The Yuanjiang River valley is deep and narrow. In Manhao and Yuanjiang counties, the valley bottom is less than 400 m. above sea level. So the tropical landscape penetrates along the Yuanjiang River to its upper reaches up to about 24° N. But the valley bottom, owing to the foehn effect, receives little precipitation. Yuanjiang, for example, receives about 700 mm. of rain a year, and its dry season lasts as long as seven months. The air here is dry (with a relative humidity of only 65 per cent). The temperature runs high and the accumulated temperature reaches 8,800°C. (the highest in the Southwest Region), thus forming a dry and hot habitat. The vegetation is that of a tropical savanna, and there is savanna soil known as "arid red soil". Under such a dry and hot climate, the soil forming process is rather weak, mineral weathering is low, and the desilicification and allitic weathering are not as marked as they are with laterite. The siallitic ratio of the clay particles in the tropical savanna soil in Yuanjiang is as high as 2.1 to 2.4. Intense evaporation causes salts to accumulate towards the top layer, so that the degree of base saturation may reach 70 to 90 per cent, and the soil shows neutrality or a slight alkalinity (pH 6.0 to 7.0), which is entirely different from laterite. Here the dry climate makes it impossible to plant rubber and other crops, but sisal and sea island cotton may grow in this area.

From this we can see that for areas west of Ailao Mountain in this subregion, the accumulated temperatures are lower than they are in the South China Region, while their upper limit (elevation) is much higher than it is in that region. Tropical and quasi-tropical zones are delimited mainly in accordance with the growth of natural vegetation and tropical crops, in addition to the value of the accumulated temperatures. Because the natural vegetation has developed over a fairly long time, it reflects the characteristics of climate and natural environment of each locality. As the natural conditions in the western tropical monsoon area vary from those in the eastern tropical monsoon area, the same amount of accumulated temperature has different effects on the growth of plants and tropical crops. In other words, the accumulated temperature here is more effective.

Plant growth has its optimum temperature beyond which growth weakens or stops. For instance, the optimum temperature for a rubber tree is about 24 to 26°C. If the temperature exceeds 35°C., the tree growth stops and may even result in damage. The temperature in the hottest month in the tropical basins of Xishuangbanna is less than 26°C. and the average temperature in the three summer months is around 25°C., both within the optimum range for the growth of tropical plants. Conversely, in many places on Hainan Island, the summer temperature is higher than 27°C. and for quite a number of days the extreme maximum exceeds 35 to 40°C. Therefore, the effectiveness of accumulated temperature for the growth of tropical plants is obviously less than it is in the western tropical monsoon area. At the same time, the diurnal range of temperature in Xishuangbanna is larger than it is in south China, averaging 12 to 13°C. in the year. A high daytime temperature facilitates plant photosynthesis and the production of organic substances, while a low temperature at night can reduce a plant's consumption of nutrients, thus helping the accumulation of nutrients. Besides, much fog in the dry season can compensate for the lack of precipitation so that the dry season is not so dry, which facilitates plant growth. On the other hand, fog can reduce nocturnal surface radiation, and so the temperature at night in winter may not drop enough to cause plants to suffer from the cold. Owing to this protective role of the fog, the lowest temperature in winter in Xishuangbanna is about 5 to 7°C., which is favourable for the wintering of tropical plants. The growth of natural vegetation and tropical crops in the tropical and quasi-tropical zones in the western tropical monsoon area is similar to that of south China, although their accumulated temperatures (7,500°C. and 6,500°C.) are 500 to 1,000°C. lower than that of south China (Table 18). The southwestern part of Tibet also belongs to the western tropical monsoon area. It is estimated that here at an elevation of 800 m. above sea level the accumulated temperature is 6,500°C., the average temperature in the coldest month is 13°C. and the extreme low is 1°C., which are similar figures to those of the quasi-tropical zone in southwestern Yunnan. There, the natural vegetation is also quasi-tropical forest.

**Table 18.   Comparison of the Accumulated Temperature Index
(°C.) Between the Tropical and Quasi-tropical
Zones in Yunnan and in South China**

Tropical zone	Yunjinghong of Yunnan	7,810°C.
	Nada of Guangdong	8,400°C.
Quasi-tropical zone	Longchuan of Yunnan	6,820°C.
	Guangzhou of Guangdong	7,990°C.

3.   Vertical Utilization of the Land and Agricultural Production

Agriculturally, the river valleys and lowlying basins in the Southwest Region are very important. Most of them have broad and level surfaces, a thick layer of Quaternary unconsolidated deposits, rich water sources and fairly fertile soils. These areas have especially high temperatures and a long history of agricultural production. They are this region's centres of grain and cash crops. This region also has a vast mountainous area with cool weather and a thin layer of soil so that it is hard to do farming there. Yet there is a great potential for terracing the fields, planting dry and cold-resisting crops, and developing forestry and animal husbandry.

At present agricultural production in the Southwest Region is generally arranged in accordance with the vertical utilization of land (i.e., "stereo-agriculture").

The low basins, less than 500 m. above sea level east of Ailao Mountain and up to 800 m. west of Ailao Mountain, have the richest amount of heat. Tropical crops and some spices and beverage crops can grow well in the humid basins or dry leeward valleys where there are water sources for irrigation. In Yuanjiang and other dry, hot valleys, for example, sisal plants, century plants and lemongrass grow well, as do three crops of paddy rice, maize and other grain crops. Occasional low temperatures may visit this area in winter and spring, and drought may occur in March and April. But measures against cold and drought can be taken in the course of cultivating such tropical crops.

The medium-high basins, at elevations of 500 to 700 m. above sea level east of Ailao Mountain and 800 to 1,100 m. west of Ailao Mountain, have a marked alternation of dry and wet seasons in a year. Coffee, bananas, pineapples, mangos, sugarcane, papayas and other tropical plants can grow well there. But the conditions for rubber and other equatorial crops to winter are inadequate. Yet rubber trees can be planted, though they grow slowly, if proper farming techniques and measures are adopted and the trees are artificially protected. The grain crops include paddy rice, maize and sweet potatoes, and three crops can be harvested in a year. Litchis and longans can grow in the humid basins and ligneous cotton and sisal plants can grow in the dry river valleys. Therefore these medium-high basins have the conditions for growing tropical crops. But in the dry, cool season, the occasional low temperatures of around 0°C., plus spring drought of varying degrees and intense erosion of the slopes in the rainy season, are all unfavourable conditions for agricultural production.

On the high basins, at elevations of 1,000 to 1,100 m. above sea level up to 1,600 to 1,800 m., the heat cannot meet the requirements of tropical crops in winter. But here it is appropriate to plant subtropical cash crops, such as tobacco, sugarcane, tea, tea-oil, tung-oil and tangerines. Two crops of grain can be reaped in a year, mainly paddy rice, cotton, peanuts, maize and sweet potatoes. Also for many years anise and the precious medicinal herb — false ginseng — have been cultivated at this altitude.

At elevations of 1,600 to 1,800 m. up to 2,400 to 2,500 m. above sea level, farming is mainly conducted in high valleys, on gentle slopes or in terraced fields. Two grain crops can be harvested in a year, but these are mainly winter wheat, rape, potatoes and beans. Paddy rice can be grown in certain favourable conditions. At present, the upper limit for paddy rice growing on the Yunnan Plateau is 2,400 to 2,700 m. above sea level, which is probably the highest location for growing paddy rice in China. On the vast slopes of the mountains are forests of Yunnan pine mixed with broadleaf tree species. On the humid mountain slopes or mountain tops are forests of evergreen oak and moss, as well as walnut, camphor and varnish trees. Therefore the chief undertaking at this altitude is forestry, which provides timber and oil, and also plays an important role in preserving water sources and conserving water and soil.

At elevations of 2,400 to 2,500 m. above sea level up to 3,000 to 3,100 m. are mountain areas where only coarse grains such as oats and beans can be grown on a limited scale. Here there is a distribution of subalpine needleleaf forests, mainly composed of *Tsuga yunnanensis*. This tree yields fine timber and is a source for tannic acid. Large tracts of grassland can often be found on some alluvial fans of the valleys and fairly dry gentle slopes can be used to graze cattle. Animal husbandry thus becomes quite important at this elevation.

At elevations of 3,000 to 3,100 m. above sea level up to about 4,000 m., the winters are very cold and the summers are also cool. Here highland barley, oats and green peas can be grown on small plots. Areas at this altitude abound in forests and woods, chiefly of spruces and firs. On the broad fossil glacier valleys are grasslands in between the woods, chiefly composed of artemisia of the grass family as well as a motley collection of other grasses, which is very favourable to grazing in summer. Besides, the subalpine belt produces capterpillars (*Cordyoops sinensis*), saffron, fritillary, musk and other precious crude drugs.

Over 4,000 m. above sea level is the area of alpine shrub meadows and firn where no farming is possible except for the digging up of medicinal herbs. This alpine belt has rich water sources; it is the source of water for rivers and for agricultural irrigation in the basins.

Chapter XII

THE INNER MONGOLIAN REGION

The Inner Mongolian Region is an interior temperate steppe zone in north China. It extends from the west side of the Greater Hinggan Mountains and the Xiliao River basin in the east to the Helan Mountains in the west over an area of 17.5° longitude. Its southern boundary corresponds to the isopleth of an active accumulated temperature of 3,000°C., of which the eastern section stretches to the watershed between the Xiliao, Linghe and Luanhe rivers. The central section is the southern contour of the Inner Mongolian Plateau, starting at Wanquan near Zhangjiakou and extending westward along the Great Wall through northern Shaanxi to the fringe of the Tenger Desert west of the Huanghe River. The western boundary coincides roughly with the isopleth of aridity 4.0. It extends from the Sino-Mongolian border in the north through the western end of the Langshan Mountains and the western foot of the Helan Mountains to the southeastern fringe of the Tenger Desert. The western boundary serves as a dividing line between the desert and desert steppe. Administratively, the Inner Mongolian Region includes most parts of the Inner Mongolian Autonomous Region, the northern parts of Liaoning, Hebei and Shaanxi provinces, the northern part of the Ningxia Hui Autonomous Region and the western part of Jilin Province.

The Inner Mongolian Region is characterized by a vast and flat terrain at an elevation of 1,000 to 1,500 m. above sea level, except for mountains and hills. Because the monsoons from the Pacific Ocean are blocked by the Greater Hinggan Mountains and the Yanshan Mountains, this region has a semi-arid natural environment. This provides favourable conditions for the growth of perennial xero-cryophilic herbs, and constitutes the largest arid steppe region in north China. The region has a long history of livestock breeding, and since Liberation, the number of livestock has increased five times. However the vast grasslands have not yet been fully utilized and there is still a great potential for breeding more livestock. The agricultural-pastoral areas and agricultural areas in the south of this region, where farming has been going on for a long time, also form an important grain producing centre in north China.

1.   Temperate Steppe Landscape

The natural vegetation in the Inner Mongolian Region is mainly grassland. With water decreasing from east to west and heat dropping from south to north, the composition of the steppe community, ecological range and corresponding soil development all reflect the gradual changes in zonality.

(1)   The Steppe Community and Its Distribution

The main characteristic of the steppe vegetation of Inner Mongolia is the predominance of perennial xero-cryophilic herbs. The constructive plants are mainly ones of the grass family, and differences in humidity result more or less in the growth of rank grasses and some semi-frutex and frutices (shrubs). Because it is severely cold, with little precipitation in winter, the stalks of the herbs wither but the roots remain vigorous to become the perennial grass species. The leaves of the grasses are narrow and often curved to adapt to the arid climate. Some steppe plants have shallow roots that crawl horizontally (*Aneurolepidium chinense*) to absorb water from the topsoil.

Needlegrass (*Stipa sp.*) and Chinese wild rye (*Aneurolepidium chinense*) are the most representative varieties of the grass family found here. The former is a thickly growing grass, and the latter a rhizome grass with well-developed root-stems that creep horizontally like a network. There are many species of needlegrass. With increase in aridity, the major species gradually change from *Stipa capillate* and *S. krylovii* to *S. gobica* and *S. glareosa* from east to west. The rank grasses are mainly of the composite and pulse families, including the *Tanacetum sibiricum, astragalus spp.* and *Medicago ruthenica.* The xerophytic shrubs are mainly peashrubs (*Caragana sp.*). Most of these plants of the grass and pulse families are favourite fodder grasses for domestic animals in all seasons. This is why the Inner Mongolian grasslands have always been one of China' major livestock breeding centres. Among the rank grasses of the pulse family are various herbs, such as Mongolian milk vetch, ballonflower, Chinese thoroughwax and lady bell, and therefore the temperate grasslands are also a major base for gathering medicinal herbs.

The aridity in the Inner Mongolian Region rises from 1.2 in the east to 4.0 in the west. Therefore, the types of grasslands are temperate steppe with grass family and rank grass in the east, temperate steppe with thick-growing grass in the centre, and temperate steppe with short thick-growing grass and short semi-frutex in the west. The height of the grasses and vegetation decreases gradually from east to west. In terms of the composition of vegetation from east to west, the quantity of rank grass decreases gradually while xerophytic shrubs and semi-frutex increases. This reflects the gradual rise in the aridity of the climate.

The eastern steppe in Inner Mongolia is China's most fertile grassland with a thick growth of grass covering 60 per cent of the land. The average height of this grass is 40 cm., there are a great variety of grasses and their nutritive value is high. Most of the plants here are Baikal needlegrass (*Stipa baicalensis*) and Chinese wild rye, but there are also many kinds of rank grasses, such as *Tanacetum sibiricum, Astragatus adsurgens* and *Artemisia laciniata.* On the shady side of hills or in sandy lands there are woodlands of poplar and birch. This type of grassland is called steppe with grass and rank grass. Roughly the Hulunbuir grassland, the Xilingol grassland, the southern section of the Greater Hinggan Mountains and the Xiliao River valley belong to this type. Some of the latter two areas have been reclaimed for both farming and stock raising. Northwest of the Manzhouli to Xilinhot line is a typical steppe or dry steppe.

The grass on the typical steppe is generally 30 to 50 cm. high and grows thinly, and it covers about 30 to 50 per cent of the land. The community is made up mainly of *Stipa capillata* and *S. krylovii*, which grow in clusters and in dry conditions. They are mixed with a considerable quantity of rank grass and a small quantity of Chinese wild rye. Xerophytic shrubs are rare. To the west of Xilingol League, the main component of the grass community is first *Stipa krylovii* and then *S. capillata*. Rank grass here is rare. Layers of xerophytic shrubs dominated mainly by peashrubs also grow here and there.

Around Wendurmiao and west of the Jining-Erenhot Railway, from the northern foot of the Yinshan Mountains and Langshan Mountain to the Sino-Mongolian border is mainly a desert steppe. The main species of thick-growing grasses in this area are *Stipa gobica* and *S. glareosa*, only 10 to 25 cm. high and covering only 30 per cent of the land. Short semi-frutex and shrubs that grow under dry conditions are found plentifully. As the number of semi-frutex and shrubs increase in proportion, the plant communities begin to resemble bushes. In the western part of Inner Mongolia, the desert steppe gradually passes into desert with the increase of aridity. The steppe vegetation here includes a considerable quantity of desert semi-frutex, such as *Salsola passerina* and *Hololachne soongarica*. There is also *Stipa gobica, Artermisia arida* and *Salsola passerina*, only 10 to 15 cm. high, and the coverage of the land is less than ten per cent.

The riverside and lakeside areas on the Inner Mongolian

grasslands are salinized meadows or marshlands with *Achnatherum splendens, Puccinollia tenniflora, Suaeda glauca* and *Carex duriuscula* as the main plants.

The geomorphological feature of the Inner Mongolian Region north of the Yinshan Mountains and west of the Greater Hinggan Mountains is that it is mainly a highland at an elevation of 1,000 to 1,500 m. above sea level. It has a slightly undulating surface without conspicuous mountains and valleys. This is called the "Inner Mongolian Peneplain". It provides a boundless expanse of temperate steppe over a vast ground surface and forms a typical great steppe landscape.

There are also many deserts and sandy lands in this region (deserts in dry steppe areas are called sandy land). From east to west are the Hulunbuir Sandy Land, the Khorcin Sandy Land, the Lesser Tenger Sandy Land, the Muus Sandy Land, and Hobq Desert and the Ulanbuh Desert (Fig. 28). These deserts are scattered over small areas and account for only 10 per cent of the total desert area in China. They are quite dif-

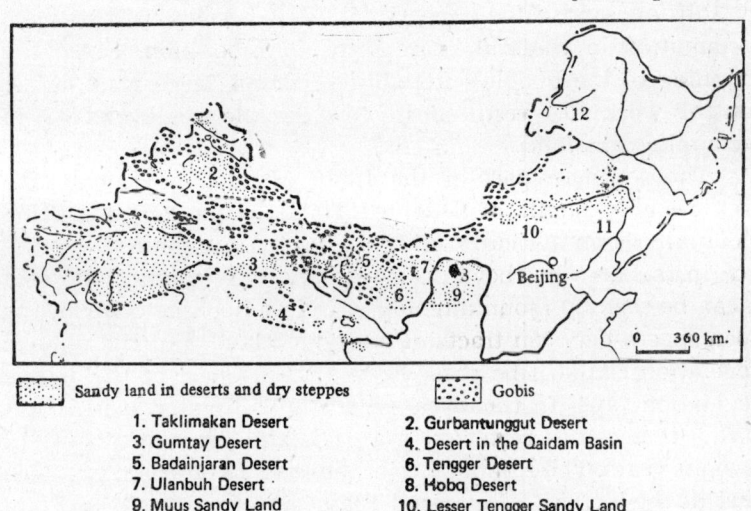

Sandy land in deserts and dry steppes   Gobis

1. Taklimakan Desert
3. Gumtay Desert
5. Badainjaran Desert
7. Ulanbuh Desert
9. Muus Sandy Land
11. Khorcin Sandy Land
2. Gurbantunggut Desert
4. Desert in the Qaidam Basin
6. Tengger Desert
8. Hobq Desert
10. Lesser Tengger Sandy Land
12. Hulun Buir Sandy Land

Fig. 28   A Sketch Map of the Deserts in China

ferent from the large deserts concentrated in the Northwest China Region west of the Helan Mountains. The sandy lands in this Inner Mongolian Region are mainly alluviums from rivers or lakes that were moved to their present location by strong winds. As there is more precipitation in this region than in the northwest desert region, most of the sandy lands here were originally covered by plants, such as *Artemisia arenaria*, *Festuca ovina* and *Caragana sp.*, and there were also sparse arbors on the Khorcin Sandy Land. Most of the sand dunes are completely fixed in place or semi-fixed.

The tracts of shifting sand in this region are mainly a result of the serious destruction of the natural vegetation over many years in the past. According to historical records and archaeological data, the northern part of the Ulanbuh Desert was a farming area 2,000 years ago. The sand shifted to this location only after the natural vegetation was destroyed by long years of excessive reclamation and grazing. The Muus Sandy Land used to be a fertile grassland, but it was covered by shifting sands along the Great Wall because of excessive reclamation in the 250 years prior to Liberation. Since the founding of the People's Republic of China, large-scale desert control work has resulted in considerable achievements in reclaiming this land.

The southern part of the Inner Mongolian Plateau, the area roughly south of Duolun, Taibus, Huade and Daqing Mountain, is an agricultural area. Most of the natural vegetation in this area has been destroyed and only small sections of it can be seen on mountain slopes, in low flood lands or in the open spaces between tracts of cultivated land. But the natural vegetation can still be recognized as being part of the steppe vegetation type. In this area, when the cultivated land is left waste, it becomes restored to a grassland again in about six to eight years. The Hohhot Basin, the Rear Bend Plain (western part of the Yellow River Bend Plain) and the Yinchuan Plain all have been reclaimed for spring wheat and broom corn millet (*Panicum miliaceum*). Part of the fields is also irrigated for paddy rice. On the borders of fields grow small-leaf poplars, elms, dryland willows and date trees. Apples, pears and grapes have been successfully cultivated on diluvial land with good drainage conditions on the southern side of Daqing Mountain.

) The mountainous vertical zone also displays the features of steppe vegetation. The types of vegetation on the southern part of the Greater Hinggan Mountains are those of mountainous forest grassland and steppe. The eastern side is more humid at an elevation of 1,500 to 1,800 m. above sea level, and so it is covered with tracts of woods. The tree species on the northern side are Hinggan larch, Hinggan white birch and mountain poplar, and on the southern side, Mongolian willow and Chinese pine. Between the woods and the foot of the mountain lie grasslands with plants of the grass family. The vegetation on Daqing Mountain grows roughly between 1,200 and 1,500 m. above sea level. The dry steppe type is found on the sunny side and mixed woods of Chinese pine and junipers on the shady side. Woods of Chinese pines and oriental arborvitae are scattered in tracts between 1,500 and 1,700 m., while mountainous meadow steppe is found above 1,700-1,900 m.

(2) Features of the Temperate Semi-Arid Climate

The temperate semi-arid climate has been a leading factor in the formation of the steppe landscapes of the Inner Mongolian Region and their gradual change from west to east. The basic features of this climate are semi-arid, cold winters and warm summers, wind drift sand, and abundant sunshine. It represents a transition in the temperate continental climate from semi-humid to semi-arid conditions.

Under the Mongolian high pressure system, there are many clear and dry days in winter, and the cooling of surface radiation is therefore strengthened. The north polar air mass often moves south or southeast resulting in strong winds and fierce cold waves. There are many blizzards, but because there is a scarcity of vapour in the air, the amount of snowfall is generally small. The Mongolian high pressure system recedes and disappears in summer, and a continental low pressure system is formed. At this time the southeast monsoons drive into the Inner Mongolia Plateau. Generally the monsoon front reaches the southern border of Inner Mongolia in July and quickly retreats in late September. The rainy season here is no more than one or two months. There is a big variability in the amount of rainfall as the force of the monsoon changes.

The Inner Mongolian Region has abundant heat resources for the growth of temperate herbs and crops. There is abundant sunshine because there is not much cloud cover in all seasons, and the rate of sunshine is as high as 70 per cent or more. The annual sunshine time is about 3,000 hours. At Hailar, for example, it is 2,792 hours and at Hohhot, 2,962 hours. The rich sunshine in winter is favourable for animals that spend cold months in natural conditions. Although it is very cold in winter, the temperature rises in summer to between 19°C. and 24°C. in July, the highest recorded being above 30°C. The growth period is 100 to 150 days. The duration of a daily mean temperature higher than 10°C. begins between late April and the end of May and terminates between early September and early October. The active accumulated temperature is 1,700° to 3,000°C. The areas north of the Yinshan Mountains and the northern part of the Xilingol League and Hulunbuir area are the coldest parts of this region. There the January average temperature goes down below -20°C. The Jirem League, Juud League and Yellow River Bend Plain are warmer in winter, with a January average temperature of about -14°C.

The annual precipitation for the whole region is 200 to 400 mm., decreasing from southeast to northwest. The precipitation is concentrated in summer. Between June and September 80 to 90 per cent of the annual total rainfalls. The variability in precipitation grows larger as one moves westward, although the average remains above 20 to 25 per cent. For example, records over a period of 20 years show that the biggest annual rainfall at Hohhot was 658.7 mm. and the smallest

201.3 mm. Cyclones also pass through this region with some frequency in late spring and early summer, and the amount of precipitation begins to increase in the eastern part of this region in June. The amount of rainfall in June has a considerable impact on the growth of forage grass and crops. There was a great deal of rainfall in eastern Inner Mongolia in June 1959. As a result, the grass grew well and good crops were also harvested. There was little precipitation in June 1961, however, and both the farming and stock-breeding were greatly affected. The front of the southeast monsoon arrives at the southeast fringe of Inner Mongolia after mid-July, bringing more concentrated precipitation. However the southeast monsoon begins to retreat southward in early September. This is why the rainy season on the Inner Mongolian grasslands is so short. As the summer monsoons differ in intensity from year to year, there can be as much as a three-fold difference in the amount of precipitation between the maximum and the minimum years, and droughts are frequent.

Not only does summer precipitation have a direct bearing on drought in Inner Mongolia, but so does the amount of snowfall in the preceding winter. Because the winters are severely cold, any amount of snowfall creates a snow cover. The amount of snowfall, the time of snow accumulation and the snow depth all decrease from east to west. The stable snow accumulation period on the Hulunbuir and Xilingol grasslands in the east runs from mid-November to late March in the following year, amounting to 120-130 days. The snow depth averages 20 to 30 cm. but the deepest snow measures 40 to 60 cm. There is often no snow cover in the western part of this region because of little snowfall. A good snowfall is beneficial to both farming and stock-raising. Accumulated snow on pasture lands can partly solve the problem of having an adequate supply of drinking water for livestock during the winter, and pastures devoid of a steady water supply can thus be used for grazing. The accumulated snow thaws in spring, dampening the surface layers and increasing the moisture in the soil.

This helps to turn the withered grass green and provides water for the sprouting of new crops. The rivers, lakes and underground water also receive water from the thawed snow.

The wind force in the Inner Mongolian Region is strong all year round, especially in the northern part of this region. Winds greater than a fresh breeze force (19 to 24 miles per hour) blow here for more than 100 days a year. Most of the winter gales bring cold waves and snowstorms and they are therefore called "wind with white snow". They present a menace to grazing stock. There are more gales in spring when the fallen snow on the ground surface thaws. The temperature then begins to rise while the relative humidity drops, often resulting in dry winds that scorch and wither crops and forage grass and also cause fires on the grasslands. After the surface vegetation is destroyed, there are usually sandstorms.

The geomorphological structure in this region accounts for the arid and cold climate on the Inner Mongolian Plateau. First, the southern border area of the plateau, from Linxi to Jining, is a vast basalt platform with its surface raised southward but sloping mildly northward below the plateau surface. Second, to the east of the plateau stand the Greater Hinggan Mountains. And in the west (west of Jining) are the Yinshan Mountains (including Langshan and Daqing mountains) on the south with their peaks at 2,000 to 2,400 m. above sea level. These high mountains and raised landforms prevent the southeast monsoons from driving into this region and make the interior of the plateau all the more arid. Third, the ground surface is flat and the cold waves from the north meet no barriers so that they can sweep the whole region, aggravating the condition of low temperatures and blizzards.

The mountains and highlands on the eastern and southern borders of the Inner Mongolian Plateau also form important boundaries between the external and internal drainage areas of China. The external fringes of the Inner Mongolian Plateau are external drainage areas, with the Hailar River and the Xiliao River systems in the east and the Yellow River Bend in the west providing important sources of water for irrigation. Inside the plateau are small inland rivers that originate from the mountains on the border and flow northward or eastward with little runoff. For example, the Xilingol River that flows from the western side of the Greater Hinggan Mountains has an average annual flow of only 0.6 cu. m. per sec. over the whole distance of 135 km. However these small inland rivers play an important role in agricultural production and stock-raising as they provide water for farm irrigation as well as for sheep and cattle.

There are also many inland lakes in the Inner Mongolian Region, some of the biggest being Hulunnur and Dalinur, and numerous small ponds. Many of these are salt lakes. The fresh-water lakes are important water sources for farm production and stock-raising on the Inner Mongolian grasslands and they teem with fishes. Many of the salt lakes abound in salt or soda. For example, Dabusu Salt Lake, northeast of Xilinhot, produces "Daqing salt", and Qagannur Salt and Soda Lake in the Otog Banner on the Ordos Highland produces natural alkali.

Grasslands that are far from the rivers and lakes have not yet been fully utilized because of the shortage of water for stock-raising. Through hydro-geological surveys conducted since Liberation, hydro-geological resources on the vast grasslands have been discovered and large-scale water conservancy work has been done. As a result, there have been marked achievements in developing and utilizing the water-short grasslands and in raising their stock-producing capacity.

(3) Steppe Soil

The characteristic soil of the dry steppe is chestnut soil, a soil that is widely scattered throughout the Inner Mongolian Region. Under the vegetation of the desert steppe in the western area is brown soil. Within the bounds of the spread of these two soils, there are also areas of meadow soil, marsh soil, solonchak, solonetz and sandy soil.

The formative process of the steppe soils includes biological accumulation and calcification (mainly the accumulation of calcium carbonate). There is a clear differentiation in the soil profile. Under steppe vegetation predominated by perennial xero-cryophilic herbs of the grass family, the upper level of soil shows a humus accumulation containing considerable quantities of organic matter. The calcium carbonate in the soil is leached out and illuviated in the middle and lower levels of the profile to form a calcic layer. With an increase in aridity, the calcic layer rises to the top level, and the content of organic matter in the surface layer becomes less as the humus layer becomes thinner.

Chestnut soil is different from chernozem because its humus layer is thinner — generally 25 to 45 cm. in thickness. This kind of soil can be divided into dark chestnut soil and light chestnut soil, depending on the amount of organic matter it contains.

Dark chestnut soil is found in Hulunbuir, East Ujimqin Banner and the southern part of the Greater Hinggan Mountains, generally on the slopes of the flat highlands and hilly areas. Its content of humus is 2-4 per cent and it includes a considerable amount of phosphorus and potassium. In flat and wet places where grass grows vigorously, there is a slight gleying process that gives rise to a dark meadow chestnut soil containing 4-7 per cent organic matter. Such places are good-quality pastures, and with good water conditions and vigorous growth of forage grass, they can be reclaimed for farming on small plots.

Light chestnut soil is found in the steppe areas west of Xilinhot. It contains 1.5 to 2.5 per cent organic matter and the calcic layer is found at a depth of from 10 to 20 cm. The soil is relatively thin and its profile is not very well developed. Carbonated light chestnut soil is also found south of the Yinshan Mountains. It gives a calcareous reaction even in its surface layer. When the land with this soil is cultivated, nitrogenous and phosphate fertilizers must be applied to increase its fertility.

Brown soil in the Inner Mongolian Region is found on the highlands west of the light chestnut soil zone and north of Bailingmiao to Wendurmiao line, and in the western part of Ordos Highland. This kind of soil is characterized by more gravel and sand in its surface layer, little loam, a humus layer 15 to 25 cm. thick containing only 1.0 to 1.5 per cent organic matter, a shallow calcic layer, and gypsum and soluble salts (sodium chloride and sodium sulphate) sometimes found in its lower layer. These characteristics show that the brown soil is mainly formed from humus accumulation and calcification in the soil, and that it also has some features of the formative process of desert soil. Brown soil is therefore located in China between chestnut soil and brown desert soil.

Sandy lands are widely scattered in the Inner Mongolian Region. According to the different stages of soil development, they can be divided into arenoso of the chestnut soil type, loose-sand original chestnut soil and arenaceous chestnut soil without effervescence in its full profile. All three types are of loose texture, relatively deficient in organic matter and mineral nutrients. Their physical properties are not good, and after these soils are turned over, they are apt to form sand dunes. Thus sandy lands have limited use for forestry and stockbreeding.

Salinized soil, meadow soil and marsh soil are also widely distributed in the Inner Mongolian Region, mostly in tala (a Mongolian term referring to vast shallow depressions) or in places seasonally filled with water. The salinized soil is mostly meadow solochak with the salts mainly concentrated in the surface layer. These salts often form salt crusts that are found less often in the lower layers. The distribution of these salts is closely related to seasonal changes in the ground water. In the dark chestnut soil found in the eastern part of this region there is some soda meadow solonetz. If ditches are dug to drain off the water, and salts are no longer deposited in the soil,

forage grass can grow in this soil. Meadow soil is found on
flood lands and terraces on both sides of the rivers where Chinese wild rye, achnatherum, sedge and wild barley grow. These
are fertile lands and excellent grassing grounds. Parts of these
lands that are sheltered from winds can be opened for farming. The depressions in the tala or the flat flood lands
frequently form marshes. Along the banks of the Ursun River,
between Hulun and Buir lakes, and the Uragongol River in
the East Ujimqin Banner are marsh lands where marsh soil
has developed.

2. Regional Differentiation of the Natural Landscape

As said above, the natural feature of the Inner Mongolian
Region is a vast temperate steppe that becomes increasingly
arid as one goes from east to west. As the aridity increases, the
quality of the steppe becomes poorer. The dominant factor for
the differentiation of physical zones in this region is the distribution of soils and vegetation. The Inner Mongolian Region
can be divided into a dark chestnut soil steppe zone, a chestnut
soil and light chestnut soil steppe zone and a brown soil desert
steppe zone according to differences in aridity, soil and vegetation. This results in three subregions and seven areas.

VI_A Eastern Inner Mongolian Subregion
VI_{A1} Hulunbuir High Plain Area
VI_{A2} Southern Greater Hinggan Mountain and Xiliao
       River Plain and Hill Area
VI_B Central Inner Mongolian Subregion
VI_{B1} Xilingol Plateau Area
VI_{B2} Jining-Hohhot Basin Area
VI_{B3} Eastern Ordos Area
VI_C Western Inner Mongolian Subregion
VI_{C1} Bailingmiao Plateau Area
VI_{C2} Yellow River Bend Plain and Western Ordos Area

(1) Eastern Inner Mongolian Subregion

The Eastern Inner Mongolian Subregion is equivalent to the dark chestnut soil steppe zone and it adjoins the Chernozem meadow grassland zone of the Northeast China Plain. The subregion includes the Hulunbuir High Plain, the southern part of the Greater Hinggan Mountains and the Xiliao River Plain. The typical steppe vegetation has been found west of the Hulunbuir High Plain, but here it covers only a small area. This small area is also regarded as part of the Eastern Inner Mongolian Subregion out of consideration for its regional integrity.

The Hulunbuir High Plain is located in the northeasternmost part of the Inner Mongolian Region. It is a wide and flat area with Hulunnur Lake at its centre. It has an average elevation of 640 m. above sea level with only a few monadnocks being about 100 m. in relative height. In the middle of this area is the Hailar platform which constitutes the main part of the Hulunbuir High Plain. The Hulunbuir Tala is a downwarping section of the plain, covered by Pleistocene deposits and eolian sand. Along the Hailar River and southward to Baiyinnur are fixed sand dunes covered with growing plants, including Mongolian pines. On the Hulunbuir High Plain the fluvio-lacustrine depressions and terraces are well developed, providing favourable conditions for the establishment of grain and fodder producing centres and basic pastures.

The Hulunbuir High Plain Area is the coldest part of the Inner Mongolian Region in winter. A low temperature of -40°C. often follows a cold wave there, and most of the area has monthly average temperatures below 0°C. for six months of the year. Under the ground are isolated frozen layers as thick as 7 to 13 m. The annual average temperature at Hailar (613 m. above sea level) is -2.6°C., and the January average temperature is -27.1°C. with a minimum temperature of -49.3°C. It is warm in summer, however, and the July temperature rises to above 20°C. The annual accumulated temperature at Hailar is less than 2,000°C.

The southeast monsoons bring a certain amount of precipitation to the subregion when they cross the Greater Hinggan Mountains. The annual precipitation in this area is 323 mm., about 80 per cent of this falling between May and September and more than 50 per cent during July and August. The water and heat conditions in summer create a good habitat for the growth of perennial xerophytic and xero-mesophytic herbs. There are a great variety of grasses on the grassland, and most of them are high-quality forage grasses. Among them are Chinese wild rye and Baikal needlegrass as the main constructive species. With the grass generally 40 to 60 cm. high and covering more than 50 per cent of the land, Hulunbuir provides one of China's best pasture areas.

There is no well-developed hydrologic network in the Hulunbuir High Plain Area. The main external river is the 300-km.-long Hailar River that rises in the Greater Hinggan Mountains and flows westerward into the Ergun River. It has plenty of water, and its lower section is open to wooden rafts and small steamboats.

Hulunnur is the biggest lake in this subregion. Its size and depth have both changed considerably over the last decades. At the northern end of the lake is a shallow depression that links to the Ergun River. When the water level in this lake rises during the flood season, the water flows into the river. Both the Hulunnur and Buirnur lakes abound in fish, and lush grass grows around the lakesides.

The southern part of the Greater Hinggan Mountains and the Xiliao River Plain have a higher temperature and more precipitation than does the Hulunbuir High Plain Area. For example, at Tongliao, the January average temperature is -14.5°C. and the July average temperature is 23.9°C. The annual precipitation here is 379 mm. At the Ongniud Banner the corresponding figures are -13°C., 22.8°C. and 371 mm. Most of the grasses in this area are therefore rank grasses and the seasonal changes are relatively obvious. Small wooded areas are found on the mountains at elevations of 1,500 to 1,800 m.

above sea level. The trees are mainly *Butula ermanii*, white birches, mountain poplars, Chinese pines and Mongolian willows. There are also some shrubs. Such woodlands become smaller and more scattered farther westward where they are found only on the shady sides of the mountains. The pastures between the woodlands are dominated by plants of the grass family, marking a transition from the dark chestnut soil with steppe zone to the more typical chestnut soil with steppe zone.

The Xiliao River Plain has a vast expanse called the Khorcin Sandy Land, which is a desert area with the best water and vegetation conditions of any desert in China. Fixed or semi-fixed sand dunes account for 90 per cent of its area. On these sand dunes grow various plants of the grass family as well as shrubs. The dunes are also sparsely dotted with elms and other arbors. The plant cover on the sand dunes is generally 20 to 40 per cent. Between the sand dunes are grassy meadow moors.

The Xiliao River Plain is an important farming and stock-raising area. To protect the plain from sandstorms and to prevent the movement of the sand dunes, shelter tree belts were planted on a large scale after Liberation. Former migrating dunes near Zhanggutai (Zhangwu County, Liaoning Province) southeast of the Khorcin Sandy Land have thus been transformed into pine woods, bringing about a marked change there.

(2) Central Inner Mongolian Subregion

The Central Inner Mongolian Subregion is equivalent to the light chestnut soil steppe zone. It stretches from the East Ujimqin Banner on the western side of the Greater Hinggan Mountains in the east to the vicinity of the Great Wall on the Ordos Highland in the west. This subregion lies in a northeast-southwest belt, and can be divided on the basis of landforms and heat conditions into the Xilingol Plateau in the north, the

Jining-Hohhot Basin in the centre and the Eastern Ordos Highland in the south.

The Xilingol Plateau has the typical geomorphological features of the Inner Mongolian Plateau. Gently undulating hills alternate with vast talas. Its annual precipitation is between 250 and 350 mm., and it has an average snow cover of about 20 cm. in winter. Its water conditions are therefore good enough to ensure the growth of temperate xerocryophilic herbs. With such herbaceous plants growing well, the Xilingol Plateau is one of the most important stock-raising areas in China. But it has a relatively smooth terrain with short rivers and poor runoff on the surface. The pastures here either are supplied by deep ground water or are short of water, and many can be used for grazing only in winter, at least until the water supply is improved.

The Lesser Tenger Sandy Land south of the plateau is about 300 km. long from west to east and 30 to 80 km. wide from north to south, with a total area of 18,000 sq. km. This sandy land overlies lake deposits of the Tertiary and Quaternary periods and red clay of the Tertiary Period, most of which has been fixed or semi-fixed in place. Shifting sands cover only about 2 per cent of the total area. Vegetation grows well on fixed or semi-fixed dunes. In this area the vegetation mainly belongs to the grass family and there is some sagebrush. Furthermore there are arbors and shrubs in the east because of the increased rainfall there. The trees are elms and Manchu cherries with a scattering of spruces and Chinese pines. The sand dunes alternate with close talas that have become the major pastures in this locality. The plants grow luxuriantly, covering more than 50 per cent of the total land area. In the centre of the talas often are lakes with water supplied by ground water and drained through underground runoffs. Most of these lakes are fresh-water bodies with good-quality water (Fig. 29).

South of the Lesser Tenger Sandy Land and across the intermittent and low Yinshan Mountains is the large basalt lava

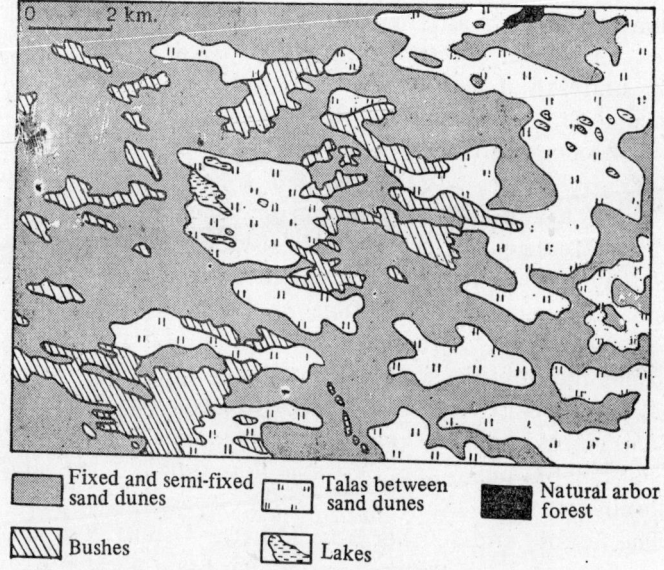

Fixed and semi-fixed sand dunes

Talas between sand dunes

Natural arbor forest

Bushes

Lakes

Fig. 29 Natural Landscape of Lesser Tenger Sandy Land

platform between Guyuan, Huade, Zhanghua and Jining. It stands 1,000 to 1,500 m. above sea level, with its hills and basins interlocking each other. Most of the land in this area has been cultivated and it is one of the important farming areas of Inner Mongolia. The crops are mainly naked oats, broom corn millet, millet and spring wheat.

Daqing Mountain west of Jining stands at an elevation of 2,000 to 2,400 m. above sea level. Its southern slopes are very steep and end in the Hohhot basin and the Bend Plain (less than 1,000 m. above sea level) with a drop of more than 1,000 m. Because of the good conditions for irrigation, most of the area has been cultivated.

The Ordos Highland is sandwiched between the Yellow River Bend in the north and the Great Wall in the south. It is a peneplain levelled by long years of erosion. Its surface is widely dotted with Cretaceous sandstone and conglomerates. It stands about 1,300 to 1,500 m. above sea level. The only exception is Zhuozi Mountain, which rises to more than 2,000 m. above sea level. In topography, the Ordos Highland is a gently undulating area interlocked with low and flat ridges and broad valleys. The east of the highland is a temperate dry steppe section with an annual precipitation of 400 mm. and an aridity of 1.6 to 2.0. The west is a semi-desert section of land with an annual precipitation of 250 mm. and an aridity of 2.0 to 2.8. The two sections are divided roughly by a line formed by the towns of the Hanggin and Otog banners and Yanchi. The natural vegetation on the fixed and semi-fixed sand dunes in the east includes *Salix cheilophilla, S. purpurea*, and other mesophytic shrubs, plants seldom seen in the west. The flood lands between the dunes are covered mainly with *Carex duriuscula* and *Achnatherum splendens* in the east, and tracts of halophilous plants (*Nitraria tangutorum* and *Kalidium gracile*) in the west.

The middle and southern parts of the Ordos Highland are occupied by the Muus Sandy Land which has a plentiful supply of surface water and groundwater due to heavy precipitation. The Wuding and other rivers run through this sandy land from north to south and flow into the Huanghe River. The groundwater under the low land between sand dunes is found at the depth of only one to three metres and is of good quality. Therefore natural plants grow well, and Ordos sagebrush (*Artemisia Ordosica*) grows widely on the sand dunes. Covering the low lands and flood lands between the sand dunes are meadows, saline meadows and swampy sections filled with willow bushes. The bushes are composed of Mongolian willows (*Salix mongolica*), sand willows (*Salix cheilophilla*) and common sea buckthorn (*Hippophae rhamnoides*). They grow vigorously and are good for grazing. Such natural oases are peculiar to the scenery of the Muus Sandy Land.

Although there are excellent water conditions here and most of the sand dunes are fixed or semi-fixed, the area of shifting sands is still expanding as a result of irrational reclamation and destruction of the vegetation before

Liberation. By now, the shifting sands account for 64 per cent of the total area of the sand dunes. The shifting sands are largely spread over the southeastern part of the Muus area, and there are densely-concentrated stretches of shifting sands at Jingbian, Yulin, Shenmu and the Uxin Banner in Inner Mongolia.

The Muus Sandy Land has relatively superior natural conditions for stock-raising, farming and afforestation. However, because of the arid climate and frequent winds, and because loose sand is widely scattered, measures must be taken to prevent further drifting of the sand in order to transform this sandy area into a good farming area.

(3) Western Inner Mongolian Subregion

The Western Inner Mongolian Subregion belongs to the brown soil desert steppe zone that covers the Ulanqab League, most of the Bayannur League, the Yellow River Bend Plain and the West Ordos Highland.

The Ulanqab and Bayannur highlands have a gentle relief with some broad and shallow basins lying in a northeast-southwest direction. The largest of these is the Erenhot Basin. The Ulanqab Highland is mainly a grassland area with *Stipa gobica* and *Artemisia frigida*, and its soil is brown soil. The Bayannur Highland is also mainly a grassland area with *Stipa glareosa*, *Artemisia arida* and Caragana (peashrubs), and its soil is light brown soil.

The Yellow River Bend Plain includes the Rear Bend Plain and the Yinchuan Plain. Tectonically this is a rift zone on the border of the Ordos Highland. It lies between the Daqing and Helan mountains, and at the foot of these mountains are gently sloping diluvial and alluvial plains. The rift zone is filled with Quaternary deposit about 2,000 m. thick from the Huanghe River. The annual accumulated temperature on the Bend Plain south of Daqing Mountain is about 3,000°C., enough to meet the needs for growing one crop a year. Irrigated by water from the Huanghe River, the Bend Plain has been well-known as an irrigated area and is thus described in a famous saying "the Huanghe River is disastrous to all, but it brings prosperity to the Bend area". A huge project to divert water from the Huanghe River was built in the Bend area after Liberation, more than doubling the irrigated acreage there prior to Liberation. The annual precipitation in the Bend area is only about 150 mm. and the annual evaporation exceeds 2,200 mm. Since there has been more stress here on irrigation than drainage, the salts in the soil have surfaced, causing secondary salinization and alkalization over a large area. Positive efforts have therefore been made in recent years to control this secondary salinization and alkalization through both irrigation and drainage. The farmlands have been extended, and this is now a large commodity grain-producing region.

The Yinchuan Plain lies between Qingtong Gorge and the city of Shizuishan on the Huanghe River. Canals have been built to draw water from the Huanghe River onto the farmland at Yinchuan, Pingluo and Huinong. Protected by the Helan Mountains in the west, the plain is free from heavy winds and shifting sand. This is the area where troops in the Qin and Han dynasties were first stationed to reclaim wasteland. The irrigation system they opened still remains today. The system has been repaired and new irrigation projects have been added since Liberation to maintain stable and high crop yields.

From Dengkou northward to the Yinshan Mountains is the Rear Bend Plain, which stands at an elevation of 1,100 m. above sea level, has relatively smooth surface and inclines mildly from southwest to northeast. The slightly rising natural levees of the Huanghe River make the land here drop on both sides. The irrigation canals to divert water from the Huanghe River run from south to north, then flow through the Wujia River into Ulansuhai Lake. The water table on the plain has risen as a result of irrigation, causing salinization of the soil.

Southwest of the Rear Bend Plain and between the Huanghe River and Langshan Mountain is the Ulanbuh Desert.

About 39 per cent of this desert is composed of shifting sands, mainly in the southeast. The rest is covered by fixed or semi-fixed sand dunes, and is a good pastureland. In the north is the alluvial plain of the ancient Huanghe River, where flat clay land is widely distributed. The terrain slopes gently from the present Huanghe River bank westward, and water can be drawn from the river for gravity irrigation. Because of the good conditions here, the alluvial plain is now being reclaimed on a large scale. Some of the land is producing nearly four tons of grain per hectare, even though only a few years ago this was just wasteland covered by yellow sand.

Through the gap between the Helan and Langshan mountains, the moving sand of the Ulanbuh Desert extends to the bank of the Huanghe River, crossing it to form the Hobq Desert on the southern bank of the river in the Bend area. Most of the dunes here are shifting ones. The desert is sparsely populated with only a few grazing points for local herdsmen.

The Helan Mountains west of the Yinchuan Plain are long and narrow, running from north to northeast. In width they are about 20 to 40 km. Most of the peaks are at an elevation of 2,000 to 2,500 m. above sea level, the highest being over 3,000 m. The western slope is gentle. It adjoins the Alxa Plateau. The eastern slope drops 1,000 m. onto the Yinchuan Plain.

3. Rational Utilization of the Grasslands and Desert Control

The grasslands in the Inner Mongolian Region cover an area of about 40 million hectares and are an important stock-raising centre for China. The forage grasses — *Agropyrum cristatum,* Chinese wild rye, *Cleistogenes squarrosa,* needle-grass, *Medicago ruthenica* and *Artemisia frigida* all have high nutritious value and few of them are poisonous. Most of them are high-quality grasses that the animals like to eat. According to a survey conducted by the Inner Mongolian Grassland

Bureau, the meadow steppe in the east has the highest productive capacity, with an average yield of 1.5 to 1.8 tons of meat per hectare. The typical steppe in the middle has a productive capacity of 0.75 to 1.125 tons per hectare; and the desert steppe in the west, under 0.75 tons per hectare. If calculated only on the basis of this natural productive capacity, the grasslands of Inner Mongolia could support twice as many animals. If the grasslands were improved, with a 50 per cent increase in grass output plus artificial cultivation and the sowing of forage grass, the stock-raising potential would be still greater.

The people of Inner Mongolia have taken a number of effective measures to construct the grasslands and control the deserts. However, there are still some problems that hinder the tapping of the full potential of the area. Some of them are as follows.

(1) Rational Utilization of Water and Grass

Surface water is scarce and unevenly distributed on the Inner Mongolian grasslands. The solution to this problem depends mainly on the discovery of new underground water resources. Since Liberation the herdsmen have done much work to improve the water supply, and 3.33 million hectares of pastures have been opened by digging wells, building small reservoirs and dams, and by drawing water from streams and groundwater. However, large areas of the grasslands are still short of water.

At the same time, the pastures that are presently being used, particularly those lying near lakes, rivers, wells and springs, have too often been overgrazed and the grass has degenerated. The grass cannot be quickly restored because the earth has been trampled compactly by animals and the soil moisture has decreased. As a result, the forage grasses that previously had high nutritious value have degenerated, the plants have become dwarfs, and the number of poisonous species have increased. These extremely degenerated pastures have thus lost their use value.

This is why the rational utilization of pasture lands is the key to the development of stock-raising on the Inner Mongolian grasslands. The main aim now is to improve the grasslands by building more water conservancy works. Apart from discovering new water resources, attention is being paid to the rational use of existing water sources, the creation of a well-arranged network of wells and the building of a complete water supply system. Redundant water sources can also used to irrigate fodder crop fields and artificial pastures. Pastures with a good water supply are now being used correctly on a seasonal basis. The degenerated pastures are being closed and irrigated for resowing in order to protect the growth of forage grasses and to restore their productive capacity.

(2) Establishment of Grain-Producing Bases

The policy for the development of animal husbandry in China involves the utilization of grasslands on a rational basis in order to increase their stock-raising capacity and to improve the quality of the livestock. Therefore, while opening water-short pastures and arranging seasonal camping grounds on rotation for rational grazing, the grassland areas are also cultivated with artificial forage grasses and fodder.

However, the Inner Mongolian grasslands adjoin the fringes of farming areas, and so this reclamation of the land has had to be done with great care. Otherwise farm land might be destroyed in the process of reclamation. The cultivated areas with the stock-raising areas have been reduced to a minimum and intensive farming and rational crop rotation are used there to increase the yield per unit and to preserve the fertility. Locations for cultivation are selected away from wind gaps and at places where the soil layer is fairly thick so as to avoid salinization. Irrigation is also given priority wherever there are water resources.

(3) Desert Control

There are great expanses of desert in the Inner Mongolian Region. Irrational reclamation, overgrazing and arbitrary tree felling prior to Liberation led to the problem of erosion and wind-blown shifting sands. The main measures taken in the areas affected by such shifting sands have been to build shelterbelts of trees and to grow grass to fix the sand in place, thus promoting an all-round development of agriculture, forestry and stock-raising. Located at the southern fringe of the Khorcin Sandy Land, Chifeng County was hit seriously by shifting sands in the past. After Liberation, more than 2,700 km. of tree belts were planted there to protect the farmland. As a result, the grain output of this county has risen sharply.

In stock-raising areas affected by shifting sands, the main measures taken have been to plant trees, bushes and grass at the same time; and to enclose trees, grass and fodder within turf-and-brick walls. In desert areas with abundant surface water (such as the Muus Sandy Land), the water sources have been used to level sand dunes so as to turn wasteland into farmland. The farmland has been extended by more than 23,000 hectares through this method in the Yulin Prefecture, Shaanxi Province, an area located south of the Muus Sandy Land.

Enclosing deserted abandoned land and degenerated pastures are also an important measure used to control shifting sands and to improve grasslands. For example, the Maowunigai area in the Ejinhoro Banner (Muus Sandy Land) had been good pastureland with a thick growth of vegetation 50 years ago, but it had been so ill used that 80 per cent of the land became sandy on the eve of Liberation. After Liberation, by a process of enclosing the sand dunes, dividing the area for rotation grazing and the planting of sand-fixing grasses and afforestation, the pastureland has been restored in 78 per cent of this area.

(4) Eliminating Rodents

The habitat of the grasslands is beneficial to rodents. The Brandt's vole, which is commonly seen on the Inner Mongolian grasslands, is the most representative species of rodent, but the ground squirrel is a superior one. In addition, there are also pikas, zokors and marmots. All of these animals are harmful to pastures and crops. They often feed on forage grass and crops, especially the forage grass that is palatable to livestock. In the areas densely populated by rodents, the ground is so crisscrossed with holes that the grasses wither from lack of water and soil. Of all these rodents, the Brandt's voles have the greatest population, averaging of 200 per hectare. A vole eats about 1 per cent of what a Mongolian sheep does in a day. Thus, wherever damage is done to the forage grass by rodents, the pastures will support two less sheep per hectare. In order to ensure the development of the stock-raising, the rodents must be eliminated from the grasslands. In recent years, great progress has been made in killing rodents on a mass scale. However, they reproduce quite rapidly, and some of the areas are still suffering from serious rodent damage.

Chapter XIII

THE NORTHWEST CHINA REGION

The Northwest China Region consists of the Xinjiang Uygur Autonomous Region, the western part of the Inner Mongolian Autonomous Region, the Gansu Corridor, the Qilian Mountains and the Qaidam Basin in Qinghai Province. The region covers a vast expanse, accounting for more than 20 per cent of the total area of China.

The Northwest China Region extends to China's frontier in the west and in the north and borders on the Inner Mongolian Region in the east along the isopleth of aridity 4.0, which stretches from Langshan Mountain through the western side of the Helan Mountains to Wushaoling Mountain. It adjoins the border of the Qinghai-Tibetan Region in the south, starting from the Pamirs in the west and moving along the northern side of the Kunlun Mountains and the Burhanbudai Mountains to the Riyue Mountains in the east. The Altun Mountains, located in the centre of China's most arid region, and the northern and western slopes of the Qilian Mountains are both desert areas, having a vertical zone structure of arid mountains similar to that of the Tianshan Mountains. Therefore both of these belong to the Northwest China Region.

Located in the central part of the Asian continent, this region receives little precipitation, and its grand basins surrounded by huge mountains are particularly arid. It is the most arid region in China. Deserts and gobis cover vast areas, the best-known deserts being the Taklimakan, the Gurbantunggut, the Badain Jaran and the Tenger. Piedmont diluvial gravel gobis are located around the edges of the basins. The Gaxun Gobi in the east part of southern Xinjiang and the Beishan Gobi in the west part of the Alxa Plateau are both well-known denuded and rocky areas.

In the arid basins, such as the Tarim and Junggar basins and the Gansu Corridor, people have long used the river water from thawed snow on the high mountains for irrigation and to build oases. At the same time they have used pastures in sandy lands and on high mountains for the development of stockbreeding. Since Liberation, both agriculture and animal husbandry have been expanded in the Northwest China Region on an unprecedented scale. The Construction Corps of the People's Liberation Army, under the Xinjiang Military Area Command, has made a great contribution to the development of Xinjiang. In the past two decades, they have reclaimed wasteland, built water conservancy works, turned large tracts into fertile farmland irrigated by crisscrossing canals and created good conditions for the all-round development of agriculture, forestry, animal husbandry and sideline production.

1. Arid Desert Landscape

The principal feature of the landscape in the Northwest China Region is the arid deserts, and the primary factor for differentiating this region from others is the difference in water conditions. Under an arid climate, the activity of water, heat, salt movement and the mechanical motion of matter are constants in the process of physical geography.

(1) Arid Climate

The Northwest China Region has a strong continental climate with scarce precipitation and a great variation in its range of temperature. It is situated in middle-latitude westerlies, where both high and low pressures are active. The region is under the Mongolian high for most of the winter half-year. During this period, the region is frequently invaded by the polar air masses and arctic air masses. Influenced by strong radiation cooling of the ground surface, the climate in the winter is mainly dry and cold.

In summer, as this region is located at the northern fringe of the continental low, the strong westerlies convey vapour quickly. Most of the exposed ground surface is then heated by extremely high temperatures. Due to the dynamical and thermodynamical influence of the air currents from the Qing-hai-Tibetan Plateau, a greater area of the northern side of the plateau is affected by the strong westerlies than in winter, and a high-altitude tropical continental air mass forms over northern Tibet and the Tarim Basin. The weather there is dry and hot. However, there is often a small disturbance of strong westerlies that form a narrow scope of convergence over the Pamirs and the southern side of the Tianshan Mountains, which gives rise to precipitation in a small area.

The primary factor that effects changes in the weather and climate of this region is the movement of the cold air the year round. Cold air invades Xinjiang roughly from three directions — northwest, west and north, but most of the cold air comes from the northwest. The invasion of cold air often leads to a violent drop in temperature with snowstorms in northern Xinjiang, causing losses of the livestock. A violent cold wave on January 24, 1969, invaded Xinjiang from western Siberia, and the temperature in the northwestern part of Xinjiang dropped by 26°C. The minimum temperature at Yining dropped to -40.3°C., an extreme for this location. The cold air from the north often moves in a very strong air current that can pass over the Tianshan Mountains. After arriving in southern Xinjiang, the air gathers on the western side of the Altun Mountains and begins to build up to certain thickness and intensity. Then it crosses the Altun Mountains to enter the Qaidam Basin, bringing a violent fall in temperature, gales and dusty weather there.

The climate in this region is dry, with little cloud cover and abundant sunshine. Especially in the eastern part of the

Tarim Basin and the northwestern part of Gansu, the average
annual total cloudiness is under 45 per cent while the relative
sunshine is above 70 per cent, with the total sunshine time
coming to more than 3,000 hours.   The area between Dunhuang
and Turpan is the most arid section of this region.   Its annual
sunshine time exceeds 3,400 hours, and it is the area with the
·greatest solar energy resources in China.   Except for northern
Xinjiang, where the total annual radiation is slightly less
(about 130 kcal. per sq. cm. per year) it is 140 to 155 kcal. per
sq. cm. per year in all other parts of this region.

The abundant sunshine and radiation give the air near the
ground surface plenty of solar energy. This not only stimulates
crop growth, but also provides the basic conditions for wide
use of the solar energy.   The lofty mountains block cold currents, but the subsidence of currents across the mountains
helps to increase the temperature.   There are great quantities
of heat resources, especially in southern Xinjiang.   And the
active accumulated temperature is 2,000° to 3,000°C. in northern Xinjiang, higher than that in the Northeast China Region.
Southern Xinjiang, with its active accumulated temperature
generally around 4,000°C. belongs to the warm temperate zone,
but the accumulated temperature at Turpan is as high as
5,400°C. and therefore this area is regarded as part of the subtropical zone in terms of heat.

The temperature variation in various parts of this region
is a salient feature of the continental climate.   The temperature in the coldest month (January) is around -20°C. in northern Xinjiang, and around -10°C. in southern Xinjiang, the
Gansu Corridor and the Qaidam Basin.   In general it is colder
in northern Xinjiang than in southern Xinjiang, in the east
than in the west, and in the mountainous areas than in the
basins.   The average temperature of the hottest month (July)
is 23°C. or above. The annual maximum range at Chepaizi in
northern Xinjiang has been as much as 55°C. greater than elsewhere in China.   The daily temperature variation is also very
large, the annual average daily range is above 11°C. in all

parts of the region, 16° to 20°C. in southern Xinjiang and the Gansu Corridor, and as high as 35°C. in the extremely arid Gobi areas of eastern Xinjiang. In extreme conditions, Dunhuang has experienced a temperature variation of nearly 40°C. in 24 hours. Therefore, there is a popular saying in many areas of this region: "I wear a cotton-padded or fur coat in the morning, but I change to a gauze dress at noon."

Precipitation is scarce in this region. The source of water vapour is mainly the westerlies in the west and the amount of precipitation decreases generally from west northwest to east southeast. The water vapour in the east comes mainly from the southeast monsoons, and the precipitation there decreases from southeast to northwest. With an annual precipitation of only about 10 mm. at Qianmu in the Tarim Basin, where the southwesterlies prevail all year round, becomes the place with the least precipitation in China. Because of the high annual average temperature (above 10°C.), evaporation is great and precipitation is often less than 1 per cent of the evaporation. This makes the area the driest in China, with an aridity of around 80.

Northern Xinjiang, influenced by currents from the Arctic, has more precipitation. There are about 200 mm. of rainfall annually in the basins there, with an aridity of about 4.0. The precipitation is distributed relatively evenly in all seasons, but there is slightly more in winter and spring. This is therefore the area with the best water conditions in the region.

In other parts of the Northwest China Region, the precipitation is generally greater in the summer. The interannual and intermonthly variability of precipitation is quite large. In southern Xinjiang and the Gansu Corridor there are often no raindrops at all for six months running, but a heavy downpour there in one or two days can account for one half or two-thirds of the annual precipitation. The great variability of precipitation is also a manifestation of the strong continental climate.

Precipitation in the mountains generally increases with

altitude. The slopes are damper than the foot of the mountains, which in turn are damper than the centres of the basins. For example, the Gansu Corridor at the northern foot of the Qilian Mountains has an annual precipitation rate of between 50 and 150 mm.; the intermontane valleys, 300 mm; and the alpine zones, up to 500-800 mm. However the precipitation gradually decreases after one reaches a certain altitude. There is little variation in the precipitation at different altitudes on the southern slopes of the Tianshan Mountains and on the northern slopes of the Kunlun Mountains because the air currents there contain too little vapour. According to the records taken at stations in the Tianshan Mountains, the altitude for the greatest precipitation is about 3,000 m.

Because of the scarce precipitation, deserts and gobis are widely scattered in the Northwest China Region, the vegetation on the ground surface is sparse, the air is dry and dry winds blow frequently. The dry winds generally occur, between April and August and often blow at a velocity exceeding 10 m. from late May to late June. During this period, there are more cold air invasions and the heating action is comparatively strong over the underlying surface so that the dry winds are quite hot, dry and strong.

Atmospheric drought, referring to the fact that the saturation deficiency of the air in the surface layer exceeds 60 millibars, occurs between early July and early August when the temperature is highest. At this time dry cold air only increases the temperature as soon as it enters, the relative humidity decreases greatly and the saturation deficiency increases. Atmospheric drought and dry winds are frequent in all parts of the Northwest China Region, which affects the growth and yields of crops.

(2) Effect of High Mountains and Grand Basins on the Formation of the Desert Landscape

The topographical features of the Northwest China Region are its towering mountains and grand basins. In the south are the Kunlun Mountains; and in the north, the Altay Mountains. The Tianshan and Altun mountains lie in the centre, and the Qilian Mountains in the southeast. Between the Tianshan and Altay mountains lies the Junggar Basin. The Tianshan, Kunlun and Altun mountains encircle the Tarim Basin; and the Altun, Qilian and Kunlun mountains surround the Qaidam Basin. North of the Qilian Mountains is the Gansu Corridor, and north of the Beishan Mountains in that Corridor and west of the Helan Mountains lies the broad and level Alxa Plateau. Except for the Beishan Mountains in the Corridor, which have an elevation of only 2,000 to 2,500 m. above sea level, all these mountain ranges are quite high. They stand at a height of more than 4,000 m. above sea level, the highest peak being over 7,000 m. and having a glacier. These mountains have played a very important role in the formation of the desert landscape of this region and in its internal differentiation.

The effect of the mountains on the formation of the desert landscape is manifested by the blocking of air currents, which increases the dryness of the climate. The main aspects of this are:

1) The mountains provide a barrier for the air currents. Cold currents are often blocked by the mountains, causing marked differences in temperature and humidity between the two sides of mountains. Only when the cold air is particularly strong can it cross the mountains through gaps or narrow passages. For example, the temperature in the Tarim Basin in January is 10° to 12°C. higher than it is in northern Xinjiang (Table 19). The Altun and Qilian mountains play a marked role in blocking the cold currents in winter. When the cold high pressure force is particularly strong, the cold current can cross the Altun Mountains into the Qaidam Basin, creating very cold weather in the basin. Because of the accumulation and subsidence of the cold air on the windward side, there is often a temperature inversion on the mountains. Temperature inversions are most obvious on the northern slopes of the Tianshan and Qilian mountains. The inversion layer in January

may be over 1,500 m. in height and is several hundred metres in thickness. This is beneficial for winter pastures in the mountainous areas. Fruit trees can also winter there when proper protective measures are taken.

Table 19. Comparison of Temperatures North and South
of the Tianshan Mountains in January

Station	Elevation (metres)	Temperature in January (°C)
Qitai	795.3	-20.9
Shanshan	420.0	-10.8
Altay	750.0	-18.6
Korla	901.4	-9.5

2) The mountains lead to a subsidence of air currents and an increase in temperature, thus intensifying atmospheric drought and dry wind on the leeward slopes. The most outstanding example of this is in the northern part of southern Xinjiang where dry winds often blow over a large area and the temperature rises. The mean temperature in the Turpan Depression in January is -10.3°C., 3.8°C. higher than it is in Yanqi in the west and 4.5°C. higher than it is in Hami in the east. The Ili and Tacheng basins are both small warm areas. Urumqi is well-known for its foehns. Whenever a cyclone moves to the northern foot of the Tianshan Mountains, the current over the northern slope of the mountains subsides and a foehn blows, resulting in a rise in temperature on the piedmont plain.

3) The mountains exert a large impact on the surface

winds. The megarelief gives rise to the prevalency of local circulation between the lofty mountains and the basins. The
prevailing winds subside near the foot of mountains or in the
valleys, where they are turned into local mountain-valley
breezes. Southern winds (mountain breezes) and northern
winds (valley breezes) prevail at Urumqi in autumn. Gales
blow most often near mountain passes. There are gales at the
Alataw Pass (the Junggar Gate) of the Tianshan Mountains
for 155 days a year. Gales also blow at the Dapancheng Pass
between the Karawucheng Mountains and Mount Bogda of the
Tianshan range for 128 days a year. The western section of
the Gansu Corridor is located in the valley of the Shule River,
lying between the Qilian and Mazong mountains, where heavy
winds blow all year round with plenty of dust. This is called
the "Anxi wind".

It is thus evident that the gale-swept areas are all related
to narrow topography, in this case mountain passes. Of course,
the barometric differences on both sides of mountains is also
a prerequisite. Strong winds bring heavy blowing snow in
winter and violent sandstorms and haze in spring. Strong
winds carrying sand cause great damage to the crops, with resultant crop failures. And moving sand menaces the oases and
buries farm land and villages. Shelterbelts have been built
around many of the oases since Liberation to reduce this
menace from heavy winds.

The grand basins in the Northwest China Region and the
Gansu Corridor have a common type of landscape (Fig. 30).

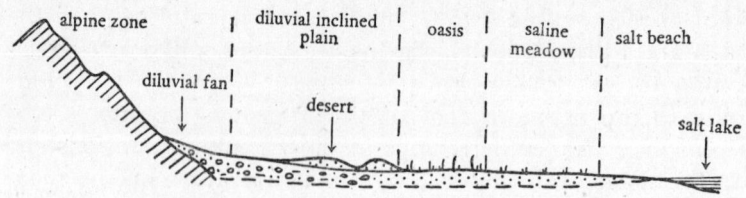

Fig. 30   Cross Section of a Desert Basin

The high mountains by the desert basins not only exert great impact on the air flow and formation of climatic features, but they also supply water for irrigation in the basins. All the high mountains have their own vertical landscape zones, in most cases starting from alpine neves and moving to alpine steppes or forest zones and mountain desert steppes down to the desert basin. Diluvial fans or diluvial and alluvial plains are widely found in the piedmont areas on the fringe of the basins. These are called gobis of the accumulation type. As the terrain slopes downward towards the centre of the basins, the deposited material of the gobis become finer and finer. Gravels are widely spread on the upper part of the diluvial plain. The streams or rivers rising from the melted ice or snow flow out of the mountain into the gobis and a great deal of this water percolates into the ground to make the groundwater level deep. The material deposited over the ground surface becomes even finer in the middle part of a diluvial plain. There it is easier to open canals to draw river water for irrigation, the groundwater is found at the depth of three or four metres, and salinization can be avoided, thus providing the most favourable conditions for building oases (Fig. 31).

Beyond the gobi zone and at the front fringe of the diluvial plain, the groundwater often seeps out of the surface in the form of springs, which are known as the groundwater discharge areas. This creates a saline meadow. Further downward towards the centre of a basin is a large area of salt marsh or desert where streams and groundwater flow into the depression to form a salt lake. According to chemical properties, the groundwater can also be divided into zones. Generally speaking, the mountain is the runoff formation zone where the groundwater contains few minerals. The diluvial plain at the foot of the mountain contains bicarbonate water. At the front of the diluvial plain there is a gently sloping ground surface covered with very fine material, and the slow-moving groundwater becomes impregnated with minerals and tends to be of a sulphate type. Farther on towards the low-lying land are

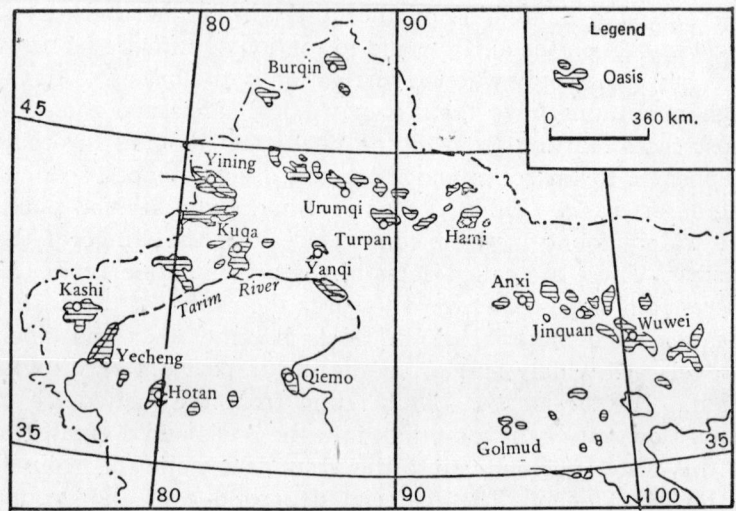

Fig. 31 Distribution of Oases in the Northwest China Region

saline meadows and salt marshlands with poor drainage.
Here the groundwater table is very shallow, even near the
surface, and the water is more mineralized and contains sulphates or chlorides.

The central parts of the various basins have different
desert landscape features. For example, the central part of
the Tarim Basin is the Taklimakan Desert; the centre of the
Junggar Basin is the Gurbantunggut Desert, and the centre
of the Qaidam Basin is composed of salt marshes and salt
beaches. But a model of the desert landscape from the piedmont area to the centre of the basin is basically the same for
all of these.

(3) Inland Rivers and Alpine Glaciers

The desert area has little surface water and lacks perennial
rivers. Except in the part of northern Xinjiang where the
Ertix River runs, the whole region is an interior drainage
area. The inland rivers rising from the high mountains and

pouring into the basins mostly percolate into the gobis and shifting sands, or the water gathers in the depressions and forms marshes or lakes. The big rivers of this Northwest China Region are the Tarim, Ili, Manas, Shule, Ruoshui and Qaidam.

After passing out of the mountains, the rivers have no permanent channels and their courses shift constantly. As a result, where old courses are abandoned the vegetation dies for lack of water and the land cracks. Wherever the new courses run, the deserts quickly turn into meadows. The Tarim River, crisscrossed with dried beds and tributaries on both sides, provides a typical example of this phenomenon.

The rainfall is scarce, but evaporation is strong and the soil is subject to little leaching. Soluble salts are therefore deposited in great quantities. Most of these salts can be dissolved by a small quantity of runoff, and so the river water is highly mineralized after flowing only a short distance.

The Tarim River is the longest inland river in China's arid region. It has three tributaries — the Aksu, Hotan and Yarkant. If the Yarkant is taken as its headwater, the Tarim is 2,200 km. long. The Tarim River, however, is usually referred to as only the lower section from the confluence of the three tributaries, a length of 970 km. The Aksu, which is derived from the Tianshan Mountains and has abundant water, accounts for about 76 per cent of the flow of the Tarim. The Yarkant and Hotan rivers discharge water into the Tarim only during the flood season. The lower reaches of the Tarim have often changed course, sometimes flowing eastward and joining the Konqi River to flow into the Lop Nur, and sometimes flowing southward into Taitema Lake. After a dam was built in Weili County in 1952, the lower section of the Tarim became separated from the Konqi River and now exclusively flows into Taitema Lake. Large-scale reclamation has been going on along the middle and lower reaches of the Tarim in recent years, and big reservoirs have been built so that the section of the Tarim from the Daxihaizi Reservoir downward no longer flows in most years.

The piedmont diluvial and alluvial plains in this region contain abundant groundwater resources. For example, the piedmont plain of the Qilian Mountains — the Gansu Corridor — contains 5,000-6,000 million cu. m. of groundwater. The groundwater has played an important role in transforming the deserts and expanding production. Large numbers of pumping wells have been sunk to obtain this groundwater for irrigation, turning once unreclamable wasteland into beautiful oases. The building of karezes in Xinjiang to obtain groundwater for irrigation is a crystallization of the ingenuity of the people of various nationalities there. A karez is an irrigation system of wells connected by underground channels to make use of the groundwater in arid regions. Little evaporation takes place while the water moves in the channels, thus greatly raising the utilization rate of the groundwater. There are now more than 1,100 karezes in use in the Turpan area, with underground channels totalling 3,000 km. in length and a total water discharge of nearly 2,000 million cu. m. a year (Fig. 32).

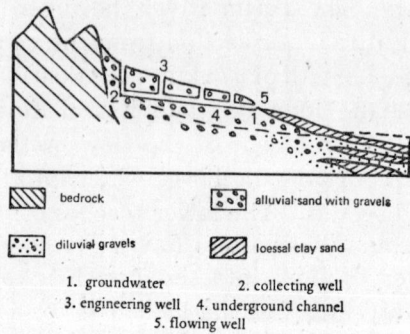

▨ bedrock	▨ alluvial-sand with gravels
▨ diluvial gravels	▨ loessal clay sand

1. groundwater   2. collecting well
3. engineering well   4. underground channel
5. flowing well

Fig. 32   Diagram of a Karez

The high mountains in this region have abundant ice and snow resources that are of great importance to agricultural development. The Tianshan Mountains are China's largest glacial area, with glaciers covering more than 9,500 sq. km. Most of these glaciers are located in the western section of the mountains where there is more rainfall. Great valley glaciers have developed there. For example, the Nanyinole-quik Glacier on the southern side of the Hantenggri Peak is 59 km. long and is the largest glacier in the Tianshan Mountains. The glaciers in the Qilian Mountains are found in the alpine zone over 4,500 m. above sea level. They cover about 1,300 sq. km. mostly in the western and middle sections of the Qilian Mountains. The glaciers of Mount Muztagata (7,555 m. above sea level) and Mount Kongur (7,719 m. above sea level) near the Pamirs, in the western section of the Kunlun Mountains, cover an area of 596 sq. km. and are scattered like stars above the snowline that lies 5,500 m. above sea level. From here eastward, the glaciers and firns in the Kunlun Mountains cover about 10,000 sq. km.

Many of the great rivers in this region are derived from the alpine glaciers and firns. The supply of melted water from the glaciers and firns has been relatively stable; more water is melted in the dry years and so the supply of water is plentiful, while less water is melted in the humid years and so the supply is scarce. Therefore the glaciers and firns serve as alpine reservoirs containing solid water. They are quite beneficial to the irrigation of the oases and for agricultural development.

(4) Desert Vegetation and Soil

The desert vegetation in the Northwest China Region mainly includes xerophilous shrubs and semi-frutex. There are only a few species, mostly of the goosefoot family, but plants of the tamarisk, composite and pulse families also account for a relatively large percentage of the plants. Because of the dry climate and high salt content in the soil, the desert plants have the following ecological features:

1) The plants generally do not cover more than 20 per cent of the ground surface and sometimes as little as 1 per cent. There are large areas of gobi and shifting dunes void of any vegetation in the extremely arid Beishan Mountain area, in southern Xinjiang and in the Qaidam Basin.

2) Some plants have degenerated into leafless plants, or else their leaves have formed special shapes (small, woolly and thorny) to reduce the transpiration. Plants such as ephedra, calligonum and wormwood are examples of this.

3) Many of the plants have large root systems so as to draw water from the soil. For example, the desert bamboo (*Psammochloa villosa*) has an underground stem that crawls horizontally over 27 m., and the roots of tamarisk can extend up to 30 m.

4) Many varieties of the goosefoot family, such as seep-weed, are juicy plants containing highly concentrated salts. They can absorb water from soil with a high salt content.

The Northwest China Region covers a vast area and its deserts can be divided into two types — the arid and the extremely arid — according to the amount of rainfall. The former includes the Junggar Basin and the eastern part of the Alxa Plateau. There the annual precipitation is 100 to 200 mm. and the aridity is about 4. The latter includes the western part of the Alxa Plateau, the Tarim Basin and the Qaidam Basin with an annual precipitation of only about 50 mm. and an aridity of over 10.

According to the properties of the surface material, the desert areas can also be divided into two groups — sandy desert and gobi. The gobis can be subdivided, in turn, into rocky and gravel types. The former are gobis subject to strong aeolian eroison, with exposed rocks and black debris over their ground surface. The latter are piedmont diluvial fans covered with gravel.

According to the different climates and surface materials, the desert vegetation can be divided into four different types:

1) The Junggar Basin has more annual precipitation than

most other desert areas and it is more evenly distributed in the four seasons. Its vegetation is mainly composed of temperate semi-arbors, mostly of the goosefoot family with the tallest plants being 7 m. in height. Under these trees are shrubs, semi-frutex and herbs. The vegetation on the fixed sand dunes covers 30 to 40 per cent of the surface. Precipitation is around 300 mm. in the Ili and Tacheng areas, where the natural vegetation is desert steppe. There is also much precipitation in the east part of the Alxa Plateau, where the vegetation is composed of temperate shrubs and semi-frutex. On the fixed and semi-fixed dunes grow semi-frutex and Ordos wormwood, covering 50 per cent of the surface.

2) In the extremely arid areas, *Sympegma regelii* and gobi goosefoot of the goosefoot family grow sparsely in the dry gullies of rocky deserts and low hills around Beishan Mountain and at the southern foot of the Tianshan Mountains, with a total surface coverage of less than 1 per cent. On the gravel gobis grow *Reaumuria soongarica* of the tamarisk family. This is a low shrub, only 20 m. tall. The plants cover no more than 10 per cent of the surface and only 2-3 per cent in some areas.

3) The vegetation in the heavy saline soils around salt lakes, along the river banks and in some depression areas is juicy low semi-frutex, mainly *Kalidium gracile* and Suaeda of the goosefoot family, *Nitraria tangutorum* and *Tamarix spp.* Saline deserts with *Kalidium gracile* cover a very large part of the Tarim Basin.

4) Light saline soil with good moisture is found along river banks in the desert region where the groundwater is at a high level. On the banks grow euphrates poplars (*Populus diversifolia*). These have been planted in a corridor arrangement along river banks, and so they are also called "corridor woods". The poplars generally grow about 10 m. high and the tallest ones reach 20 to 30 m. The longest of such corridor areas is found along the banks of the Tarim River in the Taklimakan Desert. Because of the dry climate and the low

humidity, the poplar stands are thin with a canopy density of less than 0.3. They are quite different in appearance and community structure from the deciduous broadleaf forests in the west areas.

The zonal soils in this region are gray-brown desert soil under the arid climate of the temperate zone and brown desert soil with large areas of aeolian sandy soil under the extremely arid climate of the warm-temperate zone. The parent material for these soils is gravel diluvium on the gobis, aeolian deposits on the sand dunes, weathering residue on low hills with outcrops, and some river alluvium and lake sediments. Under the influence of the climate and vegetation, these desert soils have the following features: (a) The mechanical components contain some fine particles, but more gravels and sand. (b) The topsoil contains little organic matter, less than 0.5 per cent, and there is no humus accumulation. (c) The whole profile contains a large quantity of limestone (calcium carbonate) with little leaching. Calcium carbonate accumulates in the upper layer, and the content of calcium carbonate in the topsoil (0 to 2 cm.) is often 7-8 per cent, but this gradually decreases in the lower layers. (d) The profile contains gypsum in all layers. (e) There is a certain amount of salt in the soil, mostly sodium sulphate and sodium chloride. Because of the extreme aridity, the soil in the Tarim Basin also contains salt pans of chlorides, which are rarely found in desert soil in other parts of the world. (f) The whole profile produces a medium or strong alkaline reaction (pH 8.0 to 10.0).

Gray desert soil has developed in the fine earth along the margins of the temperate desert basins. This kind of soil is mainly distributed on the inclined piedmont plain at the northern foot of the Tianshan Mountains, where there is more rainfall (about 200 mm.), the climate is wetter and vegetation covers a larger area. Gray desert soil has not only the features of desert soil in the process of formation but also the embryo stage of the steppe soil. For example, there are signs of humus accumulation in gray desert soil and the content of organic matter in the top layer is about 1.0 per cent, with a maximum of up to 1.7 per cent. The calcium carbonate in the soil is slightly leached and most of the calcium carbonate is found in the middle and lower layers.

Aeolian sandy soil is a soil that develops from aeolian sand in the desert region. Because of constant wind erosion and deposition, the formative process of this soil is quite unstable. It is very difficult to form a mature soil profile. However, as sand dunes become fixed, changes take place in the physical and chemical properties of the aeolian sandy soil. The number of sand particles in fixed dunes decreases, but the number of clay particles increases to around 5 per cent, and the content of organic matter also rises. The soil contains the ash elements and nitrogen needed for plant growth. It also preserves a certain quantity of water. As long as there is water for irrigation, this kind of soil can be transformed for farming and stock-raising.

The northern part of the Junggar Basin, the upper part of the piedmont diluvial fan at the northern foot of the Tian-shan Mountains and the eastern part of the Qaidam Basin are all desert steppe with brown soil areas. The main differences between brown soil and desert soil are that the former has a stronger biological function, a thicker humus horizon (15 to 30 centimetres), more leaching and an obvious illuvium of calcium carbonate. These features show that the formation of brown soil is based mainly on humus accumulation and calcification in the steppe soil. However, beginning at 35 to 70 cm. below the surface, the soil also contains a gypsum accumulation that reflects some of the features in the formation of desert soil. These features become more than conspicuous as the aridity increases. The annual precipitation in the Ili valley in Xinjiang is around 300 mm. and the water and heat conditions are slightly better here than in the brown soil areas. This area has gray soil with a humus horizon of 50 to 70 cm. Part of the areas with these soils has been used for dry farming.

The mountains in the Northwest China Region also have specific vertical zones. The vegetation and soils are mountain steppe with chestnut soil in northern Xinjiang and mountain desert steppe with brown soil in southern Xinjiang. As aridity decreases from south to north, the lower-limit elevation of the mountain steppe with chestnut soil zone drops from 1,100 m. in the western Tianshan Mountains to 800 m. in the northwestern Altay Mountains, and the lower-limit elevation of the mountain desert steppe with brown soil zone drops from 3,500 m. in the central Kunlun Mountains to 2,000 m. on the northern side of the eastern Tianshan Mountains.

(5) Animals in the Desert

There are a few families of animals in this region, especially in the centres of the grand deserts. The representative animals include the jerboa and gerbillus of the rodentia, such as the five-toed jerboa, earth jerboa, three-toed jerboa and long-clawed jerboa. All of these jerboas have extraordinarily long tails and hind-legs so that they can make quick leaps of from 60 to 180 cm. With hard pads on their feet, they can run fast on the sandy ground. They usually come out at night and can travel as much as 10 km. in one night.

The hoofed animals living in the desert include the wild camel, wild donkeys, Mongolian gazelles, antelopes and argalis. These are all animals capable of running quickly. Among them, the wild camel is the rarest species. It has long been listed in the first category of protected animals in China. It is found mainly in the extremely arid gravel gobi and hilly areas to the west of Xingxingxia, in eastern Xinjiang. The alhagi mannaplant (*Alhagi pseudalhagi*) and a few other plants that grow sparsely on the ground surface in this area are the staple food for wild camels.

Apart from wolves and lynxes that are widely distributed across the country, the carnivorous animals in this region include the corsac (fox), steppe cat and tiger weasel. In winter, packs of wolves run after hoofed animals on the open grounds, presenting a great menace to them and to grazing stock in particular.

2. Regional Differentiation of the Natural Landscape

In the Northwest China Region the characteristics of the natural landscape differ as water conditions change. The region forms the most arid part of China, with the annual precipitation at roughly 100 to 200 mm. in the Junggar Basin and around 100 mm. in the Gansu Corridor and most of the Alxa Plateau. Because water vapour comes from different sources, the distribution of precipitation also varies from season to season. In the east, there is rainfall in the summer but little rain or snow in winter. Northern Xinjiang has more snowfall and snow accumulation in winter than the rest of the region. Such a seasonal distribution of rainfall and heat results in regional differences in the development of vegetation and soil, and gives rise to differentiations in the desert landscape.

Due to the blocking of high mountains, there are often great differences in the vapour sources, seasonal variations, wind directions, wind intensity and heat conditions. The outline of the megal-landform strengthens the regional differentiation of the landscapes. Therefore, the principal mountain ranges can generally be taken as natural boundaries. Based on this, the Northwest China Region can be divided into six subregions and nine areas.

VII_A Northern Xinjiang Subregion
VII_{A1} Altay-Junggar Boundary Mountain Area
VII_{A2} Junggar Basin Area
VII_B Tianshan Mountains Subregion
VII_{B1} Tianshan Mountain Area
VII_{B2} Ili River Valley Area
VII_C Southern Xinjiang Subregion

VII$_{C1}$ Tarim Basin Area
VII$_{C2}$ Turpan Hami Basin Area
VII$_{C3}$ Beishan Gobi-Gaxun Gobi Area
VII$_{D}$ Alxa-Gansu Corridor Subregion
VII$_{D1}$ Gansu Corridor Area
VII$_{D2}$ Alxa Plateau Area
VII$_{E}$ Qilian Mountain Subregion
VII$_{F}$ Qaidam Basin Subregion

(1)   Northern Xinjiang Subregion

This subregion covers the whole area north of the Tian-shan Mountains in Xinjiang. Geomorphologically it is mainly composed of the huge Junggar Basin. This basin lies between the Altay Mountains, the Junggar boundary mountains and the Tianshan Mountains. Together these mountains form the outline of a scalene triangle. This subregion is not as tightly closed by mountains as is southern Xinjiang. The mountains on the northwestern side are relatively low and have many gaps where moisture from the Arctic can penetrate deeply. The subregion is therefore slightly more humid than the Tarim Basin in southern Xinjiang. It has an annual accumulated temperature of around 3,000°C., and is considered to be a temperate arid desert zone.

1) The Altay-Junggar Boundary Mountains

The Altay Mountains stand northeast of the Junggar Basin, between China and Mongolia, and run from north to west. The mountains are generally 3,000 m. above sea level, the highest peak being 4,374 m. They descend southeastward and gradually disappear into the Gobi Desert. The mountain climate is comparatively humid and the amount of precipitation rises with the height of the mountains. It is roughly 250 mm. in the low hills of less than 1,000 m. above sea level; 250 to 350 mm. between 1,000 and 1,500 m. and 350 to 500 mm., or even 800 mm., at heights of between 1,500 and 3,000 m. The temperature in these mountains is very low, with an annual accumulated temperature of less than 2,000°C. The lowest temperature at Fuyun, in the piedmont area, may drop to -52°C. in winter. Therefore the Altay Mountains have large tracts of frigid-temperate coniferous forests, composed mostly of Siberian larch trees mixed with Siberian spruces (*Picea obovata*), birches and European aspens (*Populus tremula*). The upper limit for these forests is 2,100 to 2,300 m. above sea level, and the lower limit rises from 1,300 m. in the northwest to 1,700 m. in the southeast in accord with the amount of precipitation.

The Ertix River begins in the southeastern part of the Altay Mountains and is China's only river with an arctic drainage system. The annual precipitation on the piedmont plain at the southern foot of the Altay Mountains is 150 to 200 mm. This is a desert steppe area, with sand needlegrass as the primary plant species and a mixture of low semi-frutex, short-leaf Anabasis and Ordos wormwood. The lower limit of the desert steppe rises from 500 m. above sea level in the northwest to 2,000 m. in the southeast. There are also vast pastures above the forest belts in the western section of the Altay Mountains. Therefore, the Altay area is one of Xinjiang's important stock-raising areas. The people of the Kazak nationality living in this area divide their pastures into summer, spring and autumn, and winter pastures so that they can graze their stock on rotation through the different seasons.

The Junggar boundary mountains stand 2,000 to 4,000 m. above sea level. They include some rift basins. For example, the lowest place in these mountains, Tacheng, is only 400 m. above sea level. This area is relatively humid and has an aridity of less than 4.0. Steppe and desert steppe vegetation covers most of the area, with good-quality grasses that are quite suitable for stock-raising. The Ermin River valley and the Tacheng Prefecture, where dry crops have been cultivated for a long time, are the agricultural areas in the western part of northern Xinjiang.

2) The Junggar Basin

The Junggar Basin is about 850 km. long from west to east

and 380 km. at its widest point from north to south. The terrain inclines gently from southeast to northwest, the highest section being in the southeast. This is about 1,000 m. above sea level (near Laoqitai). The northwest section is lowlying with a number of inland lakes, such as the Ulungur, Manas and Ebi lakes. The water surface of Ebi Nur (Ebi Lake), only 189 m. above sea level, is the lowest place in the Junggar Basin. The eastern part of the basin was uplifted within recent geological history to form a denudation upland that is now a vast expanse of gobi. Most of the basin is occupied by the Gurbantunggut Desert, 300 to 500 m. above sea level.

The Gurbantunggut Desert is the second largest desert in China. It has an annual precipitation of 100 to 150 mm. and has some snow accumulation in winter. Plants therefore grow in this desert, and most of the dunes are fixed or semi-fixed, covering 97 per cent of the desert. With a vegetation coverage of 40 to 50 per cent on the fixed dunes and 15 to 25 per cent on the semi-fixed dunes, the desert provides good pastures during the winter.

The mean annual temperature in the Junggar Basin is about 6°C. Winter begins early and the mean temperature for about five months of the year is below zero Centigrade. It is warm in summer, with the mean temperature climbing to 22-25°C. in July. The accumulated temperature is about 3,000°C., and the growing period is about 150 to 180 days. Wheat and sugar beets grow relatively well here. The lower part of the basin, at places such as Shihezi (445 m. above sea level), has warm summers and an accumulated temperature of above 3,200°C. so that it is suitable for growing cotton. However, since the frost period varies greatly, cold often causes fluctuations in cotton yields. Precipitation in the basin is not sufficient to meet the needs of crops, and so farming is possible only in irrigated areas. Therefore the runoff from the mountains is the lifeblood of agriculture here. The northern slopes of the Tianshan Mountains face the humid northwest current and receive much more precipitation than do the slopes at the same elevation in the Kunlun Mountains. More snow also accumulates in the Tianshan Mountains. Located at a lower line, this snow thaws earlier and most of the rivers from the Tianshan Mountains are flooded in spring. This is most favourable for the sowing of spring crops in the basin. Therefore, most of the oases in the Junggar Basin are found at the foot of the Tianshan Mountains, along the southern margins of the basin.

The piedmont area at the northern foot of the Tianshan Mountains can be divided into three landscape belts between the mountains and the centre of the basin, that is, from south to north. The first is the diluvial-alluvial fan, a gravel gobi with a big gradient (1/100 to 1/200). The annual precipitation here is about 200 to 250 mm., the soil contains little organic matter and it is poor in preserving water. However, the water table is deep and there is no problem of salinity and alkalinity. The second is the margins of the alluvial fan, which are groundwater discharge areas. The ground surface here is mainly composed of sandy clay, and the soil layer is thick. The annual precipitation is about 200 mm. and the ground surface has a gradient of 1/200 to 1/1,000. The old oases are located in this area with good water conditions. But, owing to a high water table and poor drainage, marshes have formed and there is a light degree of salinization. The third belt is the alluvial plain. This has a ground surface gradient of 1/1,000 to 1/3,000 and an annual precipitation of about 140 to 160 mm. The thick soil layer can preserve water better than that in the other two belts, and the soil offers good returns for irrigation.

The total area of oases in the southwestern margins of the Junggar Basin has increased greatly since the founding of the People's Republic of China, from 50,000 hectares before Liberation to 260,000 hectares at present.

(2) Tianshan Mountain Subregion

The Tianshan range is one of the biggest mountain systems in Asia. It stretches across the middle of Xinjiang, with a

length of 1,700 km. The western part of the mountains is
400 km. wide, but the eastern section (east of Urumqi) narrows
to about 100 km. Its major peaks stand about 4,000 to 6,000 m.
above sea level. The western part of the mountains is relatively high, but the eastern part is relatively low. The basins
on both sides of the Tianshan Mountains stand only about
1,000 m. above sea level. Therefore the mountains are high
and precipitous. Because of their high terrain and large area,
the Tianshan Mountains are defined as a subregion.

The Tianshan Mountains are a typical folded-block mountain system with many rift basins. In geologic structure and
geomorphology, they can be divided into three parts — north,
middle and south. The northern Tianshan Mountains border
closely on the Junggar Basin, with most of their peaks standing
4,000 to 5,500 m. above sea level. Mount Bogda, east of Urumqi, has a height of 5,445 m. above sea level. It is famous for
its Tianchi Lake, a well-known scenic spot in the Tianshan
Mountains. The northern Tianshan Mountains are located on
the windward side and have more precipitation than the southern Tianshan Mountains. They are widely covered by alpine
glaciers. Therefore many rivers rise from the glaciers and
many wide diluvial-alluvial fans have come into existence at
the foot of the northern Tianshan Mountains.

The vertical landscape zones in the northern Tianshan
Mountains are clearly divided. Take the mountains south of
Urumqi for instance. There are glaciers and firns in elevations higher than 3,400 m. above sea level and a frostweather-
ing zone between 3,200 and 3,400 m. where only snowlotus
(*Saussurea spp.*) and some cushion plants grow. Above 2,800
to 3,000 m. are alpine cobresia meadows. The grass grows
very thickly here and is about 10 to 15 cm. tall, covering 70
to 80 per cent of the ground. These meadows yield 1,000 kg.
per hectare and provide good pastures in summer. The thick
growth of cobresia results in the accumulation of large quantities of organic matter in the soil and the development of

alpine meadow soil. There are marshes and frozen bog soil in the valleys.

Above 2,200 to 2,400 m. above sea level are subalpine meadows with a thick growth of rank grasses, mostly dicotyledones. Between 1,500 and 2,200 m. are forest steppes and forests. On the sides of these mountains with the most humid climate, woodlands can be found as low as 1,200 m. There are no forests above 2,700 m. on the mountains near Yiwu at the eastern end of the northern Tianshan Mountains due to the arid climate. Thus this area provides a direct transition from the mountain forest steppe with chernozem zone to the alpine cobresis and sedge (Carex) with meadow soil zone.

The forests on the northern Tianshan Mountains are made up of schrenk spruce (*Picea schrenkiana*), often appearing as tracts in shady areas and at the bottom of valleys. Because atmospheric humidity is less on the Tianshan Mountains, most of the schrenk spruce woods are pure and not mixed with other firs. This makes the northern Tianshan Mountains quite different from the mountains in the Northeast China Region that are greatly influenced by marine currents. The schrenk spruce, 25 to 30 m. tall, stands erect, with its slender crown looking like a pinnacle. There is a reserve here of over 400 cu. m. of good timber per hectare.

The soil under the spruce woods is gray-cinnamon forest soil, a type that develops under mountain forests in semi-arid and arid areas. It is a transitional form of soil, standing between cinnamon soil and gray forest soil. Differentiations in the soil profile are quite clear. The humus layer is 20 to 30 cm. thick and the surface layer contains 12 to 25 per cent of organic matter. There are distinct signs of clayization in the middle of the profile and a calcic layer below 50 to 60 cm. depth. The soil produces a neutral to light alkaline reaction, with a pH value of between 7.0 and 8.0. The soil not only reflects some typical features in the formation of cinnamon soil (clayization and carbonate accumulation) but also some in the formation of gray forest soil (humus accumulation). Therefore we call it gray-cinnamon forest soil. It is a product of the special bio-climatic surroundings in mountain forests of the arid areas.

Mountain grasslands (mainly sheep fescue and needle-grass) and desert grasslands (sand needlegrass and low semi-frutex grass) are located on the sunny side below forest belts or in forest belts. Because precipitation decreases on the north-ern Tianshan Mountains from west to east, the lower limit of the desert steppes on the northern slopes rises from 1,000 m. above sea level in the west to 1,500 m. in the east, and to 1,700 m. on Balikun Mountain at the easternmost end of the Tianshan Mountains.

The piedmont areas on the northern side of the Tianshan Mountains are gently undulating hills and longitudinal valleys, 1,100 to 1,800 m. above sea level, with an annual precipitation of 300 to 400 mm., much more than is received on the plain areas. The soil here is mainly mountain chestnut soil. They are natural pastures in which forage grasses grow well. Be-cause of a temperature inversion in winter, the piedmont areas are relatively warm and are therefore good for grazing live-stock, and the winter grazing time can last for as long as five months. These areas are also important dry farming areas in Xinjiang, the lower limit of the dry farmland being about 1,200 to 1,300 m. above sea level.

The middle Tianshan Mountains comprise a series of parallel mountain ridges, interspersed with many rift basins. The ridges generally do not exceed an elevation of 3,500 m. above sea level. The Ili River basin in the west is one of the biggest intermontane basins in the Tianshan Mountains. Sur-rounded by peaks on three sides, this basin is open in the west so that humid air currents from the west penetrate deep into the basin. With an annual precipitation of more than 300 to 500 mm. (increasing from west to east), the basin is the dampest area in Xinjiang. It is covered by thick snow in winter. On the northern side of the basin are high mountains that block cold currents, and so the Ili River valley is relatively warm. For example, Ining city (804 m. above sea level) has an annual mean temperature of 7.7°C. and a mean daily temperature of -11°C. in January. This is much warmer than it is in the Junggar Basin. The natural vegetation in the Ili River basin is mainly temperate steppe with waterweeds growing thickly. The Kunes Grasslands on the upper reaches of the Ili River are a breeding centre for the famous Ili horses (called "heavenly horses" in the ancient times). The valleys on the lower reaches of the river, where wheat, cotton and rice are grown, are important farming areas in Xinjiang.

The southern Tianshan Mountains lie near the Tarim Basin and are the tallest peaks of all, many standing 5,000 to 6,000 m. above sea level. The highest one is Mount Tomul (7,439 m.).

The natural landscape of the southern Tianshan Mountains is quite different from that of the northern Tianshan Mountains. As the flow of air currents are blocked by the northern Tianshan Mountains, the aridity of the southern Tianshan Mountains is quite serious. The Tarim Basin south of the Tianshan Mountains is far drier than the Junggar Basin, and therefore the desert penetrates deep into the mountains here. The natural vegetation is mainly mountain desert steppe and steppe without any forests. Small tracts of schrenk spruce and birches are found growing sparsely in a few shady and damp gullies on the sunless side of the high mountains. There are not many shrubs under the trees, and most of them are meso-xerophilous thorny shrubs. No herbal plants, found on the northern side of the Tianshan Mountains, are under the trees on the southern side.

The Turpan-Hami Basin and the Yanqi Basin, are also part of the rift basins in the Tianshan Mountains, but their natural landscape belongs to the extremely arid desert of the warm temperate zone. For this reason, they are considered part of the southern Xinjiang subregion.

(3) Southern Xinjiang Subregion

This subregion is an extremely arid desert area of the warm

temperate zone in China. Its annual precipitation is generally under 50 mm. Apart from the Tarim Basin, this subregion also includes the western end of the Gansu Corridor (the Beishan gobi, Anxi and Dunhuang) and the Turpan and Yanqi basins.

1) The Tarim Basin

The Tarim Basin is the largest inland basin in China. It is surrounded by high mountains on all sides, with only a 70-km.-wide gap opening in the east to link it to the Gansu Corridor. The basin stretches about 1,500 km. from west to east and its widest part is 600 km. from north to south. Its relief inclines slightly from southwest to northeast, with the elevation dropping from 1,400 m. above sea level to 800 m. The Tarim River runs along the northern fringe of this basin.

With an aridity of 24 to 64, the Tarim Basin is covered by the largest desert area in China. The Taklimakan Desert lies at its centre. This is almost joined by the Gumtag Desert in the east. Together they cover an area of 327,000 sq. km., or 52 per cent of China's total desert areas (not including the gobis). Shifting dunes, mostly 100 to 150 m. high, with the highest standing 200 to 300 m., are a feature of this desert. They occupy about 85 per cent of the desert area. Small fixed dunes with tamarisks growing on them are often found in places where the groundwater level is high, near rivers and lakes. These are about two to four metres high and are called "red willow domes".

The lake known as Lop Nur, only 780 m. above sea level, is the lowest part of the Tarim Basin. It is located in a Quaternary tectonic depression. It has changed its locality several times in human history. Due to uplifting of Beishan Mountain by geologic forces, the lake was forced to move 30 to 50 km. westward from 1932 to 1942. Furthermore, the lower reaches of the Tarim and Konqi rivers have constantly changed course in this area and have joined the Lop Nur to create a vast alluvial and lacustrine plain. The river and lake deposits along the lower reaches of the Shule River and in the Lop Nur depression, eroded by wind, have formed "Yardang" landforms, which are wind-eroded mounds alternating with wind-eroded hollows. These wind-eroded mounds are generally one to five m. high. They have formed parallel to the main wind direction, roughly from northeast to southwest. The clay mounds often have salt crusts on their tops and are therefore called "white-dragon mounds". South of the Turpan-Hami Basin is the Gaxun Gobi.

Many of the rivers that rise in the Kunlun and Tianshan mountains run deep into the desert, and some (the Hotan River) even pass through it. The valleys of these rivers have become natural oases in the desert and have thick growths of euphrates poplar and bloomy poplar forests, tamarisk shrubs and reed meadows. Moreover, the desert has abundant thermal resources with an accumulated temperature of 4,000° to 5,000°C., a frost-free period of 180 to 240 days and an annual sunshine time of 3,000 to 3,500 hours. Large tracts of wasteland can be reclaimed for farming in the valleys with good water and vegetation conditions. Many new oases have been built along the lower reaches of the Tarim River in recent years, and a total of 50,000 hectares of new farmland have been opened. The two new reclamation areas at Kala and Tikanlik, along the lower reaches of the Tarim River, have extended from the margins of the basin to the centre of the desert. The Taklimakan Desert is no longer what it was once said to be, an "uninhabited wilderness", but it has some potential for reclamation and development.

The zoning of the landscape on the margins of the Tarim Basin is roughly similar to that at the southern fringes of the Junggar Basin (the northern foot of the Tianshan Mountains). As the Kunlun Mountains have been considerably uplifted in recent times, the extent and slope of the piedmont diluvial-alluvial plains are fairly big. The slope of the upper part of the diluvial-alluvial fan is mostly six to eight degrees and the extent of the fans in the Pishan area reaches as far as the southern foot of Mazhatag Mountain (a low hill in the centre of the basin). On the other hand, as the southern Tianshan Moun-tains were little uplifted in recent times, the diluvial-alluvial plains there are relatively small and do not extend much to the plains.

The zonal soil of the Tarim Basin is brown desert soil. However, the types of soil are relatively complex due to vari-ations in the landforms, composition of deposits and hydrogeo-logical conditions. Brown desert soil is seen only on low hills, in gobis and on piedmont diluvial fans. Saline meadow soil is widespread on the margins of diluvial fans and by riversides with ground water as deep as one to three metres and contain-ing one to three grams of minerals per litre. Euphrates poplar forest soil is well developed under euphrates poplars and bloomy poplars on river banks. The original trees, scrubs and meadow vegetation have withered or died out on old alluvial plains far away from present river courses, and so the soil there is extremely dry. The ground is covered with takyr soil and residual solonchak. Meadow solonchak, solonchak and lake-side solonchak are found in lakeside areas where the content of minerals in the groundwater increases.

There are no forests in the vertical zones on the Kunlun Mountains at the southern fringe of the basin because of the extreme aridity. For example, in the Setula mountainous area in the middle section of the Kunlun Mountains, desert vegeta-tion with mountain brown desert soil can be found up to 3,500 m. above sea level. Between 3,500 and 4,200 m. is mountain desert steppe with mountain brown soil. Above 4,200 metres is alpine meadow steppe and dry steppe with alpine steppe soil (alpine baga soil). The annual precipitation here is about 250 to 350 mm. The vegetation is mainly *Orinus thoroldii, Pen-nisetum flaccidum* and needlegrass. Alpine pastures are found on the mountains where there are humus layers 10 to 15 cm. thick.

2) The Turpan-Hami Basin

The Turpan-Hami Basin is an intermontane rift basin in the Tianshan Mountains. On its northern side are Mount Bogda and Mount Karlik, which are high and steep and stand at elevations of more than 4,000 m. above sea level. On the southern side is Juelotag Mountain (about 1,500 m. above sea level), which links with the Gaxun Gobi. Moreover, the climate on the southern side of this mountain belongs to the extremely arid type of the warm temperate zone and its natural landscape is the same as that of the Tarim Basin. Therefore it is included in the Southern Xinjiang Subregion.

The Turpan Depression and the Hami Basin are separated only by the Gumtag sand hills. The Turpan Depression is 245 km. long and 75 km. wide and its relief inclines southward. In the southern part of the basin are vast lowlands, mostly at elevations below sea level. Aydingkol Lake, the lowest place in the depression, is 154 m. below sea level. It is the lowest point in all China. The terrain of the Hami Basin declines from east to west, and Shalan Lake in the southwest of the basin is only 81 m. above sea level.

The Turpan Depression is a low and closed area. The air currents from northwest subside after crossing the Tianshan Mountains so that the temperature here increases greatly, giving rise to foehns. Moreover, as the surface heat is not apt to diffuse quickly, it is an area for especially hot summers, often called the "region of fire" in China. Summer at Turpan lasts four and a half months. It begins in early May, a month earlier than it does in the Changjiang River valley. The mean temperature in July is around 34°C., higher than at Wuhan, and the absolute maximum temperature is 47.8°C., the highest in China. In the middle of the Turpan Depression is a range of red sandstone hills that extend from west to east, with exposed rocks. The surface of these hills glitter in the summer sun like burning flames. These are the famous Huoyan (flame) Mountains. The accumulated temperature in the Turpan Depression is 5,400°C., the annual sunshine time is over 3,000 hours, and the frost-free period is 220 to 270 days. Because of the plentiful thermal resources, the depression is a producing centre of long-staple cotton and a home of melons and fruit.

Two crops ripen here in a year, just as they do in the Tarim Basin. During the day, the strong sunshine, high temperature and strong photosynthesis are good for saccharide accumulation in plants. At night, the temperature drops, plant respiration weakens and saccharide consumption decreases. This is why melons and fruit grown there are of specially high quality. Both raisins and Hami melons are known throughout China.

The climate at Turpan is extremely arid. The annual amount of precipitation is only 16 mm., and the minimum (1968) less than 3 mm. At the same time, annual evaporation is more than 3,000 mm. Agricultural production, therefore, depends entirely on irrigation. Today, in addition to many karezes, wells have been sunk for irrigation. The amount of cultivated farmland is now two and a half times that before Liberation. In Turpan County alone, shelterbelts totalling 1,300 km. have been built to protect 70 per cent of the farmland from sandstorms.

(4) Alxa-Gansu Corridor Subregion

This subregion covers the vast area north of the Qilian Mountains, west of the Helan Mountains and east of the Beishan Gobi. Precipitation here decreases rapidly from east to west, generally from 150 to 50 mm. The subregion belongs to the temperate arid desert zone.

1) The Gansu Corridor

To the south of this Corridor are the Qilian Mountains, with the high peaks towering more than 5,000 m. above sea level. To the north are the Longshou, Heli and Mazong mountains (known collectively as the Beishan Mountains), most of which are 2,000 to 2,500 m. above sea level with some peaks 3,600 m. high. The relief of these mountain areas is gentle and tends to be a peneplain. The Gansu Corridor itself is about 1,000 km. long and dozens of kilometres wide. Most of it is at an elevation of 1,100 to 1,500 m. above sea level. It is composed mainly of the piedmont inclined plains of the

Qilian Mountains.   As the Beishan Mountains are intermittent ranges with many wide gaps, the Gansu Corridor links directly with the Alxa Plateau to the north at some places.   The rivers in the corridor all belong to the inland drainage system arising in the Qilian Mountains.   Fifty-one streams converge into three river systems — the Shiyang, Ruoshui and Shule rivers. The Ruoshui is the longest, passing through the gobi and flowing northward into Juyan Lake (the Sogo Nur and the Gaxun Nur).   The total runoff where the water comes out of the mountain is 7,200 million cu. m., providing an abundant source of water for irrigating the oasis farmlands.

Due to the uplifting, the Gansu Corridor has been separated into three inland basins, namely, the Yumen-Anxi-Dunhuang Plain, an extremely arid desert area that belongs to the Shule River system and is part of the southern Xinjiang Subregion; the Zhangye-Gaotai-Jiuquan Plain, mostly belonging to the Ruoshui River system; and the Wuwei-Minqin Plain belonging to the Shiyang River system.

The Gansu Corridor has an accumulated temperature of 2,500° to 3,000°C. and a relatively ample water supply.   This explains why there is developed agriculture in the oases.   The corridor has been the passage between the East and the West since ancient times, and it is now one of the grain and cotton producing centres of northwest China.

The composition of the landscape in the Gansu Corridor can be illustrated by a cross-section of the area from the Qilian Mountains to Juyan Lake, as shown in Fig. 33. In this area there are different types of soil as the geomorphology changes. The salts in the residuum also change regularly according to their solubility, appearing in the following order: calcium carbonate (hard to dissolve), calcium sulphate, sodium sulphate and sodium chloride (easy to dissolve).   The composition of chemical elements in the groundwater varies correspondingly. The groundwater in the diluvial-alluvial fans contains 0.2 to 1.0 gram of minerals per litre, mainly calcium bicarbonate. The groundwater of the Corridor plain contains 1 to 3 grams

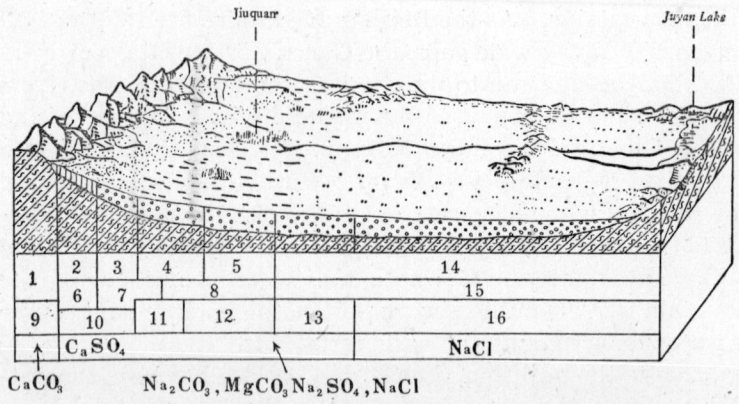

1. piedmont slope,   2. new diluvial fan,   3. sand dune,   4. old diluvial fan,   5. groundwater discharge area,
6. alluvial plain,   7. gravel gobi,   8. sand gobi,   9. oasis,   10. saline gobi,   11. sierozem,   12. gray desert soil,
13. gypsum gray brown desert soil,   14. saline meadow marsh soil,   15. loose solonchak,   16. crusty solonchak,

**Fig. 33 Diagram Illustrating the Landscape from
the Qilian Mountains to Juyan Lake**

per litre, chiefly bicarbonates and sulphates. The ground-water in the lower reaches of rivers and near the salt lake contains 3 to 10 grams of minerals per litre, mainly sulphates and chlorides. Tens of thousands of pumping wells have been drilled in recent years and large quantities of groundwater in the Corridor have been used to expand the area of the oases and to increase crop yields.

The oases in the Gansu Corridor cover a wide area, and the sand dunes, sparsely scattered near or in the oases, each cover an area of under 1,000 sq. km. Due to the good water conditions, tamarisks, *Nitraria tangutorum, Artemisio arenaria* and *Calligonum mongolicum* grow thickly on the fixed and partly fixed sand dunes at the fringes of the shifting sand. They provide abundant plant resources and natural shelterbelts along the margins of oases.

2) The Alxa Plateau

This refers to the vast area north of the Gansu Corridor, south of the Sino-Mongolian border, east of the Ruoshui River and west of the Helan Mountains. Its elevation varies from 1,000 to 1,400 m. above sea level and its relief inclines from north to south. There are some mountains on the plateau that separate it into several lowland sections where deserts are located. For example, the Yabrai Mountains, which run from northeast to southwest, separate the desert area into two big deserts — the Badainjaran and Tenger.

The Badainjaran is the third largest desert in China with big and high sand hills densely spread over it. Most of these are 200 to 300 m. high, and the highest over 500 m. Lakes are located between the sand hills. Because there is more precipitation in this area, plants such as *Calligonum mongolicum, Artemisia sphaerocephala* and *Psammochloa villosa* can grow sparsely on the dunes and sand hills. The plant-covered parts account for about one-third of the total surface of these sand hills. The lakes and basins are used mainly for grazing, and fixed human settlements such as Badainjaran are found around the lakes and in the basins.

The Tenger Desert is located in the southeast of the Alxa Plateau. It contains moving sand dunes that alternate with lake basins and beaches. There are as many as 422 lake basins in this desert. They provide the main pastures in the desert. The dunes here are also covered with a thin vegetation.

(5) Qilian Mountain Subregion

The Qilian Mountains and the Qaidam Basin are both located on the northern part of the Qinghai-Tibetan Plateau and are at an elevation of over 2,500 m. above sea level. However the Qaidam Basin has the features of the typical desert basin landscape, while the Qilian Mountains have the features of an alpine landscape in the desert region. This is why they are both included in the Northwest China Region.

The Qilian Mountains consist of a series of northwest to west mountains and valleys about 1,000 km. long. The mountain system is wide in the west and narrow in the east, the widest part being about 300 km. between Jiuquan and Qaidam.

Most of the peaks stand over 4,000 m. above sea level, the highest, Mount Tuanjie in the southern Shule Mountains, being 6,305 m. Both the northern and southern sides of the Qilian Mountains drop to the plains with clear faults. The relative height between the northern side and Gansu Corridor is over 2,000 m. while that between the southern side and the Qaidam Basin is only over 1,000 m. The top part of the Qilian Mountains above 4,500 m. is covered with firns and glaciers. The melted snow and ice are of importance to the development of agriculture, livestock breeding and industry in the Gansu Corridor and in the Qaidam Basin.

Seven ridges of the Qilian Mountains run parallel from north to south between Jiuquan and the Qaidam Basin. Between these ridges are wide valleys mostly 3,000 to 3,500 m. above sea level. They are vast mountain grasslands and have always been pastures for the herdsmen of the Mongolian, Tibetan and other minority nationalities.

The vertical landscape zone of the Qilian Mountains is relatively clear. Lenglongling Mountain (an eastern section of the Qilian Mountains), for example, has a piedmont desert steppe with sierozem zone below 2,300 m. above sea level. Between 2,300 and 2,600 m. is a mountain steppe with chestnut soil zone where the precipitation is over 300 mm. And between 2,600 and 3,400 m. is the forest with gray-drab forest soil zone where the precipitation is more than 500 mm. The forests are mostly distributed on the shady side of the mountain and grow sparsely. On the sunny side at the same altitude are blackseed junipers (*Juniperus saltuaria*), Tibet Junipers (*J. tibetica*) and mountain grass areas. The principal soil here is mountain chernozem, and the different slopes give rise to a clear difference in landscapes. Between 3,400 and 3,900 m. above sea level is an alpine meadow zone with a precipitation rate of 600 mm. and both slopes covered by thick growth of grasses. Above 4,200 m. are alpine firns and glaciers with the precipitation rate being over 600 mm.

(6) Qaidam Basin Subregion

The Qaidam Basin is a great desert basin surrounded by the Kunlun, Altun and Qilian mountains. It is 850 km. long from west to east and 250 km. wide from north to south at its widest point. The basin covers an area of about 220,000 sq. km. Around it are well-developed piedmont diluvial plains that slope downward towards the centre of the basin. The basin is 2,600 to 3,000 m. above sea level and has a peculiarly high and cold landscape for desert basins in the Northwest China Region. It is cool in summer and extremely cold in winter. Precipitation is scarce, but the wind is strong. The mean temperature falls below -10°C. in January and is above 15°C. in July for most years, though it sometimes rises to over 30°C. For example, the highest temperature at Golmud once reached 33°C. (July 1959). Therefore the absolute annual amplitude of temperature variation is 60°C. The annual growth period lasts from mid April or late April to late September or early October, and the active accumulated temperature varies from 1,300° to 2,000°C. with a stable duration of four months. This is sufficient to meet the needs for the growth and ripening of temperate crops.

The precipitation in the basin is extremely scarce. The annual precipitation decreases rapidly from east to west. For example, the precipitation at Caka, in the east, is 200 mm., but it decreases to less than 20 mm. in the west of the basin. The degree of aridity in the east is 2.0 to 9.0, but it rises to 20 in the west. Because of the extremely dry climate, no agriculture is possible in the basin without irrigation. More than 40 inland rivers rise from the Kunlun and Qilian mountains and run into the basin, bringing it abundant water. New oases have been built along the Qaganus, Xiangride, Golmud and Bayin rivers since Liberation, and animal husbandry has also been greatly expanded.

Light brown soil is found on the desert grasslands in the east of the basin while gray brown desert soil is widespread in the desert areas of the west. Because of the extremely dry climate, gypsum accumulates in the surface layer at the west end of the basin, forming gypseous gray-brown desert soil.

It is thus obvious that the landform of the inland basin encircled by the high mountains is the basis for the Qaidam Basin's landscape and the dry continental climate is the leading factor of its development and evolution. Both water and wind have had an important effect on the development of the present landscape. The features of the landscape are fully manifested in the wide distribution of gobis and deserts, the salinization of soil, the sparse and low xeromorphic vegetation and the inland centripetal drainage system.

The weathered matter around the Qaidam Basin, carried there from the mountains by intermittent floods, has formed vast piedmont diluvial plains. The diluvium and the weathered matter from the loose rock formations of the Tertiary Period have given rise to various types of aeolian landforms under the action of erosion and deposition by the strong dry winds from the west. The sand dunes have continually moved eastward, causing damage to the reclaimed land, towns and transport routes. Large quantities of salt have accumulated in the centre of the basin from the surrounding high mountains. The soluble salts have not only formed salt lakes and beaches in the depressed areas of the basin, but they have also led in a high degree to the salinization of the soil, mineralization of the groundwater and formation of the halophilous desert vegetation.

The landscape in the Qaidam Basin, from the piedmont area to the centre of the basin, is similar to that of the Tarim Basin and the Gansu Corridor (Fig. 34). Large areas in the northwest and middle of the basin are covered by salt deserts without any plants. The water in the Qarhan and other salt lakes has a one-metre-thick salt cover on its surface. Aeolian land is found mostly in areas around Mangyan and Lenghu in the northwest of the basin. This is the largest aeolian area in China. It is in this area that the loose Tertiary rocks, eroded by wind, were turned into parallel aeolian hills and aeolian badlands, the highest of which are 50 m. high. The vegetation, soil and animals in the basin all belong to the typical arid desert type. The vegetation is drought-enduring and salinity-resistant, including *Eurotia ceratoides, Haloxylon ammodendron, Reaumuria soongorica* and *Kalidium gracile,* which are widely distributed in the deserts of the Northwest China Region. In the Qiangtang Plateau there are cold-desert cushion plants which are resistant to cold and wind. Therefore, the vegetation of the Qaidam Basin is very similar to that of the Xinjiang desert, and the community similarity coefficient between them is 48.8 per cent, but the coefficient between the basin and the Qiangtang Plateau is only 1.6 per cent. Wild camels have been found in the east of the basin while yaks, which are characteristic of the Qinghai-Tibetan Plateau, have not been seen here. The degree of aridity in the Qaidam Basin is above 2 to 20, but it is smaller than that on the Qiangtang Plateau, where the annual precipitation is less than 100 mm. However the temperature is low and evaporation weak. It is obvious that the geographical features of the Qai-

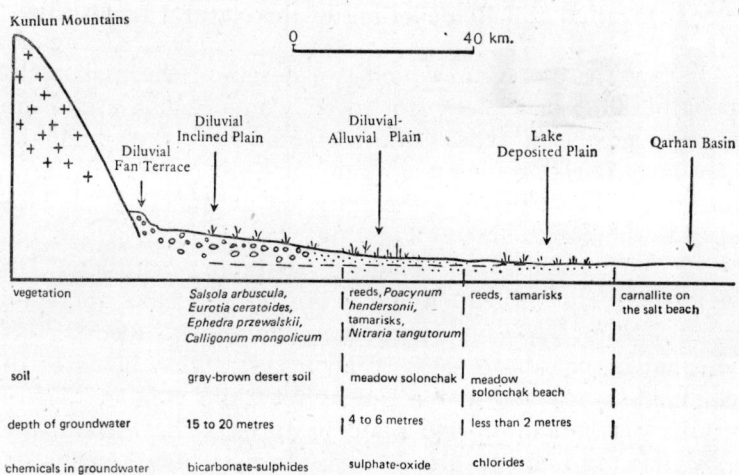

Fig. 34 The Zoning of Landscape in the Qaidam Basin from the Foot of the Kunlun Mountains to the Qarhan Salt Lake

dam Basin are different from those of the cold desert of the
Qiangtang Plateau or from the alpine steppe of the Qinghai
Plateau.   In addition to the usual features of an arid desert,
the Qaidam Basin has its own features, such as high elevation,
low accumulated temperature and vast salt beaches. For this
reason, it not only is separated from the Tarim Basin and the
Gansu Corridor in topography, but it is a unique subregion in
the Northwest China Region.
        The Altun Mountains in the west of the basin are 750 km.
long.   They are connected with the Kunlun Mountains in the
west and stand at an average elevation of 3,600 to 4,000 m.
above sea level.   The Altun Mountains are the most arid mountains in China without forests.   Alpine or subalpine meadow
grasslands are found only above 3,500 m. and alpine cold deserts on the peaks above 5,000 m. Therefore, the narrow eastern
section of the Altun Mountains is placed in the Qaidam Basin
Subregion and its northern slope is used to separate it from
the Tarim Basin area.

3.   Utilization and Remodelling of the Natural Landscape

        Except for the Alxa, which is a desert of the high plain
type, all arid deserts in the Northwest China Region are of the
intermontane basin type. The high mountains around the
basins have fairly ample precipitation and are covered by large
areas of glaciers and firns that provide an abundant surface
runoff to the desert areas. For this reason, the deserts of the
intermontane basin type provide favourable conditions for
development and utilization and large tracts of land, and they
are suitable for farming, forestry and livestock breeding.   It
is estimated that there are still about 14 million hectares of
reclaimable wasteland in the Northwest China Region. There
are also vast mountain and plain pastures. The reclaimable
wastelands are mainly spread along the margins of basins, in
the valleys of the big rivers and around ancient and contem-
porary lake depressions. Most of these are concentrated in

Xinjiang, where the reclaimable wastelands are estimated to be about 10 million hectares. For example, the wasteland on the alluvial plain of the Tarim River now contains euphrates poplar meadow soil and meadow soil. With some improvement, this land could be used to grow crops. The wasteland at the northern foot of the Tianshan Mountains contains sierozem, and the depth of the groundwater here is above five metres. The soil within one metre of the surface contains only 1 per cent of salt and can be used for farming.

Many big farms have been built in these areas since Liberation, turning the centuries-old deserts into fertile oases. The total area of cultivated land throughout Xinjiang has increased two and a half times since Liberation, making Xinjiang one of the important grain and cotton producers in China.

(1) Imbalance in the Distribution of Water and Soil Resources

The key problem in achieving full use of the arable land in the Northwest China Region is how to obtain sources of water for irrigation. The water and soil resources are unevenly distributed throughout the region. Most of the areas have soil for farming, but are short of water. The rest have abundant water, but are short of arable land. Generally speaking, the mountain areas, where the runoff forms, are areas with abundant water. But these places are not good for farming because there is no arable land and the temperature is fairly low. The diluvial-alluvial fans outside the mountain gaps are often gravel or gravel-sandy gobis without arable land, where water cannot be used. Large quantities of river water percolate through the surface here to become groundwater that is gradually mineralized and becomes inferior in quality in the course of its movement.

As to the annual distribution of runoff, precipitation is concentrated in summer, and there is insufficient water for spring sowing. During the flood period, floods occur and pass away swiftly. The peak discharge is often scores of times to more than a hundred times that of the average flow. With violent force, these floods often cause great damage. After the floods drain off, however, there is not enough water for irrigation, thus restricting agricultural development in the oases. Because the surface matter is coarse and loose, water percolates through almost all the river beds. The average percolation is 40 to 70 per cent of the flow. Smaller streams often stop flowing soon after they enter the alluvial fans. For example, the 489-km.-long middle section of the Tarim River, from Alar to Kala, loses nearly 80 per cent of its runoff due to percolation and evaporation. Percolation also occurs in the canals and reservoirs, thus reducing the rate of water utilization.

Results have been achieved in the prevention of percolation of water from the canals by using cobbles for embankments and cement for grouting, or by covering them with pitch. Water loss has dropped from 30 or 80 to 5 or 30 per cent in some cases in the main canals. The prevention of percolation from the canals also helps to control the groundwater table and to reduce the salinity of the soil.

There are abundant groundwater resources in the Northwest China Region. The reserve of fresh groundwater in the Gansu Corridor is 5,000 to 6,000 million cu. m. The Junggar and Tarim basins are also vast artesian basins. Large efforts to exploit groundwater by drilling wells for irrigation and drainage have been important to helping ease spring droughts, lower the groundwater table, improve the saline soil and extend the areas of oases.

(2) Damage by Wind-drift Sand and Measures to Fix Dunes

China's desert area covers 1,095,000 sq. km., and about two-thirds of its deserts are located in the Northwest China Region. These deserts are covered mainly by shifting sand. The sand dunes move at a speed of about 5 to 20 m. a year, and at a rate of 40 m. where the wind is particularly strong. The moving dunes cause great damage, as they bury villages and towns, devour farmland and endanger transport routes. For example, villages in the vicinity of the Bayintaohai in the Alxa Banner are often invaded by shifting sand and have to be rebuilt once every ten years. And a new farm built on what used to be sandy land with purple willow scrubs near Korla, in southern Xinjiang, was turned into a chain of barchan (crescent-shaped dunes) ten years after the natural vegetation was destroyed. The dunes have since moved forward at an annual speed of 10 to 15 m.

The people in the Northwest China Region have done a great deal to fix sand dunes in place by growing grasses on them and to build shelterbelts to stop the wind. Apart from shelterbelts on the margins of oases, networks of shelterbelts have also been built in oases to protect the farmland and reduce wind velocity, keep down evaporation, increase soil moisture and reduce the salinity of the soil. For example, Minqing County in Gansu Province used to be seriously affected by wind-drift sand, but the people there have built 830 km. of forest belts and have enclosed sand dunes by growing grasses over 133,000 hectares. The grain output in this county has greatly increased since Liberation. Many highways and railways have been built through gobis and deserts that were not accessible in the past, and the traffic flow has been smooth thanks to the effective measures taken to prevent the shifting of dunes. Checkerboard mechanical sand obstacles have been set up along the southeastern fringes of the Tenger Desert. These have effectively prevented the movement of dunes eastward and have therefore ensured normal railway traffic.

(3) Control of Salinity in the Soil

Most areas in the Northwest China Region are closed inland basins without outlets for the runoff and salts. Because the climate is dry and there is strong evaporation, a heavy accumulation of salts has formed in the basins over a long time. Solonchak is widespread and the salt content in this is very high.   The surface layer of the solonchak contains 2-5 per cent salts, while the solonchak in southern Xinjiang and the Qaidam Basin contains from 10-20 per cent.   Most of the solonchak in the Northwest China Region contains chlorides, sulphates or soda, which are all harmful to the plants.   However, salt pans or salt crusts make good raw materials for the chemical industry.

Irrigation is a prerequisite for agricultural production in arid areas.   Yet because of poor drainage systems and because salts cannot be completely washed out of surrounding wastelands, reclaimed land in this region often suffers from secondary salinization as a result of a quick rise in the groundwater level and the accelerated accumulation of salts in the soil after reclamation.   This is very common in the Northwest China Region.   The chief method for preventing secondary salinization in newly-reclaimed areas is to build drainage systems under an overall plan for rational irrigation, or to reclaim wasteland in separate plots with part of the land (mainly low-lying land) left for draining off salts.   Rice-growing has also been introduced in southern Xinjiang in recent years to improve the solonchak.

In short, bringing in water for irrigation, building shelterbelts for fixing sand dunes, improving soil and controlling the salinity are the effective means for transforming desert land into agricultural land.   These means are interrelated because Nature is an integrated whole and can only be remodelled with comprehensive measures.

Chapter XIV

THE QINGHAI-TIBETAN REGION

The Qinghai-Tibetan Region includes the Qinghai-Tibetan Plateau and extends over 2,500 km. from west to east and 1,200 km. from north to south at the widest points. It covers a total area of two million sq. km., is the largest region in China and has the highest plateau in the world. It includes the whole Tibet Autonomous Region, most of Qinghai Province, the northwestern part of Sichuan Province, the southwestern part of Gansu Province and the southern border area (the Kunlun Mountains) of the Xinjiang Uygur Autonomous Region.

The Qinghai-Tibetan Region is connected to the Northwest China Region by the Kunlun Mountains. In the east it borders on the Loess Plateau along a line starting from Riyue Mountain in the northern section and passing through Xiahe and Lintan. The borderline between it and the Sichuan Basin in the southern section is roughly the contour line of 3,000 m. and more above sea level. It is separated from the Southwest China Region by a line linking Kangding, Daocheng and Deqen in the southeastern margin and stretching westward to the boundary with other countries in the south. It adjoins Kashmir by the Pamirs and the Karakorum Mountains in the west.

There was little knowledge about the physical geography of this region in the past. After Liberation, scientific survey teams were sent to the region and much first-hand information was obtained. Chinese mountaineering teams scaled Mount Qomolangma — the world's highest peak — twice, on May 25, 1960, and on May 27, 1975, and measured its elevation as

8,848.13 m. with a mean error of plus or minus 0.35 m., the maximum error being plus or minus one metre.

1. Alpine Cold Desert, Meadow and Steppe Landscape

The Qinghai-Tibetan Plateau is a unique physical region. Its existence not only produces a deep effect on the natural environment in the surrounding regions and in the whole of East Asia, but it also has its own special physiographical features. The formation, evolution and regional differentiation of its physical complex mainly depends on its elevation and the resulting moisture and thermal differences. The plateau is located in the middle-latitude westerly belt and subtropical zone, but it does not have the landscape of a temperate or subtropical region. Its landscape is that of alpine cold deserts, meadows and steppes.

(1) The Youngest Plateau

The Qinghai-Tibetan Plateau is characterized by its height, vastness and lateness. In terms of height, the ground surface of the plateau stands 3,500 to 5,000 m. above sea level. Its terrain roughly slopes from northwest to southeast. The northern part has an elevation of 4,500 to 5,000 m. above sea level, or more. The valley of Ngari Prefecture (an area of 350,000 sq. m.) is higher than 5,000 m. Therefore, Ngari Prefecture is sometimes called "the plateau on the plateau".

The central part of the plateau where the Huanghe and Changjiang rivers arise stands about 4,500 m. above sea level, but the southwestern part, at Aba in Sichuan and Gannan in Gansu, drops to around 3,500 m. The plateau surface is relatively gentle. Except for a few high mountains, most of the mountains on the plateau are round and have gentle slopes, with relative heights of only several hundred metres. They look like mountains from a distance, but like flatland nearby.

The huge mountain ranges that stand at the fringes of the plateau, however, are mostly 6,000 to 7,000 m. in height. In the north are the Karakorum and Kunlun mountains, and in the south are the Himalayas, the Gandise and Nyainqentanglha ranges. In the centre of the plateau are the Tanggula and Hohxil ranges and the Bayanhar Mountains of the Kunlun Mountain System. In the area of 5,000 sq. km. around Mount Qomolangma, there are four peaks over 8,000 m. above sea level and 38 others above 7,000 m. The existence of so many high peaks on the plateau is something rarely seen in other parts of the world. Mount Qomolangma is often called the "top of the roof of the world" or the "third pole of the Earth".

The plateau covers a vast area. Except where the southeastern part is dissected by rivers and the plateau's surface is separately preserved at the top of the interfluves, all parts of the plateau have retained their integral surface. They represent peneplain levelled by long-time erosion and denudation, beginning in the late Cretaceous Period and extending to the Neocene Period. Their area, about two million sq. km., or 20 per cent of the total area of China, equals the combined areas of the United Kingdom, France, the Federal Republic of Germany and Italy.

The characteristic of lateness is applied to the Qinghai-Tibetan Plateau because its mountains were formed in recent geological history. They were uplifted violently during the second episode of Himalayan movement, between the Pliocene Epoch and the early Pleistocene Epoch. In other words, their present geomorphological features were formed during the last three to five million years, and they therefore constitute the youngest macromorphologic unit in the world. According to the theory of plate tectonics, the uplifting of the Qinghai-Tibetan Plateau has resulted from a collision between two continental plates, namely the Eurasian Plate and the Indian Plate. The Indian Plate has moved northward, sliding under the Eurasian Plate. This has raised the edge of the Eurasian Plate and formed a belt of ultrabasic rocks and mixed rocks in the valley of the Yarlungzangbo River. This river is located along the suture line between the two continental plates, and is the most clear boundary that is known between the two plates. The intense seismic activity in the Himalayan region at present reflects the continuing movement of these plates. As the plateau has been uplifted only recently tectonic movements and magmatic activities are frequent, and there are abundant geothermal resources. Most of the underground heat fields are found in the valleys of the Yarlungzangbo and Xiangquan rivers, that is, along the suture line between the plates. Some of these heat fields emerge in the form of intermittent hot springs and geysers, which are rarely seen elsewhere in China. The compressive stress of the plate collision has affected a wide area, and the extensive uplifting of the Qinghai-Tibetan Plateau and the faulting and upheaving of the Gangdise and Tanggula ranges and the Kunlun Mountains are all the result of the plate movement.

The recent discovery of giraffe and three-toed horse fossils from the early Pliocene Epoch in Biru County (4,500 m. above sea level) on the Qinghai-Tibetan Plateau and in Gyirong County at the northern foot of the Himalayas (4,100 m. above sea level) shows that this area was once much lower than it is today, and that the climate was humid and hot. At that time the landscape consisted of tropical forests and savannas, and the elevation was perhaps less than 1,000 m. The present plateau has resulted from the intense upheaval in the last several million years since the Pliocene Epoch. The Indian Plate has continued to move northward at a rate of about 6 cm. a year. The Himalayas have thus been squeezed by this process and have kept rising, with the axial section rising faster than the rest. Paleobotanical studies have provided vivid proof of the recent rise of the Himalayas. For example, the vegetation on the 5,700 to 5,900 m. belt of Mount Xixiabangma, which is now covered by ice and snow, was once that of warm-temperate mixed conifers and broadleaf forests, as fossils from the late Pliocene Epoch (about three million years ago) show. Such forests now appear in the Himalayas only between 2,500 and 3,100 m. above sea level. This means that the mountains have risen nearly 3,000 m. in a little more than three million years. At the village of Yali (4,300 m. above sea level) in Nyalam County, on the southern side of Mount Xixiabangma, fossil evidence shows that the vegetation used to be alpine scrubs (mainly thorny honeysuckles and azaleas) during the post-glacial period of the Holocene Epoch (about 10,000 years ago). It is now alpine steppe (mainly annual bluegrass and Carex). That shows this place has risen nearly 500 m. in the last 10,000 years of the Holocene Epoch.

The uplifting of the Qinghai-Tibetan Plateau has led to the cooling of the climate, affected the formation of soil and evolution of vegetation, and also has provided conditions for the development of Quaternary glaciers. The intense uplifting of the mountain systems along the margins of the plateau has effectively blocked humid currents from entering the plateau, and has turned the interior of the plateau into an arid region. The area of the lakes has decreased, leaving a vast area of cold deserts and alpine steppes. Therefore, extensive and intense uplifting since the Neocene Period has been the leading factor in creating the physiographical features of the Qinghai-Tibetan Region.

(2) Climatic Features of the Plateau

The profound influence of the Qinghai-Tibetan Plateau on the circulation of atmosphere was discussed in Chapter III. As a result of the existence of the plateau at an elevation of over 4,000 m. above sea level, the region (except for the eastern and southeastern parts) has the following climatic features:

1) Because the ground surface of the Tibetan Plateau is under intense radiation, the air temperature at the ground surface is higher than it is in the atmospheric layer at the same altitude in other areas of the same latitude. This is why the Tibetan Plateau is a heat source. Calculated at the vertical

temperature gradient of 0.5°C. for every 100 m., the annual mean temperature at Lhasa, 3,658 m. above sea level, when converted to 100 m. above sea level, is about 26°C. This is 9°C. higher than it is at Jiujiang in the same latitude in the east part of China. In winter it is obviously warmer at Lhasa, and the mean temperature in the coldest month is around 0°C., equivalent to that in the Huaihe River Basin. This is quite different from the situation in the mountain areas on the plains to the east.

2) Owing to the high terrain, the air on the plateau is thin. The mass of the air at 5,000 m. is only half what it is at the sea level, the amount of carbon dioxide is less than a half, the air contains little vapour and is clean and the percentage of sunshine is high. For example, the annual sunshine time at Lhasa is 3,005 hours, about 1,000 hours longer than in places of the same latitude in eastern China. Lhasa is therefore called "the city of sunshine".

The annual sunshine time at Tingri is as high as 3,393 hours, similar to that at Hami in Xinjiang. The value of the solar radiation is very high. The annual total amount of radiation at Rongbu Temple (28°13′ N. and 5,000 m. above sea level) at the northern foot of Mount Qomolangma is 199.9 kcal. per sq. cm., 75 per cent more than it is at Changsha on the same latitude in the east.   Such high values are rarely seen in other parts of the world.

3) As the atmosphere on the plateau is thin, the sunshine ample and the radiation intense, the temperature at the ground surface increases repidly during the day and drops quickly at night. This results in a big daily temperature range. However, as there is an abundant heat source on the plateau, the winter temperature is not so low and therefore the annual temperature range is relatively small. At Tingri (4,300 m. above sea level), for example, the daily temperature range is 18.2°C., about two and a half times that at Nanchang on approximately the same latitude. In the Ngari Prefecture, more than 5,000 m. above sea level, the daily temperature in August can reach

10°C. or even higher, but the temperature falls to below zero at night and the small streams and pools freeze with the ice as thick as two cm. The daily temperature range in this prefecture is about 20°C. Such features of a big daily temperature range and a small annual temperature range are conspicuously different from those in the lowlands of the same latitude in eastern China (Table 20), but they are somewhat similar to those on the Yunnan Plateau.

Table 20. Comparisons of Annual and Daily Temperature
Ranges Between Cities of Tibet and Eastern
Cities of the Same Latitude

Places	Latitude (N.)	Elevation (m.)	Annual range (°C.)	Daily range (°C.)
Lhasa	29°42'	3,658	18.1	14.8
Chengdu	30°40'	506	20.2	7.4
Tingri	28°35'	4,300	22.1	18.2
Nanchang	28°40'	49	23.1	7.4

4)   Owing to high elevation, the thermal conditions of the plateau are very poor and the accumulated temperature during the period when the daily mean temperature is higher than 10°C. is far lower than it is in subtropical lowlands of the same latitude. For example, the accumulated temperature at Gyangze (28°55' N. and 4,040 m. above sea level) is only 1,482°C., even lower than the index of 1,700°C. for the southern boundary of the frigid temperate zone. It is obvious that an elevation difference of 4,000 m. makes the thermal conditions in this region appear to have shifted 20° northward into the frigid-temperate zone. However, due to the ample sunshine, big daily temperature range, intense solar radiation and increased ultraviolet rays and infrared rays of the solar spectrum, the accumulated temperature value on the plateau has a different meaning for crop growth from the same values in lowlands of the same

latitudes. Thus the crop-growing capacity for the climatic zone of the Tibetan Plateau is by no means a simple repetition of that for the latitudinal zones in the lowlands. For example, winter wheat is now grown not only in the valleys around Lhasa but also in areas 4,100 m. above sea level north of Lhasa. Highland barley (*Hordeum nudum*) has been grown in Rutog County in Ngari Prefecture 4,900 m. above sea level. This is the highest point for crop growing in the world. Long sunshine time, intense solar radiation and a big daily temperature range all help to promote the synthesis of hydrocarbons in the crops, and the low temperature at night helps to reduce the consumption of nutrients. This is why the weight of wheat per thousand grains is generally 45 g., and sometimes even over 50 g., which is 15 to 20 g. more than it is in the other winter wheat growing areas of China. The vegetables grown in Tibet are also bigger. A radish may weigh more than 10 kg. and a potato 0.5 to 1 kg.

The weather and climate in the areas south of 32°N. on the Qinghai-Tibetan Plateau are characterized by monsoons, that is, the winter half-year (dry season) is controlled by westerlies and the summer half-year (rainy season) by humid air currents. The precipitation comes mainly from monsoons of the Indian Ocean and the rainy season is concentrated in the period from May to September. The precipitation decreases generally from southeast to northwest, that is, from about 800 mm. at Markam and Songpan in western Sichuan to 400-500 mm. at Lhasa, Nagqu, Yushu, and Xiahe and 200 to 300 mm. at Tingri, Xainza, Baingoin Lake and Madoi. Precipitation is less than 100 mm. in Ngari Prefecture in the northwest, and the annual rainfall at Gar is only 60 mm.

The Himalayas, lying transversely along the southern fringe of the plateau, stand like a climatic barrier. The low-lying valleys to the south, such as Medog and Zayu, are warm and humid, presenting subtropical and quasi-tropical sceneries with an annual precipitation of 2,000 mm. They are quite different from the high and cold landscapes on the northern side.

The annual precipitation at Qusum on the southern side (3,200 m. above sea level) is 1,450 mm., four times that at Xigaze on the northern side (3,850 m. above sea level). The rainy season in the southeast starts earlier, ends later and is much longer than that in the northwestern part of the plateau. There is a great deal of rainfall at Zhamo on the southern side of the Himalayas in May, prior to the arrival of the summer monsoons, and the rainy season lasts through mid-October, a period of more than five months. There are 150 rainy days a year in the Aba Autonomous Prefecture of western Sichuan, while at Gar, in the westernmost part of the plateau, the precipitation is not only small, it is also concentrated in summer. The rainfall between July and August accounts for about 70 per cent of the annual total.

Although the amount of rainfall is small on the plateau, the aridity during the period when daily mean temperature is higher than 10°C. is lower than one for most parts of the plateau because of the low temperature and weak evaporation. Therefore the plateau is a humid region. So far as the water conditions are concerned, the Qinghai-Tibetan Plateau is quite different from the Northwest China Region where the aridity exceeds four.

Aridity throughout China is generally calculated on the basis of the accumulated temperature during the period when the mean daily temperature exceeds 10°C. (see formula in the footnote on p. 76) This duration is very short in most parts of the Qinghai-Tibetan Plateau. It is therefore obvious that aridity calculated according to this formula cannot reflect the actual humidity on the Qinghai-Tibetan Plateau. At the same time such a calculation of aridity is contradictory to the actual vegetation and soil types there. For example, the aridity at Lhasa, calculated according to the formula, should be 0.78, and Lhasa should be regarded as a humid region. But Lhasa's natural vegetation is steppe with scrubs.

Some people have suggested that the accumulated temperature during the period when the mean daily temperature exceeds 5°C. should be used for calculating aridity in this region. It would then be smaller than 0.37 for humid zones, 0.38 to 0.75 for semi-humid zones, 0.76 to 1.50 for semi-arid zones and bigger than 1.50 for arid zones. Others say that relative humidity can more accurately reflect the relation between humidity and natural vegetation in the Tibetan Region. The annual mean relative humidity is more than 70 per cent for wet and hot forest areas, 60 to 70 per cent for humid and cool forest areas, 50 to 60 per cent for semi-humid meadow areas, 40 to 50 per cent for semi-arid steppe areas and smaller than 40 per cent for high cold semi-desert or desert areas. These suggestions conform to the actual physiographical conditions of the Tibetan Plateau. In any case, it is obvious that different values for climatic indices need to be worked out for this region on the basis of specific natural conditions.

(3) Glaciers and Permafrost

All the high mountains on the Qinghai-Tibetan Plateau stand above the snowline and many have valley glaciers, but the round top of Mount Muztagata (7,546 m. above sea level) at the western end of the Kunlun Mountains is covered with a cap glacier (icecap). Although the Karakorum Mountains are the largest mountain glacier area of the middle and low latitudes in the world, most of its glaciers are located within the boundaries of India and Pakistan. The northern branch of the Karakorum Range is located on the boundary between China and Kashmir. The main peak, Mount Qogir, is the second highest peak in the world. It stands 8,611 m. above sea level and has a 30-km.-long valley glacier on its northern side. Glaciers also cover an area of 1,600 sq. km. within 5,000 sq. km. around Mount Qomolangma, and about 722 sq. km. of this are located within China.

The distribution and features of the Tibetan glaciers reflect the local climatic conditions. First, the big valley glaciers are often dotted with a multitude of ice pinnacles (seracs),

with relative heights of 30 to 50 m., that resemble karst pinnacles. A serac cluster usually stretches for a distance of 3 to
7 km. They present a peculiar sight and exist as large clusters
only in the Himalaya and Karakorum mountains. The formation of these seracs results from intense differential thawing.
Mount Qomolangma is situated at a low latitude and the angle
of solar radiation at noontime in the summer is 70° to 85°. The
radiation is therefore intense. Furthermore, the northern slope
is relatively dry due to less rainfall. All this is favourable for
evaporation and sublimation. Due to the low humidity at the
top of a serac, there is more evaporation and sublimation there,
and the thawing is checked. On the other hand, the humidity
at the base of a serac valley is high and the thawing increases
under the intensive solar radiation. This promotes the development of the differential thawing and increases the height of
the serac. The serac clusters are therefore the product of low-
latitude high mountains under exceptional climatic conditions.

Second, the northern slope of the Himalayas and the other
high mountains on the Qinghai-Tibetan Plateau are relatively
arid due to the low temperature and little precipitation. The
southern slope of the Himalayas is very humid due to the warmer climate and ample precipitation. This results in a comparatively large difference between the glaciers that develop
in the two parts of this region. The former are called continental glaciers while the latter are called marine glaciers.
The snowline on continental glaciers is high. For example, the
snowline of the East Rongbuk Glacier on the northeastern slope
of Mount Qomolangma is located at 6,200 m. above sea level,
the highest snowline in the Northern Hemisphere.

The small amount of precipitation has greatly restricted
the scale of glacial development. Moreover, the ice temperature
is low, the volume of melted water is small and the movement
of the glacier is slow. The annual speed is generally no more
than 40 m. On the other hand, the marine glaciers have a low
snowline, about 1,000 m. lower than it is for mountains in the
interior of the continent at the same latitude. The snowline

of the Aza Glacier near Zayu is 4,600 m. above sea level, similar to that in the central part of the Qilian Mountains where the latitude is 10° higher. The ice temperature is higher (close to 0°C.), and the thawing inside and under the glacier is intense. Therefore the moving speed is faster than it is for continental glaciers, an annual speed of 300 to 400 m. The end of the glacier extends to about 2,500 m. above sea level and penetrates into mixed conifer and broadleaf forests. The Aza Glacier is found at 29°N., but its bottom is even lower than the glacier on Mount Bogda of the Tianshan Mountains near 44°N. This is unusual for glaciers in China, and it is closely related to the climate in the southeastern part of the Himalayas.

The Qinghai-Tibetan Plateau is China's largest region of permafrost. It is also the highest and largest permafrost region of the middle and low latitudes in the world. The stretch of frozen earth between the Tanggula Range and the Kunlun Mountains is 550 km. wide. The lowest elevation where permafrost is found rises as the latitude decreases. The elevation for the permafrost area at Xidatan in the Kunlun Mountains is 4,300 to 4,400 m.; that at the headwaters of the Changjiang River, 4,500 m.; that at Tanggula, 4,800 to 4,900 m.; and that on the northern slopes of the Himalayas, 5,300 m. The thickness of the permafrost varies from dozens of metres to more than 100 m. For example, the permafrost area near the Kunlun Mountain Pass for the Qinghai-Tibetan Highway is 140 to 175 m. thick. It is the thickest layer of permanently frozen soil known in China, and is presumed to be a product of the Quaternary Ice Age.

The depth of seasonal thawing in the frozen earth is about 1 to 4 m. The frozen earth at the surface begins to thaw in early or middle May, the thawing reaches its climax in late August or early September, and the ground begins to freeze again in late September. This partial thawing of permafrost often leads to the formation of exceptional preglacial landforms, such as freeze-thaw slides, solifluction, frost-heaving fissures and polygonal earth, all of which have ill effects on road building.

(4) Interior Drainage System and Lakes

The Qinghai-Tibetan Plateau is the main source for the major rivers of Asia, and these rivers radiate from the plateau. The Changjiang, Huanghe, Nujiang, Lancang and Yarlungzangbo rivers all flow to the east or southeast; the Indus and Sutlej rivers flow to the southwest; and the Yarkant, Yurunkax and Karakax are inland rivers that flow northward into the desert. The rivers on the plateau often flow in tectonic depressions and form wide longitudinal valleys. When they cut through mountains to reach the piedmont plains, they form very steep gorges. For example, the Yarlungzangbo River flows through a wide valley before it turns southward near 95° E. to cut through the Himalayas. This turn is known locally as the "Big Bend" of the Yarlungzangbo River. As the river goes through the Himalayas, the difference in relative elevation from the top of the peaks along the river to the valley below is 5,000 to 6,000 m. The narrowest section of the river is less than 80 m., the river gradient is great, the flow is swift, and shoals and rocky shallows are found here and there. The velocity of water flow along some sections measures at 16 m. per sec. There are also wide and flat valleys and large marsh mucks in the upper reaches of the Huanghe and Changjiang rivers, but when these rivers run down over the edge of the plateau, they cut through the mountains in deep gorges. The rivers receive their water supply from thawed snow on the upper reaches, as well as from the groundwater, so that their flow is generally stable. The big water head and swift flow of the rivers provide an abundant potential for energy.

Roughly speaking, the vast areas north of the Gandise Range and west of the Tanggula and Hohxil ranges are an internal drainage region made up of many internal drainage basins. The region covers more than 600,000 sq. km. The rivers here are short and have less water. They are mainly supplied by thawed snow and are frozen for most of the year.

There are many lakes on the Qinghai-Tibetan Plateau, mostly concentrated in the northern part of the Tibetan Plateau and on the Qinghai Plateau. This is the highest lake region in the world. Statistics show that the lakes in this region make up more than two-fifths of the total lake area in China. They form one of the biggest lake areas in the country, the other being the plain area along the middle and lower reaches of the Changjiang River. Most of the lakes on the plateau are inland lakes and saltwater lakes. Qinghai Lake, covering 4,426 sq. km., is the biggest semi-salty inland lake in China. Nam Co Lake in northern Tibet, standing at 4,718 m. above sea level and covering 1,940 sq. km., is the second largest in China and also the highest lake in the world. "Nam Co" is a Tibetan term that means "heavenly lake".

Most of the bigger lakes on the plateau are tectonic lakes, located in tectonic depressions or along fault zones. Their water is therefore deep. The smaller lakes, with shallow water, are mostly barrier lakes created by debris from landslides that block rivers or glacial lakes created by the movement of glaciers. Most of the former are found in southeastern Tibet, while the latter are in the southern and southeastern areas, where alpine glaciers are active.

Most of the lakes on the plateau are saltwater lakes, but there are also a few freshwater lakes, such as Ngoring and Gyaring. The salt content in the saltwater lakes decreases during the rainy season or when snow thaws, but it increases at other periods forming salt and borax deposits. The lake area has decreased ever since the Holocene Epoch, as the climate on the plateau has become dry and cold.

(5) Vegetation and Soil on the Plateau

The elevation, frozen earth, water and heat conditions on the plateau have had a deep impact on the formation of vegetation and soil. As the humidity on the plateau decreases from southeast to northwest, the vegetation changes from alpine meadow to alpine steppe to alpine cold desert.

The northern Ngari Plateau, standing more than 5,000 m. above sea level, has a low temperature, annual precipitation of about 50 mm. and strong winds. Plants grow sparsely there and their number of species is limited. Most of them are cushion plants of the low semi-frutex type, covering only 5 to 10 per cent of the land. Many are of the goosefoot family and the composite family, including *Ceratoides compacta* and *Ajania tibetica,* which grow only 15 to 20 cm. high. These plants are small and short, and resemble cushions as their stems creep along the ground. They grow in this way to accommodate themselves to the extraordinary climate on the northern Ngari Plateau. As the height of the plants is strongly checked by severe cold, aridness and heavy wind, the stems grow prostrate on the ground and branch out at the base, forming flat cushions or dome-like cushions. The branches and leaves grow thick inside the cushions, protecting themselves from the cold, and preventing excessive loss of water and damage by strong winds. For example, the stem of *Myricaria prostrata* grows only one cm. high, but its branches and leaves stretch out to as many as two metres.

The alpine steppes are found mainly in zones higher than 4,500 m. above sea level in the central part of the Qinghai-Tibetan Plateau. Taking aridity during the period when the mean daily temperature is greater than 5°C. as the index, this area belongs to the semi-arid region. The plants here are dwarf ones and resistant to cold and aridity. The grasses, mostly purple needlegrass (*Stipa purpurea*) and alien needlegrass (*Stipa aliena*), are no higher than 20 cm. They are mixed with cryophilic Cobresias, rank grasses and cushion plants, but no scrub layers are found. The most common cushion plants are *Arenaria musciformis* and *Androsace tapete.* Because of the special climatic conditions, the structure of the plant communities on the alpine steppes is distinctly different from that on the temperate grasslands of the Inner Mongolia Region. The differences are: (1) there are generally no scrub layers; (2) the grass patches are mainly composed of thick, dwarf and cold-resistant grasses, and there are almost no rhizomes; (3) the plants are often mixed with cold- and aridity-resistant cryophilic Cobresia, which is absent on the temperate grasslands; (4) there are cushion plant layers that are peculiar to the alpine zones, but are absent on the temperate grasslands. The ample amount of solar energy, thin air and strong ultraviolet rays are good for photosynthesis and promote the synthesis of protein. Although the grasses in the alpine zones are dwarf varieties and cover only 20 to 50 per cent of the surface, they contain much coarse protein and offer nutritious fodder for animals. The area thus provides favourable conditions for the development of stockbreeding.

The southeastern part of the plateau is more humid. For example, Yushu and Golog prefectures in Qinghai Province are covered by large areas of alpine meadows made up of thin patches of grass, thick patches of rhizome Cobresia and rank grasses. The thin patches, which grow as high as 80 to 100 cm., mainly include *Clinelymus sibiricus, Poa pratense, Avena tibetica* and *Festuca ovina*. The rank grasses mostly belong to the buttercup, rose, composite and pulse families. Their flowers are brightly coloured and their flowering seasons differ. Because these grasses grow fairly high, the meadows not only provide pastures in summer, but also supply large quantities of fodder for winter. On the low-lying lakesides and floodlands there are often small bog meadows, predominated by *Cobresia tibetica* of the sedge family. These form many grass-covered hillocks. Mesophytes or hygrophytes of grasses and rank grasses grow between these grassy hillocks. The bog meadows produce high yields of forage grass and are therefore good pastures in winter. There are large areas of waterlogged lowlying depressions on the Zoige Plateau in western Sichuan Province, where cold marshes are widely located and the climate is damp and rainy. This is the well-known "grassland area" that the Red Army passed through during the Long March. The main constructive species here are Carex and Cobresia of the sedge family.

The mountain slopes between 4,500 and 5,000 m. above sea level are alpine dwarf Cobresia meadows. Their constructive species is *Cobresia pygmaea,* 3 to 5 cm. high, that cover 90 per cent of the ground surface. There are a limited number of species and the community appearance is monotonous. The other plants are also short and lie prostrate like cushions, such as *Androsace tapete, Arenaria musciformis, Leontopodium varum* and *Gentiana scabra.* Such meadows are widely distributed throughout Tibet and constitute 35 per cent of the grasslands there. They are used as pastures in summer.

Because of the wind-blocking action of the Himalayas, the southern side of the mountains is warm and humid. It is also clearly marked by vertical zones (Fig. 35). For example, the

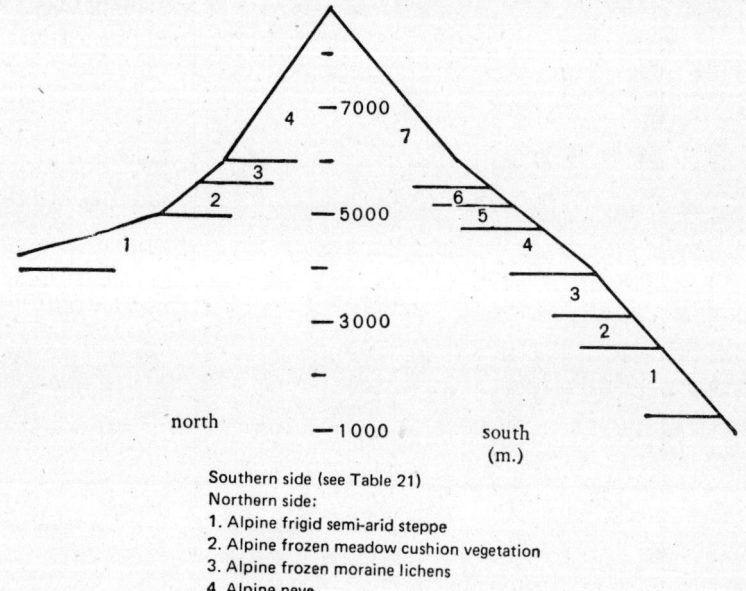

Fig. 35 **Vertical Zones of Mount Qomolangma**

southern side of Mount Qomolangma, within the boundary between the valleys at 1,600 m. above sea level and the alpine glaciers, can be divided into seven zones (Table 21). Below 1,600 m. are tropical monsoon rain forests that lie beyond the Chinese boundary.

The valley around Medog at the southeastern corner of

Table 21.　Zones on the Southern Side of Mount Qomolangma

Zone	Above sea level (m.)	Vegetation	Soil
1	1,600 to 2,500	Subtropical mountain evergreen broadleaf forest	Mountain yellow brown earth
2	2,500 to 3,100	Warm-temperate mountain needleleaf and broadleaf mixed forest	Mountain acid brown earth
3	3,100 to 3,900	Frigid-temperate mountain needleleaf forest	Mountain bleached podzolic soil
4	3,900 to 4,700	Subalpine cold bush meadow	Subalpine bush meadow soil
5	4,700 to 5,200	Alpine frozen meadow cushion plants	Alpine meadow soil
6	5,200 to 5,500	Alpine frozen moraine lichens	Alpine moraine soil
7	above 5,500	Alpine neve	

Tibet stands less than 800 m. above sea level. It is covered with quasi-tropical monsoon rain forests, and its natural landscape is similar to that of Xishuangbanna in Yunnan Province. Therefore, this area is called the "Xishuangbanna of Tibet".

In the southeastern part of the plateau, where the rivers deeply cut down, the vertical zones are well defined. The valley here is generally covered by warm-temperate and temperate needleleaf and broadleaf mixed forests (mountain brown earth) over 2,000 m. above sea level, subalpine frigid-temperate needleleaf forests (mountain dark brown forest soil) between 2,500 and 4,300 m., and alpine bush meadows between 3,700 and 4,300 m. The elevations of the upper and lower limits of these vertical zones rise from the margins of the plateau to the interior. This is in conformity with the gradual decrease of rainfall from the margins of the plateau to the interior.

The horizontal distribution of soil on the plateau also shows well-defined phases, changing from alpine meadow soil to alpine steppe soil to alpine desert soil from the southeast to the northwest. The moist and thermal conditions south of the Gandise Range and the Nyainqentanglha Range are greater, and so more humus accumulates in the alpine meadow soil south of these ranges than in the areas north of them, and the soil is darker in colour. This is also true of the alpine steppe soil. The humus accumulation and calcification in the alpine steppe soil south of the ranges is relatively greater and therefore the humus layer is thicker.

The alpine meadow soil is formed under the cold and semi-humid climate, and the soil itself has more moisture than do other alpine meadow soils. It is widely covered with meadow plants and the compact root systems provide favourable conditions for humus accumulation in the soil. Therefore the surface layers of this alpine meadow soil have 3 to 10 cm. of thick sod, and the root systems are closely interwoven so that they resemble felt. This is called "alpine meadow felt soil". The humus layer is 9 to 20 cm. thick and the surface layer contains 6 per cent of organic matter. The soil registers a slightly acidic or neutral reaction. The moist and thermal conditions on the western Sichuan Plateau and on the eastern part of the Tibetan Plateau are better, and the degree of humus formation in the alpine meadow soil there is slightly higher. The humus layer is about 15 to 30 cm. thick, the content of organic matter is about 10 to 15 per cent, and the soil colour is darker. It is therefore called "alpine black felt soil".

The alpine steppe soil develops under a frigid and semi-arid climate and the soil is relatively dry. As the coverage of plants is smaller (about 30 to 50 per cent) the humus accumulation in this soil is less than that in alpine meadow soil. The surface layer has fewer roots and the organic content is only 1.5 per cent. There is also calcification in the soil, the lower part of the soil profile showing a vague calcic horizon, but the whole body of soil produces an alkaline reaction. It is called "saga soil", which means that it is white calcareous sandy soil.

(6) Animals on the Plateau

Because of the cold climate, the growth period of grasses on the Qinghai-Tibetan Plateau is quite short, insects are rare and birds are scarce. Only those species which can adapt themselves to the alpine cold desert and alpine steppe can live on the plateau. The main animals are wild yaks and chirus, which are found in flocks on the plateau. Wild yaks are the most typical animals. They live up to 6,000 m. above sea level and are accustomed to the cold climate on the plateau. The yak is covered with long and thick hair that hangs down to protect it from the cold and to shelter it from rain and snow. Domesticated yaks are raised at an altitude of over 3,000 m. above sea level.

Chirus are widely found on the plateau. The males have vertical horns with joints, which are sometimes used in traditional Chinese medicine. In addition, there are Tibetan donkeys, bharals, and woolly hares, A big flock of bharals may number between 50 and 80 members. There are also Tibetan jackals, Tibetan brown bears and snow leopards, as well as wolves and lynxes. The rodents include the Kashmir pika, Kowslow's pika, alpine vole, Tibetan marmot, gray-tailed hare and red pika. Most of these rodents live together in groups in caves. The pikas and marmots are particularly numerous. The most common species of birds are vultures and big crows that feed on dead animals and dead human beings. The birds can fly as high as 5,000 m. above sea level and yellow-peak mountain crows were once observed at a height of 7,070 m. Mountaineers have also seen rock doves flying over an 8,300-m. ridge from south to north. Cinerous vultures also circled the same ridge.

The dense forests in the mountain areas in the southeastern fringes of the plateau and at the southern foot of the Himalayas provide favourable conditions for the sheltering of birds and animals. Here there are a great variety of animals, including giant pandas, lesser pandas and golden monkeys.

2.   Regional Differentiation of the Natural Landscape

Since the Quaternary Period, the uplift around the fringes of the plateau has been strong and extremely high mountains have arisen, thus preventing the penetration of the humid currents and turning the plateau into an arid region. As a result, the glaciers have shrunk, lakes have become small and vast areas of alpine steppe and cold desert have been formed.

As there was no continental ice cap during the Quaternary Period, the modern vegetation in this region has developed from the Tertiary vegetation. There were still temperate broadleaf forests or mixed coniferous and broadleaf forests in many parts of the plateau during the Neocene Period. However, during the uplifting of the plateau, the climate became arid and cold and the trees gradually became extinct, but not all of them. At present, in some places, there are still dwarfed remnants of the original species. At 4,700 m. above sea level

there are Aspleniums, a paleotropical relic plant. Other tropical plants have also been found at high altitudes on the southern slope of the Himalayas, such as *Qhiorrhiza L.* under the
fir trees and some genera of the Acanthaceae family under
Chinese hemlocks and spruces. It is obvious that these tropical
plants survived the rapid upheaval of the Himalayas and have
long co-existed with the firs and spruces. Moreover, there are
paleotropical karst pinnacles in many parts of the plateau, one
of them being found on Amdobei Mountain, 5,100 m. above
sea level, the highest place in the world where paleotropical
karst pinnacles are located. Some foreign scholars (K. Ward,
for example) once held that the Ice Age completely destroyed
all the natural landscape in this region, including its vegetation. This is not true.

In short, the formation of the physiographical features of
the Qinghai-Tibetan Plateau has mainly resulted from its high
elevation and vast area. Consequently the influence of latitudinal zonal factors in this region has been vehemently disturb-
ed. This is why in this region alpine steppes and meadows can
be regarded as a basic zone for making zonal decisions. It is
very difficult to compare the natural zones of this region with
any of the natural zones in the eastern monsoon regions. The
differentiation of subregions on this plateau is closely related to
the moisture and thermal conditions, especially the differences
in the amount of moisture. The Qinghai-Tibetan Region is thus
divided into the following subregions:

VIII$_A$ Western Sichuan-Eastern Tibetan Subregion

VIII$_B$ Eastern Plateau Subregion

VIII$_C$ North Tibetan Plateau Subregion

VIII$_D$ Ngari Plateau Subregion

VIII$_E$ South Tibetan River Valley and Himalayas Subregion

   VIII$_{E1}$ Southern Side of the Himalayas Area

   VIII$_{E2}$ Southern Tibetan Valley Area

(1) Western Sichuan-Eastern Tibetan Subregion

This subregion is located in the southeastern part of the Qinghai-Tibetan Plateau. It is a transitional zone bordering on the Central China Region and the Southwest China Region. It extends to the Jiajin, Daxiangling and Xiaoxiangling Mountains in the east and to the forests of Dengqen, Sog County and Lhari in Nagqu Prefecture of Tibet in the northwest. Dissected by the Jinsha, Lancang and Nujiang rivers in the southeast, the edge of the Qinghai-Tibetan Plateau in this subregion is divided into sections. Based on this dissection and the elevation of the river valleys, the southeastern part of the Qinghai-Tibetan Plateau can roughly be separated into three types of landforms from northwest to southeast: (a) The northwest hilly plateau which is shallowly cut by rivers and in which the valleys are flat and wide, the cutting depth being only 100 to 300 m. Lying between the valleys are round hills with gentle slopes that are roughly distributed north of Songpan, Luhuo and Dainkog — the boundary between the Tibetan Plateau and the Qinghai Plateau. (b) The central mountainy plateau, which is deeply incised by rivers, with a certain area of plateau surface (3,500 to 4,500 m. over the top of the interfluvial ridges). The bottoms of the valleys drop to about 2,500 m., and the difference between the valley bottoms and the plateau surface at most places is 1,000 to 2,000 m. This mountain area is roughly distributed north of Lixian, Jiulong, Daocheng and Deqen, that is, between 28-32°N. (c) The high mountains with gorges are in the south, where the plateau surface has been intensely dissected and completely destroyed, and most of the ground surface is crisscrossed by high mountains and deep valleys, the bottoms of which often drop to below 2,000 m. Most of the mountains in the central mountainy plateau are unbroken. This is true of the Shaluli and Daxue mountains, which run from northwest to southeast for several hundred kilometres. Gongga Mountain, which is one of the Daxue Mountains, rises 7,590 m. above sea level. As it faces the southeast monsoons and receives adequate rainfall, its glaciers are well developed. One valley glacier is as long as 16 km. ending at 3,000 m. above sea level in a forest belt. Some of the mountains in the southern high mountain with deep valleys area (Yulong Mountain, for example) have high altitudes, but they are scattered and stand in isolation.

The basic zones in this hilly plateau area, mountainy plateau area and the high mountain with deep valley area vary distinctly. The basic zone for the hilly plateau area is a mountain frigid-temperate zone, or subfrigid zone. Alpine meadows and steppes with black felt soil cover most of the hilly plateau area. The basic zone for the mountainy plateau area is a warm-temperate zone to temperate zone. Alpine meadows with black felt soil also cover much of this area. The basic zone for the high mountain with deep valley area is a subtropical zone; but, because the watersheds are narrow and the mountain bodies are broken, the alpine meadows are small and thinly scattered. Therefore the hilly plateau area is designated as being part of the Eastern Plateau Subregion; the mountainy plateau area, as part of the Western Sichuan-Eastern Tibetan Subregion, and the high mountain with deep valley area as belonging to the Southwest China Region. The differences in the natural environment are also manifested by the variety of domestic animals found there. Most of the animals in the hilly plateau and mountainy plateau areas are yaks, cattle yaks (offspring of a bull and a female yak) and sheep, while the major domestic animals in the high mountain with deep valley area are goats and pigs.

The annual accumulated temperature in this Western Sichuan-Eastern Tibetan Subregion is generally between 1,000° and 3,000°C. The mean temperature in most of the valleys during hottest month is about 12° to 18°C. The frost-free period is 120 to 200 days. The western part of this subregion is affected by southwestern monsoons in the summer half-year at the same time as the eastern part is under the southeastern monsoons. After the southwestern monsoons cross the Gaoligong and Nushan mountains and the southeastern monsoons cross the Jiajin and Xiaoxiangling mountains, their force becomes weaker. The annual rainfall in the subregion is generally 600 to 900 mm. The bottoms of deeply-incised gorges are relatively dry as a result of foehns, and the annual precipitation there is less than 500 mm. For example, in the valley of the Lancang River from Deqen upstream, in the valley of the Jinsha River from Derong upstream and in the valley of the Nujiang River near Boxoi there are bushes growing in a relatively dry climate and mountain grey-cinnamon soil.

The vertical variations in this subregion are obvious and somewhat complex. There are two main characteristics. First, the horizontal zones of the plateau extend down into the deeply-incised valleys as if they were hanging down into these valleys. They are therefore called "hanging down spectrums". Second, the vertical zones are characterized by the composition of various spruces and firs. Thus this subregion is one of China's most important frigid and temperate forest areas.

In the valleys are mixed temperate coniferous and broadleaf forests composed of Chinese hemlock and maple, but also including subalpine dark coniferous trees such as firs, spruces and red birches (*Betula albo-sinensis*) and subtropical evergreen broadleaf trees, such as Chinese magnoliavine and deciduous cinnamon. The soil is of two types, mountain brown earth and cinnamon soil. The former is neutral or slightly acidic and its surface layer contains more organic matter, while the latter is alkaline and its surface layer contains less organic matter. The latter is found at a lower altitude than the brown earth belt.

Above these mixed coniferous and broadleaf forests are subalpine dark coniferous forests, which have a vertical range of about 1,000 m. As the climate tends to become dry and cold from east to west in this subregion, the upper limit of the subalpine coniferous forest belt is at 3,500 m. above sea level in Lixian (Zagunao), 4,100 m. on the Zheduo Mountains and 4,300 m. on the Chola Mountains. The main species of the subalpine coniferous forests are firs and spruces, the latter being found at a lower altitude than the firs because they are capable of standing more dryness and cold. Therefore the spruces become more and more predominant from east to west in this subregion, and the firs almost disappear in the forests west of Garze. The soils under these coniferous trees are dark brown earth and brown coniferous forest soil. The dark brown earth is mainly found in the coniferous forests composed of spruces where there is less moisture, or in small-leaf forests (red and white birches) under 3,500 to 3,700 m. above sea level where the soil is more saturated with salt and produces a neutral or acidic reaction. The brown coniferous soil is found mainly under azalea and fir forests, where the climate is cold and wet, liver mosses grow in abundance and the soil is moist all year round. There is a great deal of leaching and illuviation in this soil, and it produces a strong acidic reaction. Its profile contains a podzolic layer and a humus illuvium.

The different locations of mountain slopes have an effect on the distribution of the vegetation. For example, at 2,500 m. above sea level in the Jinsha River area, mixed temperate coniferous and broadleaf forests and frigid-temperate dark coniferous forests are found on the shady side of the slopes while alpine oaks (*Quercus semicarpifolia*) and alpine pines (*Pinus densata*) are found on the sunny side. The vegetation clearly changes at the southern boundary of this subregion where Yunnan pines of the Southwest China Region are found on mountain slopes below 3,200 m. above sea level. In the dark coniferous forests of the subregion highland barley and wheat are liable to frost attacks and the harvest is unstable, while in the small-leaf forests (mainly red and white birches) the crops are better insured against such damage.

The dense forests and vertical bioclimatic belt in the Minshan and Qionglai mountains have become the natural habitat for such rare and precious animals as the giant panda and golden monkey. The giant pandas mainly live in alpine chinacane woods. The northwestern part of the Pingwu County in Sichuan Province has been designated as the Wanglang Natural Preserve.

Above the forest belt are subalpine bush meadows that spread widely between 3,300 and 4,200 m. above sea level. The plant community here is composed of Carex of the sedge family, *Clinelymus nutans* and *Helictotrichon tibeticum* of the grass family, and rank grasses. As the rank grasses form a big part of the community and grow high (40 to 60 cm.), the pastures are varicoloured. There are also a few shrubs, such as alpine spiraea, honeysuckle and azalea.

Alpine meadows are located above the subalpine bush meadow belt, between 4,200 and 4,500 m. above sea level. The main plants of these alpine meadows are Carex and Cobresia of the sedge family. These plants grow no higher than 10 cm. They spread on the ground surface and resemble a carpet of felt. Because there are no bushes and few rank grasses, the plant community does not look very attractive. There are a few typical alpine plants, such as *Arenaria musciformis* and snow lotus (*Saussurea gnophaloides*), and so there is still some difference between the alpine meadows and the subalpine bush meadows.

Under the alpine meadows in this subregion is black felt soil. As the cilmate is more humid and warm here than in other parts of the Qinghai-Tibetan Plateau, the surface layer contains more organic matter and there are earthworms burrowing in the soil. Therefore the organic matter quickly decomposes and the soil is darker in colour. Brown felt soil is sometimes found beneath subalpine bush meadows. It is a soil of transition between black felt soil and brown coniferous forest soil, and it is characterized by dark brown or light brown illuvium. Its surface layer contains a high percentage of organic matter, about 14 to 22 per cent. The whole profile is heavily leached and produces an acidic reaction.

The southwestern part of this subregion includes the river basins of the middle and lower reaches of the Yarlungzangbo River and its tributaries. The valleys here are more deeply incised and lie 2,000 to 3,000 m. above sea level. Monsoons from the Indian Ocean enter the region along these valleys. This makes the climate quite humid. Tangmai, the lowest place in the subregion, has an annual mean temperature of about 12°C. and an annual precipitation of around 1,000 mm. (Bomi- and Yigrong, 2,250 m. above sea level, have annual mean temperatures greater than 10°C. and an accumulated temperature of 3,110°C.) The mean relative humidity in the valleys is 60 to 70 per cent. Forests are therefore found on the mountain slopes on both sides of valleys. In the Bomi area, there are the mountain evergreen broadleaf forests (oaks) with mountain yellow brown earth from 2,000 to 2,500 m. above sea level, mixed mountain coniferous and broadleaf forests (spruces, alpine pines and oaks) with mountain brown earth from 2,500 to 3,200 m., subalpine coniferous forests (spruces and firs) with mountain bleached podzolic soil from 3,200 to 4,000 m., and alpine bush meadow with black felt soil and meadow felt soil from 4,000 to 4,500 m.

The climate is fairly dry in the valleys along the middle and upper reaches of the Yarlungzangbo River west of Nangxian because of the dry western wind that moves in along the river in winter and spring. The valley slopes east of Nangxian are covered by forests, and west of Nangxian, by dry grasslands and bushes. Therefore Nangxian is taken as the boundary point between this subregion and the South Tibetan Valley and Himalayas Subregion. The climate east of Nangxian is relatively humid, the annual precipitation is 500 to 600 mm. and the valleys are located 2,700 to 3,100 m. above sea level. The vertical vegetation zones in the valleys, or hanging-down spectrums, are composed of alpine bush meadows, subalpine dark coniferous forests and mountain coniferous forests. The area around Nangxian is the dividing line between the steppes and forests in the valleys of the Yarlungzangbo River. There alpine pine woods are gradually replaced by sparse woods of particularly huge junipers. The grasslands are mainly composed of xerophytes or meso-xerophytes.

The composition of different bioclimatic belts at different altitudes has resulted in the vertical distribution of farming, forest and animal husbandry for the landuse. The alpine meadow with black felt soil zone makes up the greatest part of this subregion. Black felt soil has a great potential for fertility, and so this zone has always provided fine pastureland. After improvement, the pastures should produce more forage grass and therefore provide an even greater potential. The mountain slopes and valleys are covered with dense forests that offer a large reserve of timber. Spruces and firs account for 90 per cent of the timber, and they are of good quality. The spruces on the upper reaches of the Bailong River grow up to 40 m. in height.

(2) Eastern Plateau Subregion

The Eastern Plateau Subregion includes most of Qinghai, the Nagqu Prefecture of Tibet, the northwestern part of Sichuan and the southwestern part of Gansu. Most of this subregion stands at 4,000 to 4,500 m. above sea level, but the elevation of the northwestern part of Sichuan and the southwestern part of Gansu drops to 3,000-3,500 m. The ground surface is only slightly dissected and the plateau surface is well preserved. It is a gentle undulating plateau with differences in relative height of 300 to 500 m. On the plateau are some wide valleys and basins. This is where the upper reaches of the Huanghe, Changjiang, Nujiang and Lancang rivers begin. The subregion is bordered by the Kunlun Mountains to the north and the Nyainqentanglha Range to the south. In the southeast the subregion meets the Loess Plateau and Western Sichuan Dissected Plateau; and in the west, the North Tibetan Plateau Subregion.

A number of high mountain ranges stand on the plateau surface in this subregion. These are the Kunlun Mountains, the Tanggula Range and the Nyainqentanglha Range from north to south. The part of the Kunlun Mountains to the east of the Karamiran Pass (about longitude 87°E.) is called the East Kunlun Mountains. The range runs from northwest to southeast and branches out in the east into three sections — the north, central and south. Between the parallel mountains are shallow and flat valleys and basins that have widths of several dozen km. For example, the upper reaches of the Huanghe River, the Qumar River, and the upper reaches of the Changjiang River are all wide valleys lying between sections of the Kunlun Mountains.

The northern section of the East Kunlun Mountains is composed of the Qimatag, Burhanbudai, and Jishi mountains along the southern fringe of the Qaidam Basin. At the east end of the Jishi Mountains are the well-known Anyemaqen Mountains (7,160 m. above sea level) which stand upright over the nearby Huanghe River valley. The tectonic activity that uplifted the mountains in this region caused a section of the Huanghe River to make a great turn in this area, forming the big bend on the upper reaches of the river. The middle section is composed of the Arg and Bayanhar mountains. The Bayanhar Mountains form a watershed between the Changjiang and Huanghe rivers. They have gentle slopes and the characteristics of the plateau. The southern section is the Hohxil Range which also has a gentle slope. Its relative height is only 300 to 400 m.

The climate in this subregion is fairly cold. The frost-free period lasts only 20 to 60 days and there are parts of this subregion where there are no frost-free days during the year. The annual precipitation is about 400 to 700 mm., and up to 800 mm. in the southeastern part of the subregion. The annual mean relative humidity is 50 to 65 per cent. This is a cold semihumid subregion. Its landscape is composed mainly of alpine meadows with meadow felt soil, and only *Potentilla fruticosa*, small-leaf azaleas, willows and Chinese junipers are found on the slopes facing the summer monsoon winds. Some of the floodlands and basins are flat and have poor drainage. They are covered by large areas of Carex and Cobresia marshes. The land is one of the major stock-raising areas in China — yaks and sheep. Qinghai Lake, the largest lake in this subregion, is surrounded by meadows and its elevation is generally around 3,000 m. above sea level. The temperature around the lake is fairly high. The annual mean temperature is 1° to 3°C. and the annual precipitation is 350 mm. With forage grasses, mainly of the grass family, growing luxuriantly, this subregion has become an important stockbreeding centre.

Yushu, in southern Qinghai, is typical of much of this subregion. It is situated in the basin of the Tongtian River, the name for the upper reaches of the Jinsha River. Here the annual precipitation is about 500 mm. With frost throughout the year, this area has a growth period of about 100 days for herbal plants. In the southern valleys (below 4,200 m. above sea level) are subalpine coniferous forests. At 4,200 to 4,800 m. are large areas of alpine meadows covered mainly by Carex and Cobresia of the sedge family, *Festuca ovina* of the grass family, and grasses of the buckwheat and composite families. There are also rank grasses with flowers of various colours. The average height of the grasses is about 10 cm., but they cover more than 80 per cent of the ground surface. The grasses are so short that the pastures here can carry only one to two sheep per hectare. From Zadoi where the Zhaqu River, the name for the upper reaches of the Lancang River, begins westward are vast expanses of alpine meadows with large flocks of wild donkeys and Mongolian gazelles, and many uninhabited areas.

1) The Zoige Marshland in Northwestern Sichuan

Zoige, Hongyuan and Aba are the marshlands that the Chinese Red Army travelled through during the Long March. The landforms here are typical of a hilly plateau area. They have an elevation of about 3,400 m. above sea level. The hills are round in shape and have gentle slopes. Among them are wide valleys with a relative height of dozens to over 100 m. The gradient along the lower reaches of the Haiqu and Garqu, both tributaries of the Huanghe River, is extremely small. Both rivers have many branches and meanders, and along these are numerous ox-bow lakes. The climate is cold and humid; the annual accumulated temperature is only 600° to 700°C. The July mean temperature is 10.9°C. The annual precipitation is 560 to 860 mm. and decreases from south to north and from east to west. Most of the rains in this area are moderate and light, and the rainy period extends for 150 days. There is not much sunshine. The aridity during the period when the mean daily temperature exceeds 10°C. is only 0.45 to 0.70, and the relative humidity averages around 70 per cent. Under such conditions, the ground surface is often so wet that marshlands are formed over large areas. Most of the marshes are filled with Carex plants and between the marshes are grass hillocks covered with meadow plants, mainly Cobresia. There are also thick layers of peat (the thickest being more than five metres), which are distributed over large areas. These big reserves of peat are an important natural resources that can be used as fuel, fertilizer and raw materials for industry. In recent years, about 130,000 hectares of marshland have been turned into pastures by draining the water. Large farms have been established for crop production in Hongyuan and other areas. The grasslands have also been improved.

2) The Headstreams of the Huanghe and Changjiang Rivers

The Huanghe River rises from the Kariqu River in Qumarleb County, Qinghai Province, about 4,400 m. above sea level. The mountains south of the Kariqu form a watershed between the Huanghe and Changjiang river systems, the lowest part having a relative height of only 20 m. The Kariqu valley is wide and shallow and is covered by grasslands and marshes. The Kariqu flows from southwest to northeast into Xingsu Lake, a basin 20 to 30 km. long and more than 10 km. wide. The poor drainage has turned it into marshes studded with many smaller lakes. East of Xingsu Lake are Gyaring and Ngoring lakes whose water surface stands at 4,200 m. above sea level. These are both freshwater lakes surrounded by meadows and marshes.

The main source of the Changjiang is the Tuotuo River, which originates from the southwestern side of Mount Geladandong, a snow-capped mountain 6,621 m. above sea level and the main peak of the Tanggula Range. There are many shoals in the river bed along the upper stream of the river and the water flows in branching channels to form a braided stream during the dry season. The gentle slopes on both sides of the valley are almost all covered by marshes and marshland meadows. In summer, some Tibetan herdsmen graze their cattle here.

(3) North Tibetan Plateau Subregion

The North Tibetan Plateau includes most of the northern part of Tibet and the western part of Qinghai. It is bounded by the Kunlun Mountains in the north and the Gandise Range in the south. In the east, the isohyet for annual rainfall of 300 mm. provides the boundary with the Eastern Plateau Subregion, which passes through Xainza, Baingoin and the headwater region for the major rivers. In the west, the isohyet for annual rainfall of 150 mm. provides the boundary with the Ngari Plateau Subregion to the west of Gerze being in the Ngari Plateau Subregion. This subregion stands 4,500 to 5,000 m. above sea level. The mean temperature in the hottest month is 6° to 10°C. and the annual mean relative humidity is 40 to 50 per cent. It is thus a cold, semi-arid region. A gentle hilly plateau, the subregion is studded with many medium-sized and small lakes, most of them salt lakes. It is also called the Gyantang Plateau (Gyantang means the vast land in the north).

The landscape is composed of typical alpine steppe vegetation with saga soil. The vegetation is mostly distributed over the sunny sides of the hills and broad valleys. The plants include purple needlegrass, alien needlegrass and annual bluegrass, with rank grasses comprising 10 to 15 per cent of the vegetation. Because of the shortness of the grass and relatively small area of the ground that it covers, the grass yield is only 300 kg. per hectare. But the good quality makes these grasses palatable for animals. Meadows are found in low-lying places with poor drainage, such as along lakesides and in floodlands, and the plants growing there are Cobresia and rank grasses that cover 70 to 80 per cent of the ground. The per-hectare yield is 3.75 to 7.5 tons. With low relief, warmer temperatures and little wind and snow, the meadows in these lake basins and valleys can be used as pastures in winter.

The saga soil contains only 1.5 per cent of organic matter and the soil profile contains much sand and gravel. It produces an alkaline reaction and is rich in calcium carbonate. Saga soil therefore has some of the features of steppe soil. The soil layer, however, is quite shallow.

Most sections of this subregion are still virgin lands and there are large herds of wild Tibetan donkeys, yaks and chirus. The areas of grasslands are quite vast, and many of them grow good-quality forage grasses. The subregion used to be regarded as a cold desert area of little value, but now we know that it can be exploited in a planned way for the development of stockbreeding. Some parts of the subregion that lie at a low altitude and have favourable moisture and thermal conditions can also be used for growing highland barley and turnips (*Brassica rapa*).

(4) Ngari Plateau Subregion

This subregion is located in the western part of the Tibetan Plateau. It includes the western section and the middle section (in Xinjiang) of the Kunlun Mountains. Lying at 4,800 to 5,000 m. above sea level, it is the coldest and highest part of the Qinghai-Tibetan Plateau. It contains a number of lake basins that lie roughly parallel to each other from west to east and that are connected into flat and wide valleys. Between these valleys are the Kunlun, Karakorum and Gandise mountains. The bottoms of the valleys and the lake surface stand 5,000 m. above sea level. Therefore the well-known mountain systems, high as they are, appear to be nothing but low hills on the plateau. The total area of the Kunlun Mountains exceeds half a million sq. km., standing at 5,500 to 6,000 m. above sea level. The northern slopes are steep and drop down into the Tarim Basin, which is less than 1,000 m. above sea level. The southern slopes are gentle and link up with the North Tibetan Plateau Subregion to become part of that plateau.

The climate is cold and dry, with an annual precipitation of less than 60 to 100 mm. and an annual mean relative humidity of 30 to 40 per cent. This therefore is a high and cold desert area with strong winds in winter and spring. The subregion is similar to that of southern Xinjiang in aridity, but the high elevation and low temperature make it quite different. The natural surroundings are mainly the landscape of the Qinghai-Tibetan Plateau. The vegetation is mainly a steppe type with ground coverage of less than 30 per cent. Dry and cold alpine plants, such as cushion oldworld winterfat (*Eurotia ceratoides*), are f und there; but *Haloxylon ammodendron*, *Nitraria schoberi* and tamarisk, typical of the desert plants in southern Xinjiang, and other halophilous plants do not grow there. Human beings are seldom seen, while wild animals such as chirus, Mongolian gazelles, yaks and wild donkeys are seen in large numbers. In winter, wild yaks often gather at the lakesides by the hundreds.

The main soil in this subregion is alpine desert soil. Due to the low temperature, aridness, small ground coverage and short growth period for the plants, the process of weathering and soil formation is very weak. A profile of the alpine desert soil shows that it is primitively developed and that the soil layer is thin.

The pastures in this subregion are relatively insignificant, and their per hectare yield is less than 150 kg. However they can still be used for animal raising. The herds of some communes now graze on pastures in formerly uninhabited areas. Farming has also been started in the lake basins and valleys where the natural conditions are more favourable. Farms in Rutog County (4,700 m. above sea level) have produced up to 2.25 tons of highland barley per hectare in the best years. Highland barley is also being grown on an experimental basis at a height of 4,900 m. above sea level, in an area without a frost-free period. This is the maximum upper limit for farming in China.

(5) South Tibetan Valley and Himalayas Subregion

The Himalayas lie on the southern fringes of the Qinghai-Tibetan Plateau, where they border India, Nepal and Bhutan on the southern side. At the west end they begin with Mount Nanga Parbat (8,126 m. above sea level) in Kashmir, and in the east they end with Mount Namcha Barwa (7,756 m.) at the great bend of the Yarlungzangbo River. Altogether they stretch about 2,400 km. at an average elevation of 6,000 m. above sea level. Most of the world's mountains that are more than 8,000 m. above sea level are found here. This is, in fact, the youngest and highest mountain system on earth. The mountains are linear, but they also form an arc that protrudes to the south.

The world's highest peak, Mount Qomolangma, stands in the middle section of the Himalayas on the border between the Tibet Autonomous Region of China and the Kingdom of Nepal. Geologically this is at the axis of the mountain arc. Around Mount Qomolangma are other peaks that stand above 8,000 m., such as Xixabangma, Lhotse, Makalu and Chooyu, where there are huge valley glaciers. On the northern side of these mountains, the glaciers generally extend down to a height of 5,200 to 5,000 m. above sea level, and on the southern side they extend down to 4,500-3,600 m., with some going down even to 2,500 m.

Mount Qomolangma is in the shape of a pyramid. It is surrounded by huge cirques on the northern, eastern and south-western sides, and its summit looks like a huge fish vertebra, more than 10 m. long and 1 m. wide. Because of strong winds, cliffs are unable to retain ice and snow above a certain line. This is why the lower part of the mountain is covered by firn while the upper part is exposed rock. The boundary between the firn and the rock on the northern side of Mount Qomo-langma is found at 7,450 m. above sea level.

Over the top of the mountain by the day float clouds that assume the shape of flags. These drift from west to east and appear like banners fluttering in the wind, with Mount Qomo-langma as their flagpole. Hence they are called "flag clouds". This is a meteorological phenomenon peculiar to the world's highest peak. They form because the surface of the mountain above 7,500 m. is mainly rock that becomes hot when it is ex-posed to sunshine during the day. This causes the surround-ing air currents and vapours to rise. The vapours then con-dense into clouds around the summit and hang over it. Such flag clouds do not emerge around the tops of the other high mountains.

The massive Himalayas stand erect from west to east like a protecting screen preventing the entry of the humid air cur-rents from the Indian Ocean into the region north of the moun-tains. They also prevent cold air masses from the north from crossing into the south. This has resulted in distinct differ-ences between the landscapes on each side of the mountains. Facing the monsoons from southwest, the southern side of these mountains is warm and humid, having features of a marine monsoon climate. The northern side, with little pre-cipitation, is cold and dry. This side has the features of a continental plateau climate. Take annual precipitation as an example. It measures 2,284 mm. at Chanlikarka in Nepal (2,700 m. above sea level) on the southern side, but only 325 mm. at the Rongbuk Monastery on the northern side. Al-though the two places are only 60 km. apart on a horizontal level, the mountain causes a seven-fold difference in the amount of annual precipitation.

The southern side is covered by all types of forests that change distinctly from bottom to top. And because the climate is humid, there are meadows but no dry steppes. On the northern side, the lowest elevation of the ground surface is around 4,000 m. above sea level and so no forests are found and the vegetation is that of an alpine cold semi-arid steppe. As the climate is comparatively arid, the lower limit of the alpine cold meadow cushion vegetation zone, the moraine lichen zone and the firn zone on the northern side are about 300 to 500 m. higher than they are on the southern side.

1) The Southern Side of the Himalayas

This area is mountainous and strongly dissected by the lower reaches of the Yarlungzangbo River and the tributaries of the Ganges and Brahmaputra rivers. The mountains here are high and the valleys are deep. The valleys drop to 1,600 m. above sea level on the southern side of Mount Qomolangma, to 600 m. south of Medog and to only 100 m. near the boundary between China and Burma.

Medog is situated in the valley along the lower reaches of the Yarlungzangbo River. This valley is only about 600 m. above sea level while Mount Namchaparwa, northwest of the valley, stands 7,756 m. high. The horizontal distance between them is only 45 km., but their elevation difference is more than 7,000 m. The vertical zones are quite distinct (Table 22). The valleys below 800 m. above sea level are free from frost or only have light frost in winter. The thermal conditions basically correspond to those in the quasi-tropical zone, and the annual precipitation exceeds 2,000 mm. Baxika on the boundary with Burma stands 157 m. above sea level and has an annual precipitation of more than 5,000 mm. Its annual mean temperature is above 20°C. It therefore is within the tropical zone. The natural vegetation in the surrounding area is similar to that of the tropical monsoon rain forests in the southern part of Yunnan Province. The tropical vegetation,

Table 22. The Vertical Zones at Medog

Elevation (m. above sea level)	Climate	Vegetation	Soil
Up to 1,100	Accumulated temperature more than 6,500°C. Mean annual temperature above 20°C. Coldest month 13°C.	Quasi-tropical monsoon rain forest, tropical rain forest	Mountain laterite
1,100 to 2,200	Accumulated temperature 3,000° to 6,500°C. Mean annual temperature 16°C.	Mountain sub-tropical evergreen broadleaf forest	Mountain Yellow earth
2,200 to 3,700	Mean annual temperature 3° to 11°C.	Subalpine coniferous forest	Mountain bleached podzol
3,700 to 4,700		Alpine bushes, meadows	Alpine brown bush soil and alpine meadow soil

in fact, extends to almost 30°N. along the valleys of the Yar-lungzangbo River.   This is the northernmost area for the location of a tropical zone in the Northern Hemisphere.

The frostline in the mountains is located roughly at 1,000 to 1,100 m. above sea level and therefore the upper limit for tropical forests reaches 1,100 m. Under 600 m. are tropical evergreen rain forests composed of Borneo camphor (Dipterocarpus), Canarytree (Canarium) and *Tetrameles nudiflora*. Between 600 and 1,100 m. are quasi-tropical monsoon rain forests made up of such tall tropical trees as *Terminalia myriocarpa, Lagerstroemia indica* and *Garcinia tinctoria*. Under the forests are *Musa wilsonii, Alpinia chinensis* and other plants often seen in tropical areas. There are also many big lianas and epiphyte plants in the forests. Rice, banana and lemon plants are grown around the villages.

On the lower part of the subalpine evergreen broadleaf forest zone (1,100 to 1,800 m. above sea level) are mainly evergreen chinquapin, *Machilus cathayansis* and magnolia trees, and also some tropical plants such as *Musa paradisiaca,* gomuti sugarpalm (*Arenga pinnata*) and *Cyathea spinulosa*. Tea trees have been introduced into the area and are growing well. Tung-oil, tea-oil and citrus trees are also grown. The upper part of the subalpine evergreen broadleaf forest zone (1,800 to 2,200 m.) and the lower part of the mountain coniferous forest zone (2,200 to 2,800 m.) are shrouded in clouds and mist all year round. The forests, mainly composed of Chinese hemlocks, are dark and humid. On the tree trunks grow mosses, and bearded lichens (*Usnea Florida*) hang from the branches. These are called mist forests or mountain moss forests and they constitute a unique section of the tropical and subtropical mountain zones. With their borders corresponding to the local mistlines, these forests indicate the existence of mountain zones that have the greatest relative humidity. Between 2,800 and 3,700 m. above sea level are spruces and firs, under which grow glossyleaf chinacanes. The trees here grow quickly and to an average height of 40 m. and an average diameter of about 70 cm. They provide an important source of timber in the southeastern part of Tibet. Two rice crops can be grown on the valley platform in and around Zayu, which stands at about 1,800 m. above sea level. The animals found here are also tropical or subtropical. They include the rhesus macaque, Assamese macaque, red-billed leiothrix and crimson-

A gorge on the Jinsha River in Yunnan Province.

The Central **Yunnan** Plateau stands 2,500 metres above sea level and is covered with Yunnan pines.

The Central Yunnan Plateau has many fault lakes; Erhai Lake is one of them.

Xishuangbanna's
tropical rain forest.

Xishuangbanna's
tropical scenery.

A savanna in the Yuanjiang area.
Some of the river valleys in
southern Yunnan are arid savannas.

Jinpinglao Mountain (the
southern section of Ailao
range, over 2,000 metres
above sea level) has dense
mountain mossy forests;
the tree trunks and
branches are covered
with moss.

Measures have been taken
to fix the sand dunes.

The Yinchuan Plain and the irrigation ditches that divert water from the Huanghe River.

The forestbelts protect shifting sand in the southern Muus Desert.

A gobi at the southern foot of the Tianshan Mountains.

The diversiform-leaved poplar forest along
the lower part of the Tarim River.

The shelterbelts of the oasis on the southwestern fringe of the Junggar Basin.

The giant panda protection area of Wanglang, Sichuan Province.

The Garqu, a source of the Huanghe River.

Source of the Changjiang River — glaciers on the southwestern slopes of snowcapped Geladandong.

Yaks on the Qinghai grassland.

Sheep on the grassland of northern Tibet.

The primeval forest 4,000 metres above sea level on the southern slope of Mount Qomolangma.

Tropical plants along the gorges of the Yarlungzangbo River.

chested parrot. Tea trees are grown on the slopes under 2,300 m.

The southern side of Mount Qomolangma is also a tropical zone. This is because the piedmont section beyond the Burmese boundary (below 1,000 to 1,200 m. above sea level) is widely covered by the tropical monsoon rain forests, mainly composed of sal trees (*Shorea robusta*) of the gurjun-oil tree family and laterite soil. This section links up with the sections within China to form a complete series of vertical zones (Figure 36).

The mountain subtropical zone (1,600 to 2,500 m.) has a warm and humid climate. Its annual mean temperature exceeds 10°C. The mean temperature is 16° to 20°C. in the hottest month and 5° to 10°C. in the coldest month. The annual precipitation at Zham is 2,800 mm., and the vegetation between 1,600 and 2,000 m. is evergreen broadleaf forest mainly made up of *Castanopsis indica* and *Schima wallichii*, and also includes plants of the laurel, tea and magnolia families. Between 2,000 and 2,500 m. are mainly *Quercus glauca* and *Lithocarpus spicata*. The animals found here include leaf monkeys, Assamese macaques and pandas. One-horned rhinoceros are also found in the valleys south of Gyirong. There is intensive biochemical weathering of the soil, with much leaching and illuviation of matter. This has led to the development of mountain yellow brown earth, a type of transition soil from mountain yellow earth to mountain brown earth. Two crops ripen each year, and rice is grown in areas under 1,900 m. above sea level.

The annual mean temperature in the mountain warm-temperate zone (2,500 to 3,100 m.) is about 7° to 10°C. The mean temperature in the hottest month is 14° to 16°C. and it is 0° to 5°C. in the coldest month. The vegetation is that of a mixed coniferous and broadleaf forest, mainly Chinese hemlocks and alpine oaks. This is the narrowest vertical zone on the southern side of the mountain. The soil here is acidic mountain brown earth. It has a pH value of 4.5 to 5.4 and contains 15

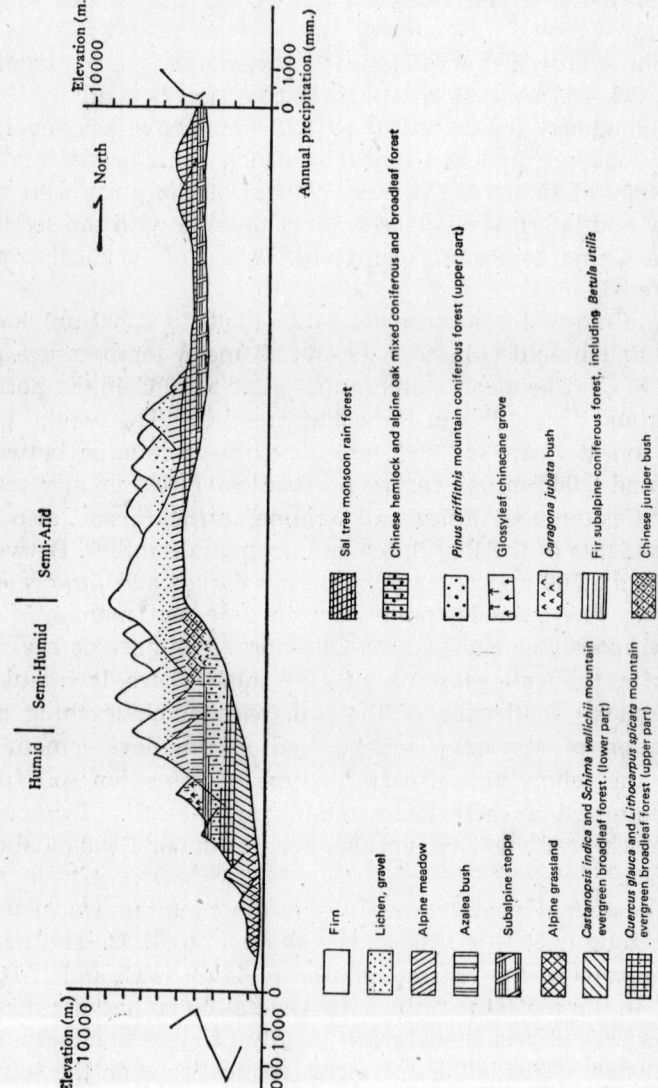

Fig. 36   Vertical Distribution of Vegetation in the Mount Qomolangma Area

Elevation (m.)
10000

North

Annual precipitation (mm.)

0   1000

Humid | Semi-Humid | Semi-Arid

Elevation (m.)
10000

2000 1000 0

Firn

Lichen, gravel

Alpine meadow

Azalea bush

Subalpine steppe

Alpine grassland

Castanopsis indica and *Schima wallichii* mountain evergreen broadleaf forest (lower part)

Quercus glauca and *Lithocarpus spicata* mountain evergreen broadleaf forest (upper part)

Sal tree monsoon rain forest

Chinese hemlock and alpine oak mixed coniferous and broadleaf forest

Pinus griffithii mountain coniferous forest (upper part)

Glossyleaf chinacane grove

Caragona jubata bush

Fir subalpine coniferous forest, including *Betula utilis*

Chinese juniper bush

to 54 per cent of organic matter. Three crops can ripen here every two years. The upper limit for the winter wheat-growing belt in the valley of the Gyirong River is 3,300 m. above sea level, and corn can be grown around 3,000 m.

The annual mean temperature in the mountain frigid temperature zone (3,100 to 3,900 m.) is 2° to 7°C. The mean temperature is 10° to 14°C. in the hottest month and 0° to -5°C in the coldest month. Located above the biggest precipitation belt, this zone has an annual precipitation of 500 to 1,500 mm. The vegetation is subalpine coniferous forest, mainly composed of Tibetan firs (*Abies spectabilis*). There are few lianas in the forest, but many *Usnea Florida* grow on the trees. This indicates that the climate is cold and humid. The isotherm of the mean temperature of 10°C. in the hottest month corresponds to the upper limit of the mountain forest. The animal species include musk deers, Himalayan pikas and willow warblers. The soil is mountain podzol, which features a light podzol layer with a pH value of 4.4 to 4.9. Silicon dioxide accumulates obviously in the profile, while ferric oxide and aluminium oxide are leached out and illuviated in the B horizon.

The subalpine frigid zone (3,900 to 4,700 m.) has a frost-free period of less than 90 days and a mean temperature of 6° to 10°C. in the hottest month. Forests cannot grow in this zone. The annual precipitation is 350 to 600 mm. The vegetation on the shady side of the mountain slopes is composed of low small-leaf bushes, mainly azaleas that grow to 40-60 cm. in height and cover 60-90 per cent of the ground. On the sunny side are subalpine meadows, mainly consisting of Cobresia and glacier Carex, but also including various kinds of cushion plants.

In the alpine frozen zone (4,700 to 5,500 m.) grow cold-resistant low meadow plants (mainly *Cobresia pygmaea* and black alpine sedge), cushion plants (mainly *Potentilla fruticosa* and *Arenaria musciformis*) and various kinds of lichens.

We have given a relatively detailed description of the vertical zones on the southern side of the Himalayas because of their significance to Chinese physical geography. The formation of these vertical zones is inseparable from the intensive upheaval of the main Himalayan range since the Pliocene Epoch. If it were not for the Himalayas, there would be no such vertical zones and the southwestern monsoons would drive straight into the Northwest China Region, turning the desert areas into luxuriant growths of grasses and trees. At the same time the fertile areas of India would become semi-deserts.

As described above, the vertical zones in this area take the horizontal tropical zone as their basic zone. The climate has the features of a tropical mountain climate: big daily temperature range, small annual temperature range and the snowy season in astronomical summer can be compared with the tropical mountainy plateau (the Yunnan Plateau). This is why there is no deciduous broadleaf forest belt of the temperate mountains in the vertical zonation (replaced by mixed mountain coniferous and broadleaf forest). It is one of the characteristics of the vertical zonation of many tropical mountain vegetations in the world.

The bioclimatic conditions of tropical mountains have many specific characteristics, so that a given vertical zone does not completely coincide with the corresponding horizontal zone. Generally speaking, the temperatures in subtropical, warm-temperate and frigid-temperate zones on the mountains in this area are higher in winter and lower in summer than they are in the corresponding horizontal zones on the plains in eastern China. For example, compared with a subtropical zone in the low-lying areas of eastern China, the mountain subtropical zone has a roughly similar frost-free period but a higher temperature in the coldest months and a lower one in the hottest months. Therefore the accumulated temperature during the period when the mean daily temperature exceeds 10°C. is only 2,400°C. at the upper limit (2,500 m. above sea level) of the mountain subtropical zone. It is more than 2,000°C. and less than 4,500°C. at the northern boundary of the subtropical zone in the eastern part of the country (Table 23). This is because the area is deeply affected by the southwestern monsoons.

Table 23. Comparison of Heat Conditions Between the Mountain Subtropical Zone on the Southern Side of Mount Qomolangma and the Subtropical Zone in Eastern China

Heat condition	Upper limit of the subtropical zone on the southern side of Mount Qomo-langma	Northern boundary of the subtropical zone in the low-lands of Eastern China
Temperature in the coldest month	5°C.	0°C.
Frost-free period	240 days	250 days
Mean temperature from June to September	15°C.	25.4°C. (Xinyang)
Accumulated temperature	2,400°C.	4,500°C.

The mean annual temperature is 7° to 9°C. more than it is in the eastern part of China at the same latitude and elevation. For example, the annual mean temperature at Rikatong, Zayu County (1,596 m. above sea level), is 15.8°C., 8.1°C. higher than it is at Huangshan Mountain in Anhui Province (1,840 m. above sea level) and the same as it is in Hangzhou, Zhejiang Province (11 m. above sea level). The northern boundary of the tropical zone in this area extends northward much farther than elsewhere, reaching its highest elevation at about 1,100 m. above sea level. And the accumulated temperature during a period when the mean daily temperature is more than 10°C. in this quasi-tropical zone exceeds 6,500°C., just as it does in the southern part of Yunnan Province. However, the accumulated temperature in the mountain temperate zone is much lower than it is in the eastern areas.   The accumulated temperature at the upper limit of the mountain temperate forest zone is only 500°C., about 1,100°C. lower than it is in the eastern areas.   This is a matter that has to be considered when plans are being made to utilize and exploit local resources.

2)   The South Tibetan Valleys

The south Tibetan valleys are the broad ones of the Yarlungzangbo and Xiangquan rivers.   They run from east to west and are located between the Himalayas and the Gandise to Nyainqentanglha ranges.   Most of these valleys stand at 3,500 to 4,000 m. above sea level.   They are a part of the Tibetan Plateau, but are separated from the plateau by the Gandise to Nyainqentanglha ranges and thus form a distinct geomorphological and physiographical unit.

There are a number of lakes in this area at the northern foot of the Himalayas.   Therefore this area is considered to be a plateau lake area.   The biggest lakes are Langa and Mapam, which form the headwaters for the three major rivers in South Asia.   The Maquan River flows in a southeast direction and becomes the upper reaches of the Yarlungzangbo River. The Xiangquan River flows in a northwest direction to become the upper reaches of the Sutlej River, a tributary of the Indus River.   And the Kongque River flows southeast into the Ganges River.   The upper section of the Maquan River runs through alpine grasslands at a height of more than 4,700 m. above sea level.

The Gandise to Nyainqentanglha ranges form the dividing line between northern and southern Tibet.   They are also the major watershed for the internal and external drainage systems in Tibet.   The Gandise Range is 60 to 100 km. wide and stands at an average elevation of 5,500 to 5,800 m. above sea level. Since the range lies on an already-high plateau, the peaks are relatively low and disintegrated. The Nyainqentanglha Range also is low for the same reason, and its main peak, 7,117 m. above sea level, is covered by firn.

Owing to the obstruction of the Himalayas, the South Tibetan Valleys south of the Yarlungzangbo River and west of Kangtog Mountain forms a distinct rain shadow belt with an annual precipitation of 200 to 300 mm. The aridity in the duration of the mean daily temperature exceeding 5°C. at Tingri (4,300 m. above sea level) is 0.92. Tingri, therefore, is regarded as part of the semi-arid area. The eastern part of the valley is more affected by warm and humid air currents from the Indian Ocean, and precipitation there gradually increases from west to east. For example, the city of Lhasa, with an annual precipitation of more than 400 mm., is in a semi-humid area.

As a result of the cold and arid climate, the vegetation in this area is mainly composed of purple needlegrass mixed with Caragana and *Potentilla fruticosa*. In addition, there are sagebrush, *Orinus thoroldii* and *Pennisetum flaccidium*. The soil is mainly alpine steppe soil. Because it is warmer in the valley area than on the North Tibetan Plateau, the steppe vegetation is better and the humus layer in the soil is thicker (about 10 to 15 cm.) than it is in saga soil. The surface layer also contains around 2 per cent of organic matter. This kind of soil is called baga soil to distinguish it from saga soil. Baga soil has clay loam with a lime accumulation in the B horizon and BC horizon, 20 to 30 cm. below the surface of the ground.

The valleys along the middle section of the Yarlungzangbo River west of Nangxian are at a height of 3,100 to 3,600 m. above sea level and have an annual precipitation of 400 to 500 mm. (409 mm. at Zetang). At the bottom of the valleys are alpine steppes with bushes, mainly *Trisetum subspicatum, Urinus thoroldii, Astraglus tibetica* and *Sophora moorcroftiana*. On the slopes are Cathay poplars, white poplars and willows, all planted in recent years by human labour. Upward, in order, are alpine steppes and alpine meadows. At the bottom of the valley of the Maquan River, 4,700 m. above sea level, is a grassland covered by purple needlegrass that extends upward to link with the alpine *Cobresia pygmaea* meadow on the Gandise Range.

The South Tibetan Valleys are relatively warm because

the Gandise to Nyainqentanglba ranges block the cold air from the north. Although the humid currents from the Indian Ocean are obstructed by the Himalayas, they can still move westward along the valley of the Yarlungzangbo River as far as Gyangze and Xigaze. Therefore the mean annual temperature at Gyangze is 5°C. higher than at Baingoin in northern Tibet, and the annual precipitation is 400 to 500 mm. As for moist and thermal conditions, the South Tibetan Valleys provide the best grasslands in Tibet. This is also the area where Tibet's best butter and sheep are produced.

The valleys of the Maquan River are high and cold, but due to the protection of the Gandise Range the low-lying lands in the valleys are still warm in winter and provide large winter pastures. The valleys along the lower reaches of the Xiangquan and Kongque rivers are down-cutting ones and lie at a low elevation, and the climate here is relatively dry and warm. Pines and honeysuckle grow in the valleys and remnants of junipers (*Sabina recurva*) are found on the mountain slopes. Apricot trees have been cultivated in the valleys at a height of 2,900 m. above sea level, and dried apricots are produced here. The most important farming areas in Tibet are located in these valleys, on the terraces and low mountain slopes along the lower reaches and tributaries of the Yarlungzangbo River. Highland barley is grown here in fields under 4,500 m. above sea level and the harvest is stable. Winter wheat has also been grown here in recent years, and its upper limit has reached 4,200 m. above sea level.

3. Development and Utilization of the Natural Resources

The Qinghai-Tibetan Plateau covers one-fifth of the total area of China. Although it has unfavourable natural conditions (high elevation, coldness and aridness), it also has some favourable ones.

First, because the plateau gradually becomes colder and

dryer from southeast to northwest, the plateau surface is marked by different horizontal zones as well as vertical zones. This has resulted in the formation of various types of forests, meadows and grasslands with abundant natural resources. The zones provide a broad vista for the development of timber production and animal husbandry. It is thought that the forest area of the frigid and temperate zones on the plateau is second only to that of northeast China. The forest area becomes even biggg, if the tropical forests in the south are included. The region includes many species for timber, and the forests are well preserved. The diameter of the pines, spruce and firs often reaches as many as two metres. There are also large reserves of Chinese hemlocks and alpine oaks. Not only is the area of grasslands and meadows bigger than that in Inner Mongolia and Xinjiang, but the quality of these pastures is by no means inferior. They can therefore be utilized for stock-raising.

Second, although the climate is arid and cold for most of the year, the sunshine is strong, sunshine time is long and the daily temperature range is big. These are favourable conditions for the growth of plants. This is why the per-unit yield of both wheat and highland barley in Tibet is very high. The per-hectare wheat yield over a large area is 7.5 to 11.25 tons. An experimental farm at Gyangze set the record in 1975 by harvesting more than 12 tons of wheat per hectare. The per-hectare yield for highland barley is more than 7.5 tons. Trees also grow rapidly. But forage grass on the plateau grows short and the per-hectare yield is low. The Cobresia and annual bluegrass growth is only enough to feed yaks. Yet the forage grass contains high nutriments and so the quality of milk and butter is quite good.

Third, the soil layer is relatively thin in most parts of the Qinghai-Tibetan Plateau, and it contains a lot of gravel and sand. But the soil layer in the broad valleys, on the lakeside and terraces is thicker and quite fertile. This is particularly true in the eastern part of the plateau where there is black felt soil and meadow felt soil, the sod layer is thick, more humus is accumulated and few mineral nutrients are lost. The soil moisture can be better preserved here because of the cold climate, and the potential fertility is high.

The Qinghai-Tibetan Plateau is thinly populated and most parts of the plateau are still undeveloped or partly developed. In the future, great efforts will undoubtedly be made to develop animal husbandry and forestry in this region.

Index

3.85

中国自然地理纲要

任美锷
杨纫章　包浩生著

✳

外文出版社出版
（中国北京百万庄路24号）
外文印刷厂印刷
中国国际图书贸易总公司
（中国国际书店）发行
北京399信箱
1985年（大32开）第一版
编号：（英）12050—68
01380（精）
01205（平）
12—E—1600